Hector Drummond is a former academic with a PhD who spent a number of years working in an academic risk institute at a Russell Group University. He is the author of *Days of Wine and Cheese*, a campus satire. He is also the creator of Skeptics in the Pub.

HECTOR DRUMMOND

The Face Mask Cult

CantusHead Books

Hector Drummond asserts the moral right to be identified as the author of this work.

Published by CantusHead Books

ISBN: 978-1-9999907-9-4

Cover image by Raul Mellado Ortiz

Contents

Introduction

One day they were out. The next day they were in.

The scientific establishment told us early in the Covid pandemic that face masks didn't work. Anthony Fauci, director of the National Institute of Allergy and Infectious Diseases (NIAID) and the Chief Medical Advisor to the US President went on *Sixty Minutes* and said they didn't work, and said there's no reason wear them. Jenny Harries, the Deputy Chief Medical Officer for England, told us not to wear them. None of the pandemic planning that had been done before Covid said we should wear them. The scientific literature didn't support their use.

Yet over a very short period the scientific and medical establishment, the big health institutions such as the WHO and the CDC, and governments all over the world completely reversed their positions and said that not only should you be wearing masks, they should be compulsory, and laws were brought in to make it illegal not to wear one in public or at work. School children were forced to wear them all day. Millions of school children are still being forced to wear them in 2022. Anyone who doubted the wisdom of this, and thought this was probably yet another Big Mistake from Big Government was treated like a pariah, abused by the media, shouted at in the street, and called a murderer.

Wearing a face mask marked you out as a fellow member of the comforting cult most people were now in. Anyone who didn't wear one, however, was an outsider, a science-denier, a dangerous maniac who was practically walking around naked in front of children. Those who refused to join the cult and wear the face nappy made the members of the cult feel scared and angry (and a little bit foolish), and were about as welcome as Carl Sagan at an Aztec child-sacrifice ritual.

The anti-maskers were right, though. Nothing much had changed in the science to justify the establishment's reversal of course on masks. Some fast-tracked research and reviews came out in spring and summer 2020 claiming to show that masks, even cloth masks, worked (or at least would help slow the virus enough to make it disappear), but this research was clearly shoddy, as you will see. The main thing that changed was that the academic establishment, which was full of terrified nerds (who regarded China as a model for the world), started shrieking – often literally, according to stories I heard – that we needed to wear masks. Their allies in the media, civil service and government liked the idea, and decided to change the narrative. The messages went out. Masks were in. Wear one, or else. The science has spoken. Or, at least, the sociologist has screamed.

This book sets out to demonstrate that masks don't work. Many of the main academic mask–pushers from spring 2020, such as Jeremy Howard and Trish Greenhalgh, who were imploring us to wear a mask, who said that any mask will do, even a scarf wrapped around your mouth, have changed their tune, and now admit that cloth masks are useless. (They want us to switch to respirator masks, like N95s and FFP2s.) But masks continue to be mandated all over the world. There are still millions of workers who have to wear one for their whole shift. Many schools still force their students, even very young ones, to wear them all day. Even in countries like the UK where it is no longer compulsory to wear masks in shops, bars and restaurants, shop assistants and waiters and bar staff are still forced to wear them by their employers. Most airlines are saying that masks will be compulsory to wear on-board, forever, with no exemptions. Hospitals and medical centres still require them, even in areas which don't have a mask mandate. And many people are still choosing to wear them because they were, and still are, terrified by their governments over a disease whose danger was vastly exaggerated. Mask use is not going away.

Parts 1 and 2 are written in the form of FAQs, where I answer the sorts of questions that often arise in the course of discussions about face masks. Anything you wanted to know about masks is probably in here.

In part 3 I take an in-depth look at various studies that have been conducted with the use of a scientific apparatus called the 'Gesundheit-II', centred around a Maryland environmental health scientist named Donald Milton. Conclusions have been drawn from these studies that far outweigh the results.

In part 4 I look at three of the main face mask reviews that have influenced UK government policy: the 2020 DELVE 'Report on Face Masks for the General Public', the Royal Society's 'Face masks and coverings for the general public' report from June 2020, and the UK's Department for Education's Evidence Summary on face masks from January 2022.

In part 5 I go through the scientific literature on face masks, looking at every randomized-controlled mask trial, as well as many other studies and reviews that examine the effectiveness of cloth, surgical and respirator masks, as well as studies that look at mask harms.

Throw away your mask. Respirator masks can be useful if you're doing DIY, but if you think they're going to stop you getting Covid, or stop you infecting people with your Covid, you've been sold a pup. If you think masks are the key to stop Covid spreading across the world then you've had a mask pulled over your eyes. Just because someone is a government scientist and is on TV doesn't mean they must be right. It's time to leave the cult.

Part 1:
Main face mask FAQs

Why does wearing a mask for a few minutes in a shop bother you?

It may be just a few minutes for you when you pop into your Waitrose for a croissant, but millions of children across the world are being forced to wear them all day long, hundreds of days. Millions of workers are being forced to wear them for eight-hour shifts every work day, many of them in hot weather, and they can't just loosely drape a scarf over their mouth. Wearing masks in such situations is intolerable to many people. It isn't 'just a few minutes'.

You people just have to suck it up, because masks work.

The scientific evidence base does not support the wearing of face masks to stop Covid-19. This is why Anders Tegnell, Sweden's chief state epidemiologist, has 'dismissed the scientific evidence for mask-wearing as "astonishingly weak"'.

See part 5 for an comprehensive look at the literature, and part 4 for in-depth analyses of the influential DELVE and Royal Society reports in 2020 which greatly influenced the UK government's switch to forcing masks on people.

Nonsense, the ever-reliable Guardian had a story saying that masks cut Covid by 53%, and the study they were talking about was in the British Medical Journal, so where do you get off saying they don't work?

That meta-analysis was hopeless. The authors themselves admitted that the 'risk of bias across the six studies [ie. the studies chosen for the meta-analysis] ranged from moderate to serious or critical'. Even Professor Stephen Reicher, the zero-Covid fanatic, felt forced to apologise for promoting this story on social media once he realised how bad the study was (it included many garbage studies, including even 'attitude' and studies, and telephone interviews).

The even more extreme zero-Covid Communist Party member Prof Susan Michie published an article in the *BMJ* the *same day* saying the study was poor and should be disregarded:

> the quality of the current evidence would be graded—by GRADE criteria11—as low or very low, as it consists of mainly observational studies with poor methods (biases in measurement of outcomes, classification of PHSM, and missing data), and high heterogeneity of effect size.

And the BMJ also published an editorial, the *same day again*, saying the study lacked serious data:

> Among 35 studies good enough to evaluate, only one was a randomised trial, and it was too small... The others were all observational studies, including natural experiments, and the effects are likely to result from "bundles" of protective behaviours rather than single interventions.

I discuss this paper in more depth in part 5.3.b.

What about country-level analyses? Don't the countries that use masks have less cases and less deaths? Didn't places that introduced mask mandates find that cases and deaths fell?

This is completely the opposite of the truth. There is no correlation between mask use and a reduction in cases or deaths in a country or state. In an article called 'Mask mandate and use efficacy for COVID-19 containment in US States' in the *International Research Journal of Public*

Health (v.5 (55), 2021), the authors Guerra and Guerra conclude that

> We did not observe association between mask mandates or use and reduced COVID-19 spread in US states…
> Our main finding is that mask mandates and use likely did not affect COVID-19 case growth. Mask mandates were associated with greater mask use but ultimately did not influence total normalized cases or post-mandate case growth… initial association between masks and lower COVID-19 growth rates that dissipated during the Fall-Winter 2020-21 wave is likely an artifact of fewer normalized cases begetting faster growth in states with coincidental low mask use.

In 'Masks, false safety and real dangers, Part 2: Microbial challenges from masks' by Borovoy et al, in *Primary Doctor Medical Journal* (9 Oct 2020), a country-level analysis of mask use against Covid deaths was performed:

> In July 2020, the Council of Foreign Relations conducted a survey of 25 countries, with the following question to their citizens: "Have you always worn a face mask outside the home in the last seven days?" The "Yes" responses ranged from 1% in Finland and Denmark, to 93% in Singapore. We then examined each of the same 25 countries for prevalence of mask use versus Covid-19 deaths per 1 million population. This data was gathered from Worldometers statistics. That data is shown in Table 1, also represented in Graph 1… As we see from the above data [in Table 1], there was no significant correlation with mask use and either increase or reduction of deaths from COVID-19; thus masking could not have caused a significant reduction in deaths. In fact, two of the countries with the highest COVID-19 deaths also had high rates of mask use: Spain at 87%

mask use and Brazil at 90% mask use. Again, masking could not have caused a significant reduction in deaths.

Ian Miller, on his Twitter account @ianmsc, does regular comparisons of countries and states looking at correlations between mask mandates and cases/deaths. He consistently finds no correlations whatsoever. (He has now published this work in his 2022 book *Unmasked*.)

The graphs he regularly posts totally devastate the pro-mask position. Take, for instance, this graph of Germany vs Sweden. Germany requires, by law, everyone to wear high-quality N95 masks, and there is high compliance, whereas Sweden doesn't require masks and most people don't wear them.

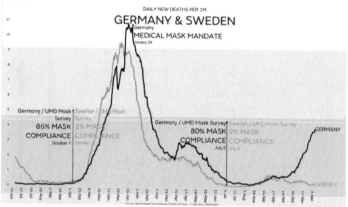

Masks work because they filter out the Covid virus, meaning my breath goes through the mask and comes out Covid-free on the other side, and vice-versa.

No. SARS-CoV-2 is vastly smaller than the holes in your piece of cloth. Did you really think that a bit of cloth placed over your face was going to stop every microscopic virus that is between 0.06-0.14 microns (micrometres, or μm) in length? That's 60-140 nanometres (a nanometre is one millionth of a millimetre)? Pull up your shirt or dress over your eyes – you can literally see the holes with your naked eye.

But I read on pro-mask site that the virus is usually attached to a Flugge droplet, an aerosol, or a bit of protein, and these are much bigger.

It is true that when they come out of someone's mouth, virions are almost always attached to something else that is larger, most usually fine aerosols, ie. tiny water droplets, as well as larger droplets. But fine aerosol droplets are microscopically small too. In 'Particle sizes of infectious aerosols: implications for infection control' by Fennelly in *Lancet Respiratory Medicine* (v.8 (9), 1 Sep 2020, pp.914-24), the author points out that 'most particles [ie. aerosols] in exhaled breath are smaller than 4 μm, with a median between 0.7 and 1.0 μm'.

In an examination of the size of the holes in cloth masks titled 'Optical microscopic study of surface morphology and filtering efficiency of face masks' by Neupane et al, in *PeerJ* (v.7, 26 June 2019), it was found that

The pore size of masks ranged from 80 to 500 μm.

This is between 80 to 714 times as big as a typical Covid-carrying fine aerosol. As many have mockingly pointed out, this is like trying to carry sand in a shopping trolley, or stopping a mosquitos with a chain-link fence.

(Bear in mind also that many of the tiny virus-carrying aerosols will be following the air flow around the fibres and through the holes. It's not like randomly shooting a whole load of ping pong balls all at once at a wall with some holes in it.)

Having said that, these analogies are somewhat misleading, as even the worst cloth mask will trap some of your aerosols, whereas shopping trolleys aren't going to carry any sand, and no mosquitos get stopped by a chain-link fence (for one thing, they have a sensory system and can fly around the wire. Then again, pro-mask debunkers never mention the fact that many aerosols will follow the air flow, so they are kind of like mosquitos, to some degree).

That's why your cloth mask becomes wet after a while, it is trapping some of the moisture in your breath. But not much. Try this. Put a pan full of water on the hob and boil the water. Put one side of T-shirt over the pan. Cover the sides of the pan with the shirt (making sure the T-shirt doesn't catch fire from the hob). Don't stretch the material, just have it how it normally is, otherwise the holes will get even bigger. Watch how much steam goes through the cloth. It's most of it. The cloth doesn't even get very wet. Cloth masks generally don't stop much water vapour, and they won't be stopping many of the aerosols that contain virions.

Have you got any close-up photos of cloth masks?

Here are some close-up images of cloth masks captured by Neupane et al under the microscope in their very useful 'Optical microscopic study of surface morphology and filtering efficiency of face masks' paper mentioned above. (The short line at the bottom of photo A is 500 microns and applies to all the images.)

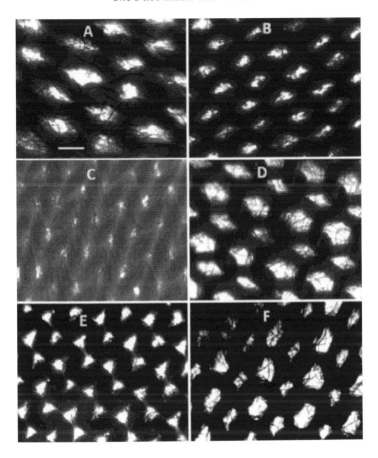

Some pro-mask sites claim that the holes in cloth masks are more like 'small tunnels than windows'. These sorts of images show that this is not true. (And even if it was true, the aerosols would mostly follow the air flow through the tunnels.)

Here are some more taken by Neupane et al in a different paper called 'A smartphone microscopic method for rapid screening of cloth facemask fabrics during pandemics', in

PeerJ. (v.8, July 30 2020). (The line at the bottom of photo E is 400 microns and applies to all the images.)

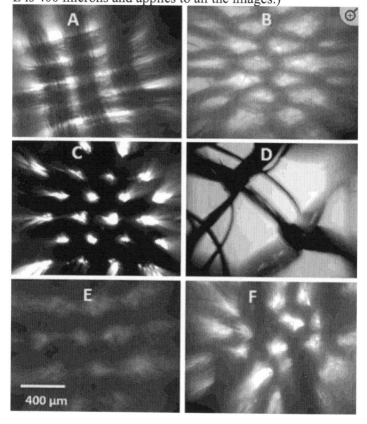

Do the aerosols that get through the mask just fall straight to the ground?

No, this only applies to larger droplets. Fine aerosols can float about in the air for long periods. Bear in mind also that aerosols very quickly evaporate, so the aerosol a virion is attached to becomes smaller and smaller, which means it can stay in the air for even longer. Some virions even become free floating particles attached to nothing at all. As this *City*

Journal article states ('Do We Need Mask Mandates?' Harris, 22 March 2021):

> One widely cited model estimates that droplets with diameters smaller than about 100 microns (a micron is a thousandth of a millimeter) evaporate before reaching the ground, leaving their contents as long-lasting aerosols; particles smaller than about five microns can stay aloft indefinitely and travel beyond droplet range.

But maybe fine aerosols don't have much virus in them compared to the larger droplets?

No, the fine aerosols have far more virus in them – according to 'Influenza Virus Aerosols in Human Exhaled Breath: Particle Size, Culturability, and Effect of Surgical Masks' by Milton, et al, in *PLoS Pathogens* (v.9 (3), March 7 2013),

> fine particles [ie. aerosols] contained 8.8 fold more viral copies than did coarse particles.

It doesn't hurt to wear a mask. There are no downsides. So why don't you just do it just in case?

There are numerous ways in which wearing a mask has considerable downsides. I cannot cover them all here, but here are a few. (Note that the scientific studies on masks have mostly ignored mask harms – as a Cochrane meta-analysis of the literature states, 'Harms were poorly measured and reported'.)

Wearing a mask that covers your airways for long periods, or even any period, is a very unpleasant experience for many people. It makes breathing difficult, and the better the mask, and the closer it fits to your face, the more difficult the breathing. It is very unhygienic, and for many people they feel, reasonably enough, degraded, dehumanised, humiliated and defeated. Over history, forcing people to wear masks is something that is usually used as a punishment and/or a sign of submission, to reduce or remove their ability to engage in normal human communication, and even to change or reduce their identity.

There is also the obvious example of the Islamic tradition of masking women, which indicates their submission.

Consider also the 'scold's bridle', a punishment mask developed in Britain in the 16th century, designed to humiliate women who were considered shrews, gossips, gluttons, eavesdroppers, or liars. This practice spread to Europe – such masks were known as 'Schandmaske' in Germany, which meant the 'mask of shame' – and the practice then spread to the New World with the Puritans.

Given the aggressive and spiteful behaviour of modern states in forcing masks on people against their wills, and despite the lack of evidence of benefit, it is entirely reasonable for people to feel that being forced to wear mask is also in this case a sign of submission. For such people wearing a mask is an unjustified intrusion upon their bodily workings, and every second they spend in a mask is intolerable. It is like being forced to wear special clothing by a victorious army of hostile invaders. In fact, it is even worse because you are having to cover your airways in doing so.

Even for people who don't feel as strongly as that, wearing a mask is still very unpleasant and most people dislike having them on, especially when they have to be worn for long periods. These are disutilities than cannot just be ignored in any calculation of the harms and benefits of masks. Even if you think the harm for each person is not great, when you multiply that by millions of people, by hundreds upon hundreds of days, you are looking at a significant overall harm, which has to be weighted against the benefits of wearing a mask, which is... zero.

There is also the huge downside that masks cover most of your face, and this disrupts the normal face-to-face communication that is so integral to the human race and human communications. And preventing people from being able to see the faces of human beings not only hinders communication, but is in itself a bad thing, because seeing the faces of other people around them is a basic human need for almost everyone. You can't see facial expressions, you can't see emotions, you can't see smiles, frowns, puzzlement, etc. You can't hear them very well. You can't properly connect with a masked human. Depriving people of that for long periods is like putting them in solitary confinement, which for good reason is considered even worse than normal imprisonment. So these are also massive disutilities.

In the Brownstone Institute article 'Facemasks Are Not a Mere "Inconvenience"', author Aaron Hertzberg argues that masks have many downsides that are not immediately obvious, and he articulates various categories such as the deprivation of personal autonomy, the sense of helplessness, the invalidation of your personal identity, the changing of your personality over time, the induction of a general feeling of being trapped in a nightmare, the stress of difficulty communicating, the distress of constant harassment, living in constant state of worry, fear, and anger, the sapping of joy from many different activities, living in perpetual stress from social enforcers, public humiliation, the distress of being under the control of someone you loathe, making people doubt their sense of reality, destroying people's sense of trust and stability, dehumanization through forced anonymity, and more.

For some academic studies on face mask harms, see part 5.8.

Why the fuss about kids wearing masks?

As Julia Donaldson, the author of The Gruffalo and a former Children's Laureate in the UK said, face masks in schools are 'alien – even dystopian'. She said of children being forced to wear masks that

> I don't think they should be sacrificed like this...
> Because of the climate of fear, people have readily
> accepted something I regard as unacceptable, and that I
> fear may now be seen as a normal part of life.

In 'Mandatory Masking of School Children is a Bad Idea' in the *Orange County Register* (13 July 2021), Neeraj Sood (Director of the COVID Initiative at the USC Schaeffer Center for Health Policy and Economics) and Jay Bhattacharya (a professor of medicine at Stanford University) say

> the long-term harm to kids from masking is potentially
> enormous. Masking is a psychological stressor for
> children and disrupts learning. Covering the lower half
> of the face of both teacher and pupil reduces the ability
> to communicate. In particular, children lose the
> experience of mimicking expressions, an essential tool of
> nonverbal communication. Positive emotions such as
> laughing and smiling become less recognizable, and
> negative emotions get amplified. Bonding between
> teachers and students takes a hit. Overall, it is likely that
> masking exacerbates the chances that a child will
> experience anxiety and depression, which are already at
> pandemic levels themselves.

In 'A Partial List of the Myriad Abuses That Facemasks Inflict on Our Children' (19 Jan 2022), Aaron Hertzberg provides a long descriptive list of just some of the ways that masks harm children, for example

> Constant mask-based fearmongering and threats and moral opprobrium has inflicted an unfathomable measure of fear and anxiousness upon children. Masks are the talisman of fear and anxiety (and everything else negative) of the covid pandemic. Anxiety disorders are something that people can relate to. But inflicted upon children, this is much more pernicious and debilitating, because they will internalize it as "how it is supposed to be/feel" and not realize that this is a messed up way of feeling all the time in the way that an adult is (usually) able to realize and understand that being anxiety ridden is not normal, and an adult also has the benefit of a contrast to a time when they were not suffering from perpetual anxiety.

Is there any harder evidence of masks harming children?

A database set up by German academics (called 'Corona children studies "Co-Ki": First results of a Germany-wide registry on mouth and nose covering (mask) in children', Schwarz et al) collected many examples of masks harms in school children. The academics say

> Impairments caused by wearing the mask were reported by 68% of the parents. These included irritability (60%), headache (53%), difficulty concentrating (50%), less happiness (49%), reluctance to go to school/kindergarten (44%), malaise (42%) impaired learning (38%) and drowsiness or fatigue (37%).

The percentages are somewhat meaningless as this is a self-selected sample, and we can't be sure that all the problems mentioned were caused by masks, but as the database had over 20,000 people on it, this is very concerning and should have seen the scientific establishment scurrying to conduct more research. Of course the opposite happened, and the academic establishment tried to poo-pooh the database as 'non-scientific'. The very same establishment that promoted as major evidence a shallow look at two hairdressers (see the first section of part 5).

Yves Van Hastel, teacher in secondary education in Antwerp, told the media

> "Those masks are not made for constant wearing and talking behind it," he writes. "They get moist. We breathe our CO_2 in and out, in and out. Students complain of a red rash around their mouths from sitting behind that mask all day. Almost every lesson they ask me, "When will this end?" If they have to, they prefer to take lessons from home. Myself and fellow teachers also suffer. We force our voice to be heard when we wear a mask. I feel more tired. I expect that many colleagues and students will call in sick with voice problems, exhaustion, colds.

The American Institute for Economic Research reported (in 'Masking Children: Tragic, Unscientific, and Damaging', by Paul E. Alexander, 10 March 2021) that

> During April to October 2020 in the US, emergency room visits linked to mental health problems (e.g. anxiety) for children aged 5-11 increased by nearly 25% and increased by 31% for those aged 12-17 years old as compared to the same period in 2019.

This is a result of lockdowns and non-pharmaceutical interventions (NPIs) in general, not just masks, but no doubt masks contribute strongly to these results. Remember that many US states have required all-day mask-wearing for children since March 2020.

Do masks harm the development of children?

Yes. Not being able to see faces is even more important for young children, because this is crucial for their socialisation and mental development. In many US states school pupils having been wearing masks all day for 18 months, and this is very damaging for their development. We are damaging a generation of children, as well as making life very unpleasant for them. Many children greatly dislike wearing masks. This is child abuse.

Children's education is also disrupted by masks. If you can't see your teacher's face for the whole day, or the faces of your classmates, your learning will be retarded.

Masks also greatly hinder children's intellectual, and especially emotional development, which relies on being able to see people's faces. 'Babies learn an enormous amount of information from faces. From language to social cues, developmental psychologists say faces are a learning tool in the same way that books are. But with the coronavirus pandemic prompting orders and recommendations around the country to wear masks in public, young children are losing out on the crucial visual tools they need for language learning, said Dr. Lisa Scott, professor of psychology at the University of Florida.

> Scott is calling on policymakers and educators to implement the use of transparent face masks — like face shields or clear masks — for caregivers and teachers of infants and young children. When learning language, babies use the mouth to help them learn the differences between sounds, such as "ba" and "da" — particularly in noisy environments, Scott said. And while wearing masks doesn't mean they won't learn language, it will be more challenging.

Kathleen M. Pike, PhD is Professor of Psychology and Director of the Global Mental Health WHO Collaborating Centre at Columbia University, and she says

Joy, anger, fear, surprise, sadness, contempt, disgust. These basic building blocks of emotional experience are written all over our faces. Legendary psychologist Paul Ekman has devoted his life's work to studying non-verbal emotional expression across cultures. His research suggests that we can largely recognize how people around the world are feeling by simply reading their faces. All of humanity expresses these seven core feelings in ways that we universally comprehend. We depend on facial expression to know and understand each other. With physical distancing, increased anxiety, and disrupted routines due to COVID19, we are primed to seek emotional connection by simply seeing each other's facial expressions.

She then says

Masks block a lot more than COVID-19 droplets. We depend on non-verbal behavior, and particularly facial expression, to express ourselves and communicate to others. Those feelings above, and many more, get expressed on our faces. In some contexts, non-verbal communication accounts for the majority of what we understand in our social exchanges. With our faces half-covered, we lose key non-verbal information, and other information, like raised eyebrows and shoulder shrugs become highly ambiguous without cues from the mouth. This loss of information is like talking on your phone in a zone with weak cell service. You know… those times when you only hear every third word and eventually the call drops. The effect leaves us feeling less able to communicate and less able to understand each other.

The *Telegraph* reports:

> Dr Yvonne Wren, director of the Bristol Speech &
> Language Therapy Research Unit, and a senior research
> fellow at the University of Bristol, said: "We know that
> the deaf community is affected by masks, but it's going
> to affect speech and language development for all
> children. All children are going to get a much less clear
> signal. They won't see people's faces and won't see
> whether they are smiling and looking stern. When we're
> talking we often fill in the blanks and use the context of
> facial expressions to understand the message. It means
> they are going to get more confused and we know
> children don't learn as well when they are in an
> emotional state".

In a press release from the American Academy of
Pediatrics, Dr. Alice Kuo, President of the Southern
California chapter of the AAP, said:

> For example, wearing masks throughout the day can
> hinder language and socio-emotional development,
> particularly for younger children.

But not to worry, the *New York Times*, in an article
reluctantly published to deal with this major issue, has a
solution, which is to completely change the results of
millions of years of human evolution:

> Sarah Gaither, an assistant professor of psychology and
> neuroscience at Duke University, said in an email, "With
> mask wearing now being required in most school
> settings, children and adults should start practicing being
> more explicitly verbal by stating their emotions out
> loud." Children will get better at reading people's eyes,
> she suggested, and at understanding emotional content
> from tone of voice.

Alternatively, we could just take off these ridiculous religious encumbrances and save ourselves the bother of pointlessly reinventing human life.

In 'Rapid Response: Psychosocial, biological, and immunological risks for children and pupils make long-term wearing of mouth masks difficult to maintain', by Peteers et al, in *British Medical Journal* 370, 9 Sep 2020, the authors say

> Facemasks prevent the mirroring of facial expressions, a process that facilitates empathetic connections and trust between pupils and teachers. This potentially leads to a significant increase in socio-psychological stress. During childhood and puberty the brain undergoes sexual and mental maturation through hormonal epigenetic reprogramming [18-21]. Several studies show that long-term exposure to socio-psychological stress leaves neuro-epigenetic scars that are difficult to cure in young people and often escalate into mental behavioural problems and a weakened immune system.

For a review of the relations between schoolchildren, masks and teachers, see 'Un-masking Children: Part 1 of 4. The Role of Children in COVID-19 Transmission in Schools' in *Rational Ground* (Burns, 11 May 2021).

For one sceptical American teacher's take on masks in schools, see 'What They Did to the Kids', by Alex Gutentag in *Tablet* (22 Nov 2021).

> As a teacher for special needs and underprivileged students, I saw the effects of school closures up close. It was a moral crime... Masks have become a constant reminder of potential transmission, and mask mandates have given rise to a wide array of new educational materials, such as dystopian singalongs and call-and-response routines that teach young children to cover their

faces in order to keep their friends safe. In some schools, students are rewarded with "mask breaks" and can be suspended for mask noncompliance. Back-to-school activities that once had names like "All About Me" now have names like "Me Behind the Mask".

In a survey conducted by the UK's Department for Education in March 2021 it was found that

> 80% of pupils reported that wearing a face covering made it difficult to communicate, and more than half felt wearing one made learning more difficult (55%).

A different survey for the UK's Department for Education in April 2021

> found that almost all secondary leaders and teachers (94%) thought that wearing face coverings has made communication between teachers and students more difficult, with 59% saying it has made it a lot more difficult

In 'Masked education? The benefits and burdens of wearing face masks in schools during the current Corona pandemic' by Spitzer , in *Trends in Neuroscience and Education* (Sep 2020), the author says

> covering the lower half of the face reduces the ability to communicate, interpret, and mimic the expressions of those with whom we interact. Positive emotions become less recognizable, and negative emotions are amplified. Emotional mimicry, contagion, and emotionality in general are reduced and (thereby) bonding between teachers and learners, group cohesion, and learning - of which emotions are a major driver.

In February 2022 the CDC lowered its standards for childhood linguistic development. (I didn't know the CDC was involved in this field, but apparently they are.)

According to the *Postmillenial* in a Feb 18 article called 'CDC quietly lowers early childhood speech standards',

> The Centers for Disease Control and Prevention has quietly changed their standards for early childhood development, as the effects of pandemic policies on children's development, from speech to reading to other basics, becomes increasingly more apparent.

For example:

> Before, the milestone guidelines said that at 24 months, or two years of age, a child should be able to say more than 50 words. This milestone has been pushed back to 30 months.

This will be in large part due to mask-wearing.

How are young adults affected?

A CDC study called 'Mental Health, Substance Use, and Suicidal Ideation During the COVID-19 Pandemic — United States, June 24–30, 2020' by Czeisler et al in the CDC's *Morbidity and Mortality Weekly Report* (August 14, 2020, v. 69 (32), pp.1049-57) said that the level of anxiety and depression in young adults aged 18-24 has increased by 63% since government restrictions began, and their use of antidepressants has increased by 25%:

> The young adults also reported the highest levels of symptoms of anxiety and depression — 62.9 percent reported either or both. Their rates of having started or increased substance use to cope with pandemic-related stress or emotions was way up there as well at 24.7 percent (it was equal or higher only among the essential workers and the unpaid caregivers).

The study also found that a quarter of them think about suicide.

But aren't masks good because they 'send a signal'?

They certainly send a signal, but this is a bad thing. Masks increase fear and anxiety unnecessarily. They remind us, as they are supposed to, to spend our lives being be scared and worried about a disease that isn't worth worrying about for most people. They remind the people who don't believe the fear-mongering about Covid to fear the state. They also turn ordinary people into state agents, because they make it easy for non-believers to be identified and shamed by mask-wearers.

The UK's official 'Nudge Unit' has admitted that this is one of the reasons they like mask-wearing – Prof David Halpern, chief executive of the Government's Behavioural Insights Team, known as the Nudge Unit, who also sits on Sage, was quoted in a 30 Nov 2021 *Telegraph* article titled 'Why face masks became the symbol of a divided Britain' as saying

> "Most of the heavy lifting [on mask enforcement]," he says, "is done when we look at each other and think 'Why aren't you wearing a mask?' and frown."

Halpern also said that

> the British are particularly good at this.

The UK Government's January 2022 face mask Evidence Summary confirms that this sort of thinking is still in operation:

> Wearing face coverings is comparatively cheap and easy to implement and supervise. It can be a visible outward signal of safety behaviour and a reminder of COVID-19 risks'.

So masks make people fear the compliant masses. They make people who don't want to wear masks wear them out of fear of other people, including friends and family. They tear apart the normal bonds of society, because instead of our different beliefs being kept in our heads, allowing us to rub along, they are forced out into the open where they are attacked and shamed, forcing you to comply or suffer.

Some scientists have explicitly admitted that an important function of masks is that they act as a symbol, though of course these scientists frame this in a positive way, eg.

a symbol of social solidarity in the global response to the pandemic.

(In 'Wearing face masks in the community during the COVID-19 pandemic: altruism and solidarity' by Cheng et al in the *Lancet*, April 16, 2020).

So you're saying masks are about enforcing compliance to the state/the establishment?

Yes. Masks are used by governments, and those influencing the government (eg. academics, unions, tech billionaires), as a psychological tool to signal compliance. If you find that you don't agree with your government's approach to Covid-19, then seeing most people around you in a mask tells you that you are in a small minority. It tells you not to bother questioning, because you're just an isolated fool. Even though most people may just be wearing the mask because they have been told to, and may also disagree with the government's approach, you don't know that. All you can see is that they are wearing the mask, so there must be something wrong with you if you don't. There's danger if you don't obey, danger that's going to come directly from the scary people around you. It's a symbol that says you'd better obey unless you want some serious trouble.

Here's an example, from an editorial in the *New England Journal of Medicine* ('Universal Masking in Hospitals in the Covid-19 Era' by Klompas et al, v.382, May 21 2020) of scientists talking about masks as useful symbols, although of course they are deluded enough to think that masks will reduce worry.

> It is also clear that masks serve symbolic roles. Masks are not only tools, they are also talismans that may help increase health care workers' perceived sense of safety, well-being, and trust in their hospitals. Although such reactions may not be strictly logical, we are all subject to fear and anxiety, especially during times of crisis. One might argue that fear and anxiety are better countered with data and education than with a marginally beneficial mask, particularly in light of the worldwide mask shortage, but it is difficult to get clinicians to hear this message in the heat of the current crisis.

Wearing a mask is just 'doing your bit'.

Masks discourage people from doing normal things, and encourages them to stay inside and watch TV or use the internet. This is not always the intention of those implementing mask mandates: the British government clearly intended the opposite effect in summer 2020 when it encouraged masking as a way to end social distancing and get people outside and back to work and back to the shops, but not surprisingly this didn't work very well. But other governments and health agencies and tech companies (who benefit from people staying inside) may have different motives.

Whatever the motive of those pushing masks, they discourage people from going outside, from meeting others, from shopping, from pursuing their hobbies, interacting normally with others, going to restaurants and pubs, playing sport, going to school, going to their University classes, going to concerts or the theatre, and so on. All this has significant effect on people's mental and physical health, and causes great damage to society. Masks scare people and kept them inside, and so masks should only ever be considered as a last resort in a dire emergency when there is solid-gold evidence of their effectiveness (and maybe not even then).

To come at it in another way, mask-wearing is a major way in which the Covid hysteria is maintained, which makes masks partly responsible for the continuation of the murderous lockdowns, which have killed so many people over the world. As I have said since they were introduced, masks are murder.

C'mon, it's not like it's killing anyone.

As psychologist Dr Gary Sidley said of the fear engendered by masks

> There is plenty of evidence to suggest that fear of attending hospital with non-coronavirus problems is contributing to the premature death of many people. In the first four months of the year, the Office of National Statistics estimated that almost 13,000 excess deaths were not attributable to SARS-CoV-2, a finding likely to be associated with the fact that admissions to Accident & Emergency departments were 128,000 lower in March 2020 as compared to March 2019. The Royal College of Paediatrics stated they had evidence of parents too scared to take their ill children to hospital. A senior oncologist predicted that treatment delays could cause up to 30,000 excess cancer deaths. And the health impact on

older people – lonely and isolated, too scared to leave their homes – is as yet difficult to quantify.

Some people like wearing a mask, so they can't be that bad.

Not many people choose to wear masks when they don't have to, and those that do are doing so because they are scared, not because they like covering their mouth with a dirty rag.

Masks increase social decay and social isolation. We don't see other people as people so much, we see them as moving figures in a landscape, as non-playing characters in a video game. We already live in a society that is becoming increasingly anonymous and disjointed (especially in the cities), and wearing masks increase this process enormously. It's telling that the people who spent years lecturing us that we aren't isolated islands and we must connect with others are now the most keen to push masks, which does the very opposite. They atomise us. They literally dehumanise us, in that we no longer see others as quite as human as we used to.

But surgeons wear masks to protect their patients from viruses when operating on them. So they must work, and you should stop complaining about them, as surgeons don't complain.

First of all, note that an operation involves someone's body being cut open and their internals exposed for a period, sometimes a long period. The situation is hardly analogous to going to a deli.

There are several reasons why surgeons started wearing masks. One is to protect themselves from blood and other bodily fluids which could spray or splash into their mouth, just as they wear special gowns to protect their clothes from these fluids. The masks can also prevent saliva droplets or bits of food or other gunk from dropping from the surgeon's mouth, nose or facial hair into what is basically an open wound.

Another important reason they were originally worn is that it was hoped they would stop bacteria from the surgeon getting into open wounds. In the early part of the twentieth century

> haemolytic streptococci isolated from wounds and puerperal fever were found to be identical with those carried in the throats of the surgical and obstetric teams

and it was thought that masks could help stop this sort of infection happening.

Note, though, that the focus here was on bacteria (a major health threat at the time), not viruses. As far as I can tell from my research into this topic it was not originally thought that masks would protect against virus particles.

But a mask filters out the bacteria and viruses from a surgeon's breath and prevent them going onto their patients' openings.

They mostly don't. As I said, it was hoped that surgical (aka medical) masks would stop bacteria, but stopping viruses wasn't even an original aim. As a 2008 British government report called 'Evaluating the protection afforded by surgical masks against influenza bioaerosols: Gross protection of surgical masks compared to filtering facepiece respirators' said,

> surgical masks are not intended to provide protection against infectious aerosols… There is a common misperception amongst workers and employers that surgical masks will protect against aerosols.

The FDA says on its official page on face masks that

While a surgical mask may be effective in blocking
splashes and large-particle droplets, a face mask, by
design, it does not filter or block very small particles in
the air that may be transmitted by coughs, sneezes, or
certain medical procedures. Surgical masks also do not
provide complete protection from germs and other
contaminants because of the loose fit between the
surface of the mask and your face.

More recently some surgical masks have incorporated
N95-style electrostatic filters in them, which are designed
(like N95s), to filter out most virions and bacteria, but they
still have their traditional loose fit, which means this
filtering effect is mostly negated. In addition their filter
usually has a weaker electrostatic charge than an N95. (For
details see 'Face masks against COVID-19: Standards,
efficacy, testing and decontamination methods' by Ju et al in
Advances in colloid and interface science (v.292, June
2021).)

There is, though, also a newer mask called a 'surgical
N95', which has a tight fit as well as an N95 filter – see the
later sections on respirator masks like the N95 for more on
this sort of mask.

Has there been research on the effectiveness of surgical masks?

There has been quite a bit of research on this. Not as much
as you might expect, but enough for us to conclude that
surgical masks probably do nothing much to prevent virions
from being transmitted to their patients. See part 5.7 for a
literature review on the effectiveness of surgical (aka
medical) masks in a surgical context, although I will
mention here a seminal 1981 study titled 'Is a mask

necessary in the operating theatre?', published in the *Annals of the Royal College of Surgeons of England*, which said

> No masks were worn in one operating theatre for 6 months. There was no increase in the incidence of wound infection… The conclusion is that the wearing of a mask has very little relevance to the wellbeing of patients undergoing routine general surgery and it is a standard practice that could be abandoned.

The study also noted that

> A review of the very considerable literature on prevention of infection in theatre shows a heavy bias in favour of history and hypothesis.

MedPage Today in 'ICAAC: Surgical Masks Don't Prevent Infection' (Phend, 16 Sep 2009) reported that

> Although surgical masks were the face of the 2003 SARS epidemic in Asia, they don't protect against pandemic H1N1 (swine flu) or any other respiratory infection, C. Raina MacIntyre, MBBS, PhD, of the University of New South Wales in Sydney, Australia, and colleagues warned. Last month, MacIntyre presented a preliminary version of these findings to an Institute of Medicine panel deliberating guidelines for personal protective equipment standards for healthcare workers. Aside from her trial, there was little but anecdotal testimony. "There are many guidelines – quite sweeping guidelines – about the use of masks without really a shred of high-level evidence to support them," said MacIntyre.

Bear in mind that when a doctor really wants to prevent the transmission of a serious disease they wear specially-designed protective headgear, or biohazard-type suits. They don't wear standard surgical masks in such cases, and they certainly don't wear trendy masks with roses on them that they bought off the internet.

(Also bear in mind that surgeon's masks aren't sterile when they put them on, as is commonly supposed. For example, in 'Gaps in asepsis due to surgical caps, face masks, external surfaces of infusion bottles and sterile wrappers of disposable articles' by Gräf and von Imhoff in *Zentralblatt fur Bakteriologie, Mikrobiologie und Hygiene. Serie B* (v.179 (6), Dec 1984, pp.508-28), the authors found that

> The surfaces of 25% of the examined disposable surgical masks and caps were considerably contaminated with saprophytic germs

even before they were used).

Aren't you anti-maskers just selfish? You just can't be bothered to save people's lives.

This is hot air. And speaking of hot air, an important reason why masks are a dismal failure is that a lot of the air simply goes in and out around the loose-fitting edges of the mask, rather than through the mask itself. As a group of fluid engineering researchers at the University of Waterloo showed

> most common masks, primarily due to problems with fit, filter about 10 per cent of exhaled aerosol droplets. The remaining aerosols are redirected, mostly out the top of the mask where it fits over the nose, and escape into the ambient air unfiltered.

Or, as these Edinburgh researchers put it in an article titled 'Face Coverings, Aerosol Dispersion and Mitigation of Virus Transmission Risk' by Viola et al in *Engineering in Medicine and Biology* (v.2, 20 Jan 2021, pp.26-35), the effectiveness of the masks should mostly be considered based on the generation of secondary jets rather than on the ability to mitigate the front throughflow.

As these aerosol experts said in their study on face masks titled 'Performance of an N95 Filtering Facepiece Particulate Respirator and a Surgical Mask During Human Breathing: Two Pathways for Particle Penetration' by Grinshpun et al, in *Journal of Occupational and Environmental Hygiene* (v.6 (10), Oct 2009, pp.593-603)

we concluded that the future efforts in designing new RPDs [respiratory protection devices] for health care environments should be increasingly focused on the peripheral design rather than on the further improvement of the filter media. The faceseal leakage was found to represent the main pathway for the submicrometer particles penetrating into the respirator/mask. Thus, we believe that the priority in product development should be given to establishing a better fit that would eliminate or minimize the faceseal leakage.

Face mask leakage can actually be seen on the many videos where someone takes a lungful of smoke or visible cold air and then breathes out with a mask on. Most of the breath goes out the sides, and only some goes through the mask itself.

The smaller the holes in the mesh, or the more layers of mask, the more the air goes in and out of the sides, because small mesh holes or more layers makes it a harder job for your air to get out through the mask, so it takes the easier route of going out the sides where there's nothing stopping it. This air isn't filtered at all by your mask, whether going in or coming out. This is why serious masks are supposed to have a tight fit around the face. But this is pretty much impossible to do with standard masks, especially the virtue-signalling designer cloth ones with patterns on them.

But even without side leakage, cloth masks are ineffective. As this review titled 'Masks-for-all for COVID-19 not based on sound data' by two University of Chicago experts on respiratory protection for the Center for Infectious Disease Research and Policy at the University of Minnesota (April 2020) says

> In sum, cloth masks exhibit very low filter efficiency. Thus, even masks that fit well against the face will not prevent inhalation of small particles by the wearer or emission of small particles from the wearer.

But coughing and sneezing…?

One of the weirdest things about the mask studies that mask proponents use as evidence for the effectiveness of masks is that many of them are just studies on coughing and sneezing. These studies generally show that masks greatly reduce the distance aerosols and other particles travel from the mouth when you cough or sneeze. No joke, that's what they're looking at.

It's hard to overstate the idiocy of this. First of all, no-one doubts that covering your mouth with a piece of cloth will prevent droplets and particles from flying off everywhere. Have these people never heard of handkerchiefs? But, more importantly, where did they get the idea that maskless people are just going to be coughing and sneezing without doing anything to cover their mouths? Virtually no-one does this, especially in these paranoid times. So how far a cough or sneeze can travel unimpeded by anything is just a total irrelevancy. Maskless people will cover their mouths when they have to cough or sneeze, just like they always have done.

The other weird thing about the pro-maskers' focus on how masks help with coughs and sneezes is… are they just expecting people to cough and sneeze into their masks? Because this seems to be the assumption underlying a lot of their talk. But they rarely quite come out and say explicitly "You should cough and sneeze directly into your masks". Some actually do say this, but most don't quite say, they just imply it. Probably because it is deeply bizarre, and unrealistic, and unhygienic. What kind of weirdo sneezes into their mask? That's whole lot of saliva and snot and bacteria that you've just deposited right onto the surface that's going to be covering your face, in some cases for the next six or so hours if you're working an all-day shift where you're expected to wear a mask all day. Or you're at a school that is forcing you to wear a mask. You may sneeze again later, especially if you have hay fever, and you could end up sneezing dozens of times a day. Who the hell does this? Or coughs a bunch of phlegm onto the inside of their mask? Anyone who does such things is in the grip of a serious delusion. How is it being health-minded to soak your face in a stew of bacteria and viruses and mucus and spit for hours? If you really do do this, you should replace your mask every time, because a wet mask is supposed to be replaced.

But let's face it, most people, even the mask fanatics, aren't going to orally ejaculate into their mask, they're going to remove their mask, or push it aside, and use their hand, or a tissue, or a handkerchief. And then they'll put their mask back on, which goes completely against the mask protocols. And you will know that all their careful studies measuring sneeze distances were about as useful as counting how many eyes of newt you've got.

I bet some scientists cough and sneeze into their masks.

You may be right. In a bizarre story on 29 July 2020 ('Spreading Germs: How many bacteria are trapped by masks?'), scientists boasted to Virginian news station WBDJ7 about how great masks are by showing the difference between coughing into a petri dish without a mask, and with a mask. Growths occurred after a few days in the former petri dish but not the latter. What this shows, although the scientists fail to appreciate this, is that if you cough into a mask (who actually does this? Perhaps these scientists do) you are coughing a whole load of bacteria into the cloth that you will be wearing next to your mouth for the rest of the day, and maybe the next few days if you don't get around to washing or replacing it. Why would anyone think this is a good thing?

I expect the American Medical Association has a rather different view than you.

Nope. The *Journal of the American Medical Association*, published by, yes, the American Medical Association, has a Patient Page dedicated to masks. (JAMA's 'Patient Pages' are a described by them as 'public service' with information and recommendations about various medical matters.) On this page they say (and this page is still current as of Jan 2022)

> Face masks should not be worn by healthy individuals to protect themselves from acquiring respiratory infection because there is no evidence to suggest that face masks worn by healthy individuals are effective in preventing people from becoming ill.

(They recommend face masks only be used by people with respiratory symptoms, those caring for them, and health care workers.)

But lots of doctors are telling us to wear masks?

Here's something to ask any doctor who says this. Ask them if they would be willing to walk into a room with no windows or ventilation which is full of smoke, with just a cloth face mask on. (Smoke particles are generally bigger than virions.) Then you'll find out what they really think. You will find that they will soon start drastically qualifying what they say, for example, 'Well, masks only have a small effect, but every bit counts', etc.

If you think this question might come across as too blunt, then ask your doctor instead about some of the studies listed in the literature review, particularly Macintyre's 2015 BMJ study, the only randomized controlled trial ever done on cloth masks. Or ask them to cite a randomized controlled trial on any sort of masks that shows that masks work. You'll soon find them getting evasive and hustling you out of the room.

Don't masks at least stop 'spray-talkers' and sneezers from spreading the virus?

The one thing we all agree on is that a face mask does probably stop at least some of the larger saliva droplets that some people spray out when they talk from going into someone else's mouth or eyes. (And the droplets from coughs and sneezes, for that matter, but as I said earlier, who is seriously going to cough or sneeze into a mask?) But that is a very different matter than stopping smaller aerosols, which are the main method of SARS-CoV-2 transmission. As the National Academies of Sciences Rapid Expert Consultation on the Effectiveness of Fabric Masks for the COVID-19 Pandemic says

The evidence from these laboratory filtration studies suggests that such fabric masks may reduce the transmission of larger respiratory droplets. There is little evidence regarding the transmission of small aerosolized particulates of the size potentially exhaled by asymptomatic or presymptomatic individuals with COVID-19.

A review article in *City Journal* titled 'Do We Need Mask Mandates?' (Harris, 22 March 2021), say

So while masks may stop short-range, face-to-face spread from large droplets, they are likely less effective—and perhaps completely ineffective—at stopping airborne spread from aerosols.

These issues have been around for a long time. In a 1920 paper titled 'An experimental study of the efficacy of gauze face masks' by Kellogg and Macmillan, in the *American Journal of Public Health* (v.10 (1), Jan 1920, pp.34-42), the failure of mask-wearing in San Francisco during the 1918 influenza epidemic was noted, and the authors said

The reason for this apparent failure of the mask was a subject for speculation among epidemiologists, for it had long been the belief of many of us that droplet borne infections should be easily controlled in this manner. The failure of the mask was a source of disappointment, for the first experiment in San Francisco was watched with interest with the expectation that if it proved feasible to enforce the regulation the desired result would be achieved. The reverse proved true. The masks, contrary to expectation, were worn cheerfully and universally, and also, contrary to expectation of what should follow under such circumstances, no effect on the epidemic curve was to be seen. Something was plainly wrong with our hypotheses.

Wasn't stopping large droplets was the original point of masks in 2020?

Yes, stopping large droplets, sent out of the mouth by talking, as well as by sneezing and coughing, was all that many mask advocates initially claimed. Their original selling point was that masks would stop these larger droplets, and that would stop transmission in its tracks.

If stopping large droplets was the original point, why did it matter whether you covered your nose?

Good question. I've never seen this discussed, but I expect that we would get more nonsense about sneezes as an answer.

Wasn't large droplets also why it was said that masks protect others from you, not you from them?

Yes. Your infected droplets would be stopped by your mask. But if someone without a mask spray-talks or coughs the virus onto your mask, you may then breathe in those virus particles from your mask. So that's why initially the mask advocates were saying a mask is to protect others, not you.

So not wearing a mask is selfish?

The propagandists who advise the governments, like the UK's Nudge Unit, liked this idea, because it meant that it didn't matter if you said 'I'm not worried about getting Covid' – the issue was that you were putting other people at risk. So whether you were bothered about getting Covid or not didn't come into it.

See, for example, this April 2020 *Lancet* paper:

People often wear masks to protect themselves, but we suggest a stronger public health rationale is source control to protect others from respiratory droplets… This measure shifts the focus from self-protection to altruism.

(In 'Wearing face masks in the community during the COVID-19 pandemic: altruism and solidarity' by Cheng et al, April 16, 2020.

Once aerosol transmission came into the picture, though, this messaging faded away, because the original asymmetry no longer existed: masks were no better at keeping aerosols in than out. (And, let's face it, most mask-wearers, other than some of the young virtue-signallers, are wearing a mask because they believe it protects them as much as it protects others.)

(Despite the change in science on droplet vs aerosol spread, we will see in part 4 that British government mask reports, even in 2022, still talk as though stopping droplets is the main point of masks.)

Didn't the CDC start appealing to our selfish natures towards the end of 2020?

Yes, after noticing that a small but significant proportion of people were still not wearing a mask despite their 'wear a mask to protect others' messaging, the CDC decided to start selling masks as protecting you as well. A 12 Nov 2020 article in the *Washington Post* called 'Wearing a mask isn't just about protecting other people, the CDC says. It can help you — and might prevent lockdowns', reports

When the White House coronavirus task force first recommended mask-wearing April 3, officials emphasized that this was not about you. It was about others... [But] The Centers for Disease Control and Prevention said for the first time, writing in a scientific bulletin posted to its website this week that "the benefit of masking is derived from the combination of source control and personal protection for the mask wearer." Masks are neither completely selfless nor selfish — they help everyone. John Brooks, chief medical officer for the CDC's coronavirus response, told The Washington Post... "the agency wants the public to understand masks are masks are "good for them."

In particular, those selfish conservatives who don't care about anyone else but themselves were targeted by this messaging:

"Overall, this seems like a win in terms of messaging that would appeal to Republicans," said Katherine White, an expert in consumer behavior at the University of British Columbia. She said this was because conservatives are strongly motivated by a personal responsibility to care for themselves.

Notice also the typical emphasis on language:

Brooks, who oversaw the publication of the new bulletin, said the language went through lengthy vetting to make sure there was agreement on the best evidence.

Forget the 'agreement on best evidence', which is not so much a matter of language, what this means is that the language was heavily vetted to make sure the most effective propaganda they could cook up was being used.

Do masks stop the virus particles they trap from ever getting out of the mask again?

No. Even when masks traps a virion it doesn't destroy the virion, or lock it away in a deep dungeon where it can never get out. The virion is loosely held by the mask fibres, but it will be regularly blown upon by the wearer's breath which will pull it away from the fibre. Eventually the virion can break free of the fibre holding it and be carried by a breath out into the surrounding environment. So for many virions the mask merely delays its passage into the surrounding air.

Dr Roger Koops, an experienced biochemist (who worked for years in Quality Assurance/Control and issues related to Regulatory Compliance), explains:

> The virus is not somehow magically "glued" to the mask but can be expelled, whether or not there is still moisture. This can happen the next time a person breathes, speaks, coughs, sneezes, hisses, grunts, etc. So, the virus can be expelled out into the environment from the face covering... the face covering acts as an intermediary in transmission. It can alter the timing of the virus getting into the environment, but it now acts as a contact source and airborne source; virus can still get into the environment. Since we know that the stability is good on most covering and mask materials, it does nothing to break down the virus until the covering is removed... as more virus molecules accumulate, more are expelled. The face covering is not some virus black hole that sucks the virus into oblivion.

The same is true of breathing in. Even those virions which your mask has trapped are not forever locked away from entering your lungs. Many virions will only be loosely held by a fibre, and this connection will be broken down by repeated breaths in and out, and after a while some of them will detach from the mask fibres and be pulled into your lungs by a breath.

Of course many of the virions that are trapped in your mask will stay there all day, but don't think that all of them will. The longer you wear a mask the more trapped virions there will be that detach from your mask and enter your lungs or the air around you.

Consider the situation where 13 million masks in Switzerland had to be recalled because they had gone mouldy. The people who had been forced to wear them before the recall said that they got a strong mould smell from the masks:

> Hospital staff in Bern then complained of burning eyes and breathing problems'. "They smelled like a moldy bathroom ... Almost unbearable!" said one employee in an interview with Euronews.

(*Euronews*, 'Masken mit Pilzbefall: "Sie rochen wie ein schimmliges Badezimmer"', 13 July 2020.)

This vividly demonstrates how masks do not permanently trap all pathogens, such as virions, bacteria, and fungi, within the mask's fibres. Some stay loosely attached to the fibres for a while before being breathed in or out.

Why was stopping larger droplets all that the pro-maskers claimed early on?

The reason for this was this was received wisdom at the WHO, and at many other health institutions, was that the main method of transmission for respiratory disease was large droplets rather than fine aerosols. For example, a 2008 British government report called 'Evaluating the protection afforded by surgical masks against influenza bioaerosols: Gross protection of surgical masks compared to filtering facepiece respirators', which was put together by the Health and Safety Laboratory for the Health and Safety Executive, said:

The main route of transmission of influenza is believed to be via direct contact with large droplets. The relative importance of aerosols in transmission is considered to be minor, but it cannot be ruled-out.

It turned out that WHO and all these other health institutions were wrong, as they have been wrong about so many things. A large group of determined scientists, who knew large droplets were not the most important method of transmission eventually forced WHO and other health authorities to acknowledge, in summer 2020, that aerosol spread was a major method of transmission.

This was partly achieved by 239 academics led by Donald Milton, who we will be meeting in part 3, and Lidia Morawska publishing a letter about the issue in the journal *Clinical Infectious Diseases* (v.71 (9), 1 Nov 2020, pp.2311–3), entitled 'It Is Time to Address Airborne Transmission of Coronavirus Disease 2019 (COVID-19)'.

One obvious reason to believe that aerosol transmission was happening was that people were getting sick after being in the same room as someone who was infected without there being any close or sustained contact, and there were plenty of other good reasons too.

Once it was finally acknowledged that aerosol spread was very important (although WHO dragged its feet over formally acknowledging this, as did the CDC) then the promotion of basic cloth masks, which don't stop aerosols, should have been greatly downgraded or discontinued (especially given the numerous and major downsides to them).

This, of course, didn't happen. Some of the scientists who pushed the aerosol spread theory genuinely believed that masks would stop aerosols as well as large droplets. Many others knew or suspected they didn't stop aerosols, but wanted them anyway. So masks continued to be stupidly or even dishonestly pushed as a simple, quick and important solution to getting rid of Covid.

(Note that Trish Greenhalgh pushed the aerosol theory while being a fanatical mask advocate, but it took her until 17 January 2022 before she admitted that aerosol transmission means that cloth masks don't work:

> It was initially assumed SARS-CoV-2 spread via droplets (in coughs and sneezes) which caused infection when they landed on the mouth, nose or eyes. For such particles, a cloth or surgical mask is an efficient form of source control to protect others from virus emitted by the wearer. Now it's understood the virus is airborne... In general, they [cloth masks] are poor filters of small airborne particles.

(In 'Time to upgrade from cloth and surgical masks to respirators? Your questions answered' in *The Conversation*, 17 Jan 2022.)

Wasn't it around then that the WHO started advocating masks?

Yes, the WHO came on board at that time with the promotion of masks *despite* the fact that they had now started to accept that aerosol spread was a factor, and despite the fact that they knew there was no good evidence for the effectiveness of masks in stopping aerosols (as they admitted in their influential mask review published on 5th June 2020; see below for more on this). But real science was swept away at this point by political game-playing, and the promotion of masks at that time by health authorities, governments and the media, backed by the WHO's cynical stamp of approval, not to mention the CDC's earlier switch on masks on April 3, went into overdrive despite the fact that the new consensus about how Covid spreads made masks irrelevant.

The mask push was driven into overdrive a bit later in 2020 by a ludicrous article in *Nature Medicine* v. 27, Oct 2020, pp. pp.94–105) by the Institute for Health Metrics and Evaluation COVID-19 Forecasting Team, titled 'Modeling COVID-19 scenarios for the United States'. They claimed that 130,000 (possibly even 170,000) lives could be saved in the USA by public mask use:

> We find that achieving universal mask use (95% mask use in public) could be sufficient to ameliorate the worst effects of epidemic resurgences in many states. Universal mask use could save an additional 129,574 (85,284–170,867) lives from September 22, 2020 through the end of February 2021, or an additional 95,814 (60,731–133,077) lives assuming a lesser adoption of mask wearing (85%), when compared to the reference scenario.

This hyperbolic claim was repeated dutifully by the lapdog media, such as the *New York Times*, and by the singing buffoon Francis Collins, who runs the NIH (search YouTube for his unbelievably cringeworthy songs.)

This paper wasn't based on any serious real-life work, it was based on IHME's computer modelling of scenarios. And despite their prestige with the media, IHME's modelling in the Covid era has turned out to be complete junk. Moreover, the authors simply assume that mask-wearing works, rather than providing any evidence to think they do, so it simply circular reasoning to point to this paper as evidence that masks work.

(The *Wall St Journal* also ran a piece, 'Case for Mask Mandate Rests on Bad Data', by Magness, 11 Nov 2020, criticising the study in regards to the estimates of mask-wearers at the time.)

So how much of Covid spread does depend on spray-talking then?

Spray-talking is unlikely to be a major source of Covid transmission, and anyone who is worried about getting it that way can just keep their distance. Or stay inside and hide under the bed.

Is keeping your distance still a good idea in general if spray droplets are not the main method of transmission?

Keeping your distance will reduce the chances of the terrified from getting Covid via aerosol transmission, because even though aerosols can travel further than droplets, they become greatly dispersed the further they travel, like with cigarette smoke. So you are still more likely to get it from being close up to someone than further away. But no amount of distancing can *guarantee* you'll never get Covid from aerosols, and the more time goes on the more likely you are to get it. Take the case of Independent SAGE member Christina Pagel, a zero-Covid fanatic, who thought that her social distancing and mask-wearing meant that she would never get Covid. She did.

Overall, though, social distancing has extremely damaging effects on society.

What about fomite transmission?

'Fomite' transmission, ie. getting infected through touching contaminated surfaces, can also occur, but is now considered to be far less important as a source of infection– the CDC said on 5th April 2021 that 'the relative risk of fomite transmission of SARS-CoV-2 is considered low'. So you can stop disinfecting your groceries now.

How do we know that spray-talking is less important than aerosols?

It turns out that the science about these things was pretty poor. Hundreds of billions of dollars has been spent on disease research over the last century, yet our understanding of some of the basic mechanisms of how diseases spread was a mess. It's not just me who thinks this, this Royal Society article from 12 Oct 2021 titled 'How did we get here: what are droplets and aerosols and how far do they go? A historical perspective on the transmission of respiratory infectious diseases' by Randall et al also thinks so:

> The COVID-19 pandemic has exposed major gaps in our understanding of the transmission of viruses through the air. These gaps slowed recognition of airborne transmission of the disease.

A useful popular summary of how things changed around with Covid can be found in the *Wired* article 'The 60-Year-Old Scientific Screwup That Helped Covid Kill' by Megan Molteni (13 May 2021) (but please ignore the melodramatic overstatements in it).

See also the *Nature* news piece titled 'Mounting evidence suggests coronavirus is airborne — but health advice has not caught up' by (Lewis, 8 July 2020).

And 'Airborne transmission of SARS-CoV-2: The world should face the reality' by Morawskaa and Caob in *Environment International* (v.139, June 2020).

Scientific opinion has now swung strongly over to the view that aerosol spread is the main method of transmission. The *Wired* article has some examples of recent research supporting this, eg:

Li's elegant simulations showed that when a person coughed or sneezed, the heavy droplets were too few and the targets—an open mouth, nostrils, eyes—too small to account for much infection. Li's team had concluded, therefore, that the public health establishment had it backward and that most colds, flu, and other respiratory illnesses must spread through aerosols instead.

An influential paper in the *Lancet* (v. 397 (10285), May 1 2021, pp.1603-1605) entitled 'Ten scientific reasons in support of airborne transmission of SARS-CoV-2' set out

ten streams of evidence [that] collectively support the hypothesis that SARS-CoV-2 is transmitted primarily by the airborne route.

A University of California study argued that not only does SARS-CoV-2 spread via aerosols, but most other respiratory diseases do as well (previously it was believed that only a few diseases, such as measles, spread this way).

SARS-CoV, MERS-CoV, influenza, measles, and the rhinoviruses that cause the common cold can all spread via aerosols that can build up in indoor air and linger for hours, an international interdisciplinary team of researchers reported in a review published in Science Aug. 27.

Over the last century and at the beginning of this pandemic, it was widely believed that respiratory viruses, including SARS-CoV-2, mainly spread through droplets produced in coughs and sneezes of infected individuals or through touching contaminated surfaces. However, droplet and fomite transmission of SARS-CoV-2 fails to account for the numerous superspreading events observed during the COVID-19 pandemic or the much higher transmission that occurs indoors vs. outdoors...

The team reviewed numerous studies of superspreading events observed during the COVID pandemic and found the studies consistently showed that airborne transmission is the most likely transmission route rather than surface contacts or contact with large droplets.

('It's not just SARS-CoV-2: Most respiratory viruses spread by aerosols', by Monroe, University of California News, 9 Sep 2021.)

An editorial review by Tang et al in the *British Medical Journal* titled 'Covid-19 has redefined airborne transmission' (v.373, 14 April 2021) says

It is now clear that SARS-CoV-2 transmits mostly between people at close range through inhalation. This does not mean that transmission through contact with surfaces or that the longer range airborne route does not occur, but these routes of transmission are less important during brief everyday interactions over the usual 1 m conversational distance. In close range situations, people are much more likely to be exposed to the virus by inhaling it than by having it fly through the air in large droplets to land on their eyes, nostrils, or lips. The transmission of SARS-CoV-2 after touching surfaces is now considered to be relatively minimal.

This *JAMA Insights* paper titled 'Indoor Air Changes and Potential Implications for SARS-CoV-2 Transmission', by Allen et al (v.325 (20), April 16 2020, pp. 2112-3) says

First, SARS-CoV-2 is primarily transmitted from the exhaled respiratory aerosols of infected individuals. Larger droplets (>100 μm) can settle out of the air due to gravitational forces within 6 feet, but people emit 100 times more smaller aerosols (<5 μm) during talking, breathing, and coughing. Smaller aerosols can stay aloft for 30 minutes to hours and travel well beyond 6 feet.

Second, high-profile and well-described SARS-CoV-2 outbreaks across multiple space types (eg, restaurants, gyms, choir practice, schools, buses) share the common features of time indoors and low levels of ventilation, even when people remained physically distanced.

In my own view the situation with hospitals suggests strongly that Covid transmission is mainly by fine aerosols rather than direct saliva droplets. Hospitals are not full of people up close talking to each other. The vast majority of patients are confined to their beds for almost all the time. The staff are all wearing masks, which stop droplet spray. Some patients have visitors, but the visitors mostly wear masks and anyway mainly sit away from the patient in a chair beside the bed. Hospitals have zealously enforced social distancing, with plastic screens everywhere. Hospitals are the polar opposite of crowded mosh-pits; there is very little opportunity for spray-talk transmission in hospitals. Despite all this hospitals are prime Covid spreaders. The same applies to care homes. Given that 'fomite' transmission is less important, and given that most masks are of little use against aerosol spread, that leaves aerosol transmission as the prime suspect in hospital (and care home) Covid spread. (This argument, I was pleased to note, appears as reason number five on the aforementioned *Lancet* paper.)

Also note that SARS-CoV-2 has relentlessly spread to billions of people all over the world despite the widespread and long-term use of masks and social distancing in many countries, which have made no difference. This is what you would expect if SARS-CoV-2 was primarily spread by aerosols, which masks and social distancing don't have much effect upon, but not what you'd expect if larger droplets were the main transmission source.

Didn't WHO produce an influential document in June 2020 making a case for masks? Why should I believe you over them?

You didn't actually read that document, did you? I did, at the time, and did an analysis of it on my website. The document not only makes no good case at all for mask use, it actually admits that there isn't much a case.

First of all, note that it doesn't go through any studies in any detail, it merely summarises what it thinks the literature has found. And what it thinks the literature has found is... not much at all:

> There is limited evidence that wearing a medical mask by healthy individuals in households, in particular those who share a house with a sick person, or among attendees of mass gatherings may be beneficial as a measure preventing transmission... Results from cluster randomized controlled trials on the use of masks among young adults living in university residences in the United States of America indicate that face masks may reduce the rate of influenza-like illness, but showed no impact on risk of laboratory-confirmed influenza. At present, there is no direct evidence (from studies on COVID-19 and in healthy people in the community) on the effectiveness of universal masking of healthy people in the community to prevent infection with respiratory viruses, including COVID-19.

After this, they concluded that

> At the present time, the widespread use of masks by healthy people in the community setting is not yet supported by high quality or direct scientific evidence.

So why did WHO recommend masks despite finding there was no evidence for their use? Their reasons were vague:

taking into account [1] the available studies evaluating pre- and asymptomatic transmission, [2] a growing compendium of observational evidence on the use of masks by the general public in several countries, [3] individual values and preferences, as well as [4] the difficulty of physical distancing in many contexts, WHO has updated its guidance to advise that to prevent COVID-19 transmission effectively in areas of community transmission, governments should encourage the general public to wear masks in specific situations and settings as part of a comprehensive approach to suppress SARS-CoV-2 transmission.

Nothing was said about [1]. [2] and [3] were pretty meaningless. [4] was irrelevant as evidence. So they basically had, by their own admission, no good reason to recommend masks. But the priestly caste of the scientific community had become fixated on masks at the time, as had Western governments and health bodies, and WHO was pressured politically to change its tune, so it did. (There were many stories at the time about WHO being leaned upon.)

Note also that nowhere in this document is there any support expressed for making masks compulsory. It merely says that governments should encourage their use.

Some have alleged that WHO's decision to support masks despite the lack of evidence was political.

Yes, and not just 'conspiracy theorists'. BBC reporter Deb Cohen tweeted on 12- July 2020 that

We had been told by various sources WHO committee reviewing the evidence had not backed masks but they recommended them due to political lobbying. This point was put to WHO who did not deny.

What about the higher-quality masks like N95s? Aren't these supposed to be better at stopping aerosol-borne viruses? What are they anyway?

Better quality masks, or respirators, are known as N95, PPF2 or PPF3. These terms are government standards, not commercial names. N95 is a U.S. government standard, regulated by the National Institute for Occupational Safety and Health. The 'N' refers to 'not resistant to oil'. FFP2 and FFP3 are EU standards, and is currently in use in the UK. 'FFP' stands for 'filtering facepiece'.

The N95 standard requires the respirator to filter out at least 95% of particles that are 0.3 microns (300 nanometres) in size. (That's what the '95' stands for.) This is actually the size that the respirator is least good at filtering: it will normally perform better for particles that are smaller and larger than 0.3 microns. This allows the respirator to trap virions, bacteria, dust, haze, pollen, smoke and smog, and so on. (In theory, at least, and under ideal conditions.)

The FFP2 standard is roughly equivalent to the N95: FFP2 masks filter out 94% of particles that are 0.3 microns in size. FFP3 is a higher standard again: FFP3 masks are required to filter out 99% of 0.3 micron particles. FFP1 is a lower standard, it requires 80% filtration.

(There are also standards on the 'inward leakage'.)

What's a KN95 mask?

KN95 is a Chinese standard, and is like a lower-quality version of the N95. In theory a KN95 mask will filter out 95% of 0.3 micron particles just like the N95. In practice many KN95s are poor quality, or even fakes, and don't work anywhere near like they're supposed to. For example,

Researchers at ECRI, a not-for-profit organization that for decades has advised hospitals, government organizations and other healthcare stakeholders on product safety, found that 60 to 70 percent of imported KN95 masks do not filter 95 percent of aerosol particulates, contrary to what their name suggests.

Despite this a lot of American mask mandates allow or even prefer the KN95 in order to preserve N95 supplies for the medical profession.

What's a KF94 mask?

KF94 mask is a Korean standard that is similar to N95 ('KF' stands for 'Korean filter').

What's an R95?

An R95 is just like an N95, except that it's also resistant to oily particles (it will last about a day in conditions with oily particles).

What's a P95?

A P95 is just like an R95, except that it's also very resistant to oily particles (it will last for about 40 hours of use).

What are N99 and N100 masks?

These are like N95s but have 99% and 99.97% efficiency.

What's a P2 mask?

P2 is an Australian standard that is similar to N95 and FFP2.

What are these masks made of?

N95 respirators are made of four plies of polypropylene media: an outer veil that is moisture resistant, a double-ply filtration layer, and an inner layer that is in contact with the skin.

The efficiency of the respirator lies in the middle filtration layer, which is developed through the processes of melt blowing and electrostatic charging.

Masks made using this sort of technology are often called 'non-woven', because the very thin plastic strands/fibres in them are not made by normal weaving techniques, but by industrial 'melt-blowing' and 'spunbond' processes. Often different layers are made using a different process. (For details see 'Face masks against COVID-19: Standards, efficacy, testing and decontamination methods' by Ju et al in *Advances in colloid and interface science* (v.292, June 2021).)

Electrostatic charging?

Yes, the key to the superior filtering performance of respirators is that they have an inner layer of fibres that have a slight electrostatic charge. This attracts small particles and causes them to stick to the fibres. Without the electrostatic charge these filters would be far, far less good at trapping tiny particles.

Why are N95s so efficient at filtering out the smaller particles? It has something to do with "Brownian motion," or a phenomenon that causes particles smaller than 0.3 microns to move in a haphazard, zig-zagging motion. This makes it more likely for the particles to get caught inside the fibers of the N95. Plus, the masks use electrostatic absorption, which means that rather than passing through the fiber, the particles are trapped.

"Although these particles are smaller than the pores, they can be pulled over by the charged fibers and get stuck," Jiaxing Huang, a materials scientist at Northwestern University, told *USA Today*.

(From 'N95 Vs. KN95 Masks: What's the Difference?' by Linder, *Popular Mechanics*, 7 Jan 7, 2022.)

Why do some of these masks have valves?

Respirators can come with or without a valve, which will open for a strong breath in and/or out (depending on the design). There is no filtration for the air that goes out the valve.

Doesn't that mean valved masks don't work?

Yes. The NHS even put out a safety alert for valved FFP3 masks in August 2021, which said that

> The exhalation valves do not filter exhaled breath. Current infection control guidance states that: "Valved respirators should not be worn by a healthcare worker/operator when sterility directly over the surgical field is required".

The British Association of Oral Surgeons also recommend against the use of valved masks, even FFP3 masks:

> Valved FFP3 masks may represent a risk by directing unfiltered exhaled breath toward a patient... FFP3 masks with an exhalation valve may be more comfortable for the user but, by design, they allow unfiltered breath to be directed toward a patient during close contact.

Cornell University admits that masks with valves are useless:

N95 respirators with exhalation valves are not effective in reducing the spread of COVID-19 and are not permitted to be used as a face covering.

(Note that an exhale valve is fine if the purpose of the mask is to prevent the wearer breathing in, for example, wood dust.)

So the N95 and FFP2/3 masks are better than cloth masks then?

In theory all these masks are far better than your basic cloth mask. Cloth masks have large holes in them, whereas the gaps between the strands in respirators are smaller.

What size gaps are there in the N95 filter?

This is a trickier question than it seems. First of all, note that a lot supposed fact-checking sites and debunking pro-mask newspaper articles simply say the answer is 0.3 microns, eg. 'The N95 filter is indeed physically around the 0.3 micron size'. That's not really right, and it looks like a lot of them are simply mixing this up with the fact that these masks are tested again particles that 0.3 microns in size.

First of all, we need to note that outer layers of N95s are usually made of spunbond fibres, while the crucial inner layer is made of melt-blown fibres. The spunbond layers have relatively larger fibres and larger gaps. In 'Face masks against COVID-19: Standards, efficacy, testing and decontamination methods' by Ju et al in *Advances in colloid and interface science* (v.292, June 2021), the authors say

> In general, this spunbonded PP layer has a fiber diameter of 20 μm and a pore size of up to 100 μm.

The pore sizes actually vary greatly, but this is little better than many cloth masks.

The thickness of the fibres in the melt-blown layer vary much more than the spunbond fibres, but they are on average much thinner – they have a 'fiber diameter in the range of 1–10 μm'. The pore sizes here are much smaller, around 20μm (not 3μm as many sites tell you). 20μm is still far bigger than the 0.7–1μm of the typical aerosol-carrying droplet.

Here are some microscopic images of N95 layers from Neupane et al in 'Optical microscopic study of surface morphology and filtering efficiency of face masks', *PeerJ* (v. 7 e7142. 26 Jun. 2019), which the authors describe as

> Representative images of (G) inner, (H) middle, and (I) outer layers of a three layered surgical mask.

(The short bar at the bottom of picture G is 500 microns long and applies to H and I as well.)

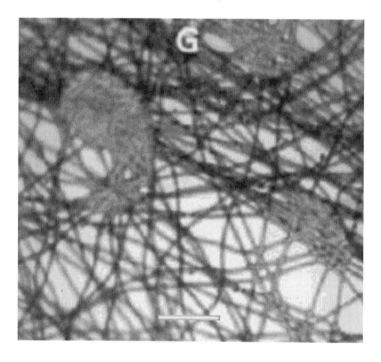

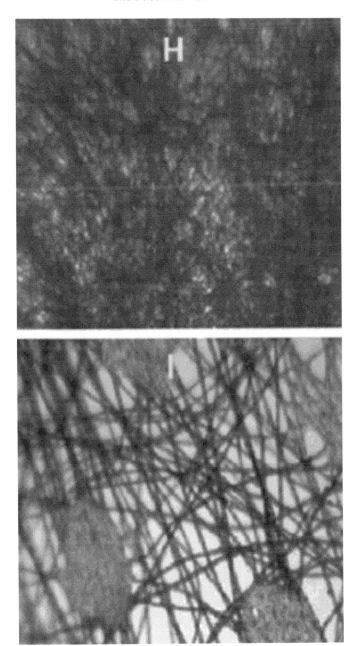

Notice that the fibres in a respirator are arranged fairly randomly – they don't form regular geometric patterns like a chain-link fence. Also, even within the one layer you've often got multiple layers of strands, so even if an aerosol gets through one gap, it may still be stopped after that. And there are multiple layers in the mas itself, which will further reduce the chances of an aerosol getting through. Plus there is the fact that very small particles like fine aerosols move in a random zig-zag motion as they are buffeted by the small air particles around them – this is 'Brownian motion', and in this context it's called 'diffusion' – which further increases their chances of getting caught. (Note that diffusion also happens with cloth masks, even though some writers, such as in the *Popular Mechanics* piece above, present it as something that is unique to respirators, and part of why they are better than cloth masks.)

However, although these features make some difference, the fact is that even with them N95s wouldn't be very good at filtering. What makes the biggest difference with an N95 filter is the electrostatic charge that is applied to the fibres, which attracts the aerosols. (Note that the main charge is in the middle melt-blown layer – the spunbond layers only have a weak charge.)

I have seen numerous scientific papers say that it is the charge that is by far the most important factor. They all give different numbers for how much worse the filtering efficiency is without the charge, as the matter is not that precise, and you get different results for different masks, but the general idea is that an N95 would only stop 5–30% of 0.3 micron test particles, rather than the 95% it is supposed to, without the charge. ('Filtering efficiency' generally refers to how good the filter is by itself at stopping aerosols, ie. not counting side leakage, but some authors use it to refer to tests that also measure side leakage.)

A paper that specifically studied this topic is 'Experimental Study of Electrostatic Aerosol Filtration at Moderate Filter Face Velocity' by Sanchez et al, in *Aerosol Science and Technology* (v.47 (6), 2013), in which the authors tested charged and uncharged filters:

> A substantial increase in overall collection efficiency was observed when electrostatically charged filter media were used. Uncharged filter media displayed a local minimum in collection efficiency (30%) around 200 nm [nanometres] at a filter face velocity of 0.5 m/s. Filter efficiencies were approximately 85%, down to 30 nm [nanometres], in the presence of electrostatically charged filter fibers.

Surgical masks, with the same sort of melt-blown layer as N95s but a weaker charge (Ju et al confirm this), typically only have a 30-50% filtering efficiency (ie. against 0.3 micron particles), and this is despite them still having a charge, only not as strong a charge as an N95. Ju et al also claim that that spunbond layer by itself with its weaker charge only has a filtering efficiency of 6-10%, despite having some charge.

The effect of removing the electric charge from surgical masks by dipping them in isopropanol was investigated in 'Filtration Performance of FDA-Cleared Surgical Masks' by Rengasamy et al, *Journal of the International Society for Respiratory Protection* (v.26 (3), Spring-Summer 2009, pp.54-70). They found that all surgical masks with electrostatic filters had their performance significantly affected by removing the charge (see Fig. 8).

So does the meme about stopping mosquitos with a chain-link fence doesn't apply to N95s?

It doesn't apply to N95s. The gaps are smaller, and the electrostatic charge makes the gap size far less relevant anyway. (The meme was mostly directed at cloth masks, but some people tried to apply it to N95s as well.)

Doesn't Germany require the use of these higher-quality masks?

Yes. For example, the Berlin government requires FFP2 or equivalent masks (without valves) to be worn by anyone over six in almost every circumstance.

Some American Universities require KN95 masks.

These masks sound great, shouldn't we be wearing these instead of the rubbish ones?

Yeah, really great, except they only work on paper, not in reality. In reality they are just as bad as the basic masks, and possibly worse. If you've never tried one, buy one and put it on. Although they have a tighter fit than a typical cloth mask their sides are still easily forced by your breath to come slightly off your skin, and so most of your inhalations and exhalations will go in and out the sides. In fact, often more of the air goes in and out of the gaps than with a basic mask because these masks are so much harder to breathe through.

Anyone who wears glasses will find this out as their glasses will fog up from the air that comes out around the nose. There is a piece of bendable metal there for the bridge of the nose, but although careful manipulation of the metal may lessen the amount of air that comes out here, it only reduces it somewhat, and anyway, the air will just go out another gap instead.

For a visually compelling test get a lighted cigarette, put the respirator on, pull it aside and inhale some cigarette smoke, then put the mask back in place, and exhale. You will soon see where all the smoke goes.

To sum up, respirator masks are supposed to filter out 94–95% of viruses (99% in the case of FFP3), and this is scientifically supported, but that only happens if all your breath goes through the mask, and assuming everything else is working exactly as it supposed to. As your breath doesn't go through the mask in any great quantity, those figures are irrelevant.

As these two scientists say in a *Newsweek* piece from 24 Jan 2022, entitled 'We're a Physician and Mathematician and a Data Scientist. N95s Won't Work for Kids',

> the effectiveness of respirators is vastly overestimated, and there is scant evidence that they stop community transmission.

(I should also note that the filters in KN95s are often found to be useless when tested, even disregarding the side gap issue – expecting a KN95 filter to work as it's supposed to is foolish.)

Germany also shows that the respirator masks do nothing in the real world. Remember the Germany-Sweden graph from earlier? Germany is doing worse despite forcing everyone by law to wear respirator masks.

If this is such a simple failure why isn't the medical establishment aware of these issues?

The medical establishment is perfectly well aware of all this. If you read articles on masks in medical magazines you will see it endlessly acknowledged that even respirator masks are useless if air can escape out the side gaps. For example high filtration efficiency and a good fit are needed to enhance protection against aerosols because tiny airborne particles can find their way around any gaps between mask and face.

('Covid-19 has redefined airborne transmission', by Tang et al, *British Medical Journal* (v.373, 14 April 2021.)

Another example:

N95 masks need to be fit-tested to be efficacious and are uncomfortable to wear for more than an hour or two.

('Disease Mitigation Measures in the Control of Pandemic Influenza' by Ingelsby et al, in *Biosecurity and Bioterrorism: Biodefense Strategy, Practice, and Science* (v.4 (4), 2006.)

And another (in 'Experimental investigation of indoor aerosol dispersion and accumulation in the context of COVID-19: Effects of masks and ventilation' by Shah et al in *Physics of Fluids* 33 (7), 21 July 2021):

leakages are observed to result in notable decreases in mask efficiency relative to the ideal filtration efficiency of the mask material, even in the case of high-efficiency masks.

Also:

Fit is critical to the level of protection offered by respirators. For an N95 respirator to provide the promised protection, it must fit the participant.

('Comparing the fit of N95, KN95, surgical, and cloth face masks and assessing the accuracy of fit checking' by O'Kelly et al, *PLoS One*. (v.16 (1), 22 Jan 2021.)

How do ordinary people cope with this issue?

They don't. In 'Assessment of Proficiency of N95 Mask Donning Among the General Public in Singapore' (*JAMA Network Open*, v.3 (5), 20 May 2020),

> Yeung and colleagues gave 3M Vflex N95 masks along with "multilingual pictorial instructions" to randomly selected adults, then performed a visual mask fit test and user seal check... Only 90 participants [out of 714] passed the visual mask fit test. About three-quarters performed strap placement incorrectly, 61% left a "visible gap between the mask and skin," and about 60% didn't tighten the nose-clip.

Bear in mind that these people knew they were being observed on how well they could fit their mask, so they had far more motivation than a person ordinarily has to do a good job with it, but they still couldn't.

In a study examining people's attempts to fit N95s themselves, titled 'Comparing the fit of N95, KN95, surgical, and cloth face masks and assessing the accuracy of fit checking' in *PLoS One* (v.16 (1), Jan 22, 2021), O'Kelly et al say

> most N95 respirators failed to fit the participants adequately. Fit check responses had poor correlation with quantitative fit factor scores. KN95, surgical, and fabric masks achieved low fit factor scores, with little protective difference recorded between respiratory protection options. In addition, small facial differences were observed to have a significant impact on quantitative fit.

This was despite the fact that

> Three out of the seven participants worked in a healthcare or healthcare-related field and had received a degree of mask fit education.

Does the media know about this?

The better-informed health reporters in the media know about this serious issue, but they usually bury this information; for example, these are the last two sentence in a BBC story about the mask rules introduced at the end of November 2021:

> It is also possible to buy FFP2 and FFP3 masks used by healthcare workers which offer higher protection.
> However, these must be fitted correctly to work.

(There are, no doubt, less well-informed health reporters who don't have a clue.)

Do governments know about this?

Of course; at least, the scientific advisors know, even if many politicians don't.

A 2014 British government review titled 'The Use of Facemasks and Respirators during an Influenza Pandemic: Scientific Evidence Base Review', commissioned by the Department of Health and produced by Public Health England, concluded that

> The effectiveness of masks and respirators is likely to be linked to consistent, correct usage and compliance; this remains a major challenge – both in the context of a formal study and in everyday practice. Given the potential loss of effectiveness with incorrect usage, general advice should be to only use masks/respirators under very particular, specified circumstances, and in combination with other personal protective practices.

What do hospitals do about this problem?

These failures with respirators are why healthcare establishments like hospitals usually require their staff to get their respirators 'properly fitted' to try to avoid these problems. This is a time-consuming procedure. This involves either a quantitative fit, or a qualitative fit.

The qualitative fit test requires the wearer to pass a smell test to check whether the respirators have been properly fitted. Here is some description of it from workplacetesting.com:

> During the qualitative test, the test subject is exposed to a non-toxic irritant, the fit test challenge agent, such as smoke. The mask wearer will then be asked to perform a series of exercises including head movements, speaking and breathing deeply. The worker is asked to alert the test monitor if the irritant breaches the seal of the mask during these exercises. The quantitative test employs a small tube or other device to take air samples from within the face plate during testing. This air sample is then evaluated to determine if, and at what level, the challenge agent was detected within the sealed airspace. Any contaminants detected within the sealed faceplate will lower the mask's overall fit factor. A mask deemed unsuitable because of a low fit factor may not be used by the subject employee.

Here is another description of the qualitative fit test from *StatNews*:

> The [smell] challenge is also made while the user moves his or her head from side to side, up and down, and while reciting the Rainbow Passage — a script designed to get the mouth and jaw moving in different ways. The goal is to test how the mask performs during simulated work activity that includes movement and talking.

Quantitative fit testing, on the other hand,

continuously measures the concentration of particles
inside and outside a mask while it is worn (see Fig 1).
For a mask with an established level of filtration ability,
such as an N95 or KN95 respirator, a higher number of
particles inside of the mask is indicative of poor fit.
When gaps are present in the fit of the mask, unfiltered
air is allowed to enter the mask, raising particle levels.
Quantitative fit testing machines use these particle
concentrations to calculate a fit factor via a standard
formula.

What guarantees that the masks continue to have a good seal after the test?

A good question. A respirator may work well at the time
of testing, but what guarantees a proper fit and seal beyond
the occasion of the testing?

Quantitative tests render the mask unusable after the test,
so a new mask must be worn. What guarantees that this one
fits properly?

Qualitative tests, on the other hand, though they do not
destroy the mask, are unreliable. In 'Correlation of
qualitative and quantitative results from testing respirator
fit', by Hardis et al, in the *American Industrial Hygiene
Association Journal* (v.44 (2), Feb 1983, pp.78-87), the
authors report that only

23 to 46% of the poorly fitting full face masks were
detected by qualitative methods.

That is, of the masks that failed the quantitative tests, only
a quarter to a half of the failures were picked up by the
qualitative tests. So passing a qualitative test doesn't even

give much assurance at the time that the mask is properly fitted, let alone later on.

The big problem is that respirators are very hard to breathe through, and almost certainly the wearer will, through small unconscious movements, slightly adjust the position of the mask on the face (even via head movements only) so that air can go in and out the gaps more easily. A couple of rubber bands around the ears hardly guarantees a perfect fit all day long.

Here is a study from *Infection Control and Hospital Epidemiology* (called 'Assessment of Healthcare Worker Protocol Deviations and Self-Contamination During Personal Protective Equipment Donning and Doffing', v.38 (9), 13 June 2017, pp.1077-83) that shows just some of the problems faced here:

> Protocol deviations were common during both EVD [Ebola virus disease] and CP [contact precautions] PPE doffing, and some deviations during EVD PPE doffing were committed by the HCWs' doffing assistant and/or trained observer. Self-contamination was common.

But surely the American Medical Association wants us to use these sorts of masks?

On the contrary, on their 'Patient Page' on face masks they say

> Because N95 respirators require special fit testing, they are not recommended for use by the general public.

This is their diplomatic way of saying what I said above. And they're saying members of the general public should *never* wear these masks. The same masks that are required use in Germany. As Yale University says (my italics):

An N95 is actually a high-efficiency respirator that must *fit tightly* to work properly.

Are there studies looking at the effectiveness of respirator masks in healthcare settings?

Yes, and they have not made for pretty reading for the N95 advocates.

A 2020 Cochrane review (which are the highest quality reviews in medicine) said

> The use of a N95/P2 respirator compared to a medical/surgical mask probably makes little or no difference for the objective and more precise outcome of laboratory-confirmed influenza infection… Restricting the pooling to healthcare workers made no difference to the overall findings.

For a literature review of other articles on this issue see part 5.6. The evidence is strongly against N95s working in healthcare settings, even though they are being worn by trained healthcare workers.

I think we just need to develop a way of sticking the mask to your face to prevent the gaps. Maybe using some sort of tape.

No thanks. Try this. Close off all the side gaps as much as you with your fingers. Or push it down around your mouth with your fingers to stop breath escaping. Making sure, that is, that your breath goes in and out through the mask, not anywhere else. Now try breathing in and out. It's pretty hard. (You can't even blow a candle out.) That's what it would feel like were the mask was properly fitted to your face so that the air really cannot get out any other way, and all your breath went in and out the mask. Breathing would be become laborious. It would require great effort just to stay alive. There's no way I would wear that for more than a minute, it's quite frightening. If that's your vision of the future of human existence, count me out.

It also becomes clear, when you do this, that regardless of all the talk about a proper 'fit', you can't really get any such thing with the mask just on your face normally. Once you let go of the mask with your fingers you can feel it become less of an effort to breathe. It's still an effort compared to having no mask, and very unpleasant, but it's not as awful as when the side gaps are closed off (and while you can still feel the warmness of your own breath, your breath isn't as hot as with the gaps blocked). That tells that you that air is getting in and out the side gaps even if you think it isn't, even if you think you have a good 'fit'.

This isn't just my opinion, and this issue has been known about for a long time. In a thorough 1920 study of mask use in the wake of the influenza epidemic entitled 'An experimental study of the efficacy of gauze face masks' by Kellogg and Macmillan, in the *American Journal of Public Health* (v.10 (1), Jan 1920, pp.34-42), the authors also concluded that the number of layers required to make the masks effective would make breathing too difficult, and anyway would result in the air going in and out the sides of the mask:

> When a sufficient degree of density in the mask is used to exercise a useful filtering influence, breathing is difficult and leakage takes place around the edge of the mask.

The FDA admits that

> the N95 respirator can make it more difficult for the wearer to breathe.

Dr Quinton Fivelman, Chief Scientific Officer at the London Medical Laboratory, admitted that

"It can be hard to breathe through high filtration FFP masks".

('UK mask mandate: The specific type of face mask you should STOP wearing', by Doyle, *Daily Express*, 17 Jan 2022.)

In general, the issue with effective masks is this. There is no way (with present technology) to get a mask that will filter out all or most of the virions in all your inhalations and exhalations, with no gaps, that anyone in their right mind would want to wear for more than a few minutes.

I should also add that even if such a mask were developed, wearing it more than occasionally would be disastrous for the immune system, which relies on having virions and bacteria coming in that challenge the immune system, helping it to develop and improve.

So you're saying that respirators are horrible to wear?

Yes. In 'Investigation of adverse reactions in healthcare personnel working in Level 3 barrier protection PPE to treat COVID-19', by Yuan et al, in BMJ's *Postgrad Medical Journal* (v.97 (1148), 2020, pp.351-4), the authors said

A total of 122 (94.57%) healthcare professionals experienced discomfort while wearing L3PPE to treat patients with COVID-19. The main reasons for adverse reactions and discomfort include varying degrees of adverse skin reactions, respiratory difficulties, heat stress, dizziness and nausea… Our study discovered that the high rates of adverse reactions experienced by healthcare personnel due to the usage of L3PPE in treatment of COVID-19 not only include previously reported skin mucosa discomfort reactions but include multiple adverse reactions linked to the respiratory, nervous and digestive systems.

In 'Effects of Prolonged Use of Facemask on Healthcare Workers in Tertiary Care Hospital During COVID-19 Pandemic' by Purushothaman et al in the *Indian Journal of Otolaryngology and Head & Neck Surgery* (v.73, 20201, pp.59–65) the authors say

> This study suggests that prolonged use of facemasks induces difficulty in breathing on exertion and excessive sweating around the mouth to the healthcare workers which results in poorer adherence and increased risk of susceptibility to infection.

Do respirators cause skin problems?

Yes, see part 5.8.b for a review of the literature on this (not that much research has been done, though).

I also look at masks and headaches in part 2, and other physical harms caused by masks in part 5.8.c.

Are we supposed to regularly replace our masks?

Respirators and modern surgical masks are supposed to be disposable and used only once. Cloth masks are not supposed to be disposable, but you shouldn't wear the same one for more than a few hours, and they should be sterilised every time you use them (this will actually reduce their effectiveness by making the holes bigger – see the question 'Does washing your cloth mask reduce its ability to trap the virus?' in part 2, but then they're not effective in reality anyway).

Professor Yvonne Cossart of the Department of Infectious Diseases at the University of Sydney told the Sydney Morning Herald that surgical masks

are only effective so long as they are dry. As soon as
they become saturated with the moisture in your breath
they stop doing their job and pass on the droplets.

Professor Cossart said that could take as little as 15 or 20
minutes, after which the mask would need to be changed.

Numerous SAGE papers have recommended that face
masks be changed every four hours.

As masks don't actually work there isn't really any point
in replacing them on the grounds of effectiveness, because
they aren't effective. They should, however, be replaced or
thoroughly sterilised regularly for hygiene reasons.

Is there a problem with poor quality or fake N95s like there is with KN95s?

Yes. Not as much as with KN95s, perhaps, but a problem
nonetheless. With mask sales now in the trillions, and
enormous money to be made, many far-East factories who
made other things started making masks instead, with low or
non-existent quality standards:

Factories in China have popped up seemingly overnight
to meet the demand. Amid the rush, the high prices
masks are commanding have led to what the *Wall Street
Journal* called a "wild west" for mask manufacturing.

One test of Chinese-made N95s found that

Out of the 31 masks tested, 13 Chinese N95 masks fail
quality standards for filtration... only 18 masks managed
to capture more than 95% of tiny particles. What's more,
many of these failing masks were not just a few
percentage points below the standard. On average, the
masks that failed the tests captured just 51% of particles.
The worst of the worst captured just 24% of particles,
which is on par with the filtration ability of a bed sheet.

***You're making light of a measure designed to help protect
against an extremely deadly disease.***

On the contrary, it is the mask wearers who make light of
the disease. If SARS-CoV-2 really is as deadly as they say,
and if masks really did filter out most of it from your breath,
then it follows that your mask is going to be full of these
deadly and terrifying viruses. Yet have you seen a single
mask wearer anywhere in the world act like this is true? If it
was true then the masks would be extremely dangerous.
They should be treated like toxic waste. Not only should you
never touch them once they're on, you should never take
them off with your hands; rather you should use disposable
gloves. They and the gloves should be placed immediately
into special toxic waste bins, like you have in labs and
doctor's surgeries. They should never be placed on any other
surface, lest they spread the virus around where it can be
picked up by someone else. You should disinfect your face
as soon as you've taken the mask off, or at least wash it
thoroughly with soap and water. (This applies triple if you're
one of these rare and strange mask wearers who sneezes and
coughs into their mask.)

But no-one, not even the most extreme mask fanatic, does
anything remotely like this. Masks are reworn over and over.
They are constantly touched and fiddled with. They are put
into pockets or handbags when they are not being worn.
They are thrown onto tables and kitchen tops. In cafes and
pubs people take them off and put them on the tables, or in
their handbags. They hang off car rear-vision mirrors, or
they sit on the back seat of the car. They mingle with
everything else in the house. They don't even get washed
much, let alone disinfected, and are reworn the next day
after spending the night on a bathroom shelf. They get

dumped all over the city streets and the countryside. Nobody at all acts like these things are full of a deadly disease, and this is because everyone knows deep down that the disease is not really that big a deal, and the mask-wearing is rather a quasi-religious ritual, not a serious health intervention.

We agree that masks aren't 100% effective in stopping aerosol virus spread. But they don't need to be. They just need to help slow Covid spread somewhat. Or be just one little bit of help in the overall battle.

The evidence base tells us that masks don't have any effect on Covid spread at all. A great many countries and states have introduced mask mandates and they haven't slowed the spread. In many of those places cases have gone up with the mandate in place. Ask yourself this: how can Covid still be spreading as much as ever, more than *two years* after it started, in those countries that have been fanatical about mask use?

Anyway, if masks are only intended to somewhat slow the spread, or to be a minor player in the 'battle' against Covid, then the overall case for forcing them on people against their will is greatly diminished. The justification given for making people wear them was that they were very effective at stopping Covid spread, so much so that in the UK the politicians said that we wouldn't have to socially distance any more if we wore masks. Even then, I would argue, the mask mandates were nowhere near being justified. Once it was accepted that masks were at best bit players in the supposed 'battle', there was never any hope that they could be justified, given the enormous individual and social harm they cause.

But masks may make that little bit of extra difference that gets the R_0 (the reproductive rate) below 1, and so they could be the difference between Covid either dying out or spreading everywhere.

This never happened, though, did it? The disease hasn't died out anywhere. It keeps on spreading around despite the enormous amount of mask wearing that has taken place in so many countries. So there's no reason to think that masks can make just that little bit of difference that gets R_0 below 1. This is wishful thinking. Mask-wearing not only doesn't cause a virus to die out, it doesn't even slow it down.

You hear this sort of talk a lot in public these days, but here's an actual example of it in a (pre-Covid) scientific paper:

> if one hypothesized that all transmission were due to aerosol particles <50 μm, and estimated a reproductive number of 1.5 for influenza (i.e. each infection generates 1.5 new infections on average at the start of the epidemic), then the use of surgical masks by every infected case could reduce the reproductive number below 1.

(In 'Influenza Virus Aerosols in Human Exhaled Breath: Particle Size, Culturability, and Effect of Surgical Masks' by Milton, et al, in *PLoS Pathogens* (v.9 (3), March 7 2013.)

Here's another:

> as the reproduction number of influenza may not be very high a small reduction in transmissibility of the virus may be sufficient for reducing the reproduction number to a value smaller than 1 and thus extinguishing the epidemic.

(In 'Professional and Home-Made Face Masks Reduce Exposure to Respiratory Infections among the General

Population', by van der Sande et al, *PLoS One* (v.3 (7), 9 July 2008).

Here's one from post-Covid times (this one doesn't explicitly claim that the R_0 is just above 1, but it can't think it's that far above):

> The available evidence suggests that near-universal adoption of nonmedical masks when out in public, in combination with complementary public health measures, could successfully reduce R_e [the R_e is similar to the R_0] to below 1, thereby reducing community spread if such measures are sustained.

(From 'An evidence review of face masks against COVID-19' by Howard et al, *Proceedings of the National Academy of Sciences*, v. 118 (4), Jan 2021.)

You could, of course, apply this logic to any possible intervention that might possible have a small effect: 'if we hypothesize an R_0 of 1.1, then if we all walked around or sat with our faces pointed upwards to avoid directly inhaling the breath of others then that could be the difference between an R_0 of 1.1 and one of 0.9, and so could defeat the virus, so the government must force people to do that until further notice'.

Notice also that even getting the R_0 below 1 doesn't magically cause a disease to die out. If masks really did do this, then as soon as people took their masks off the R_0 would go up above 1 again, and start spreading around again. So we'd have to keep wearing masks indefinitely, or at least for a few years until sufficient numbers of people have finally been infected. As we have seen in many countries and US states, wearing masks for years is a reality, which is a completely intolerable situation. But, as has happened with lockdowns, the BS artists are always giving the impression (without ever committing themselves to any explicit predictions) that just a short period of everyone wearing masks will break the back of the disease and then it will go away. Like with the 'circuit breaker' lockdowns, this never happens. These periods are, in fact, endless. You'd have to be a fool to still believe this sort of talk.

But maybe masks could be the difference between the health services being overwhelmed and being okay?

This also never happened. The health services in Sweden and US states that didn't see much mask wearing didn't get overwhelmed and crash. So there's no reason to think that masks can make just that little bit of difference that, in an amazing coincidence, was just enough to stop the health services being overwhelmed. They don't make any difference in their effect on health services, and health services are in a very similar position that they always have been even in non-mask areas. How many more years is this going to go on for before the maskers notice reality?

Even if masks only reduce the virus in your breath by 10%, that's still 10% less people dying.

No, this doesn't follow. Even if masks reduced the amount of virus the average person exhales by 10%, it doesn't follow that there's any reduction in cases, as that 90% of virus-laden breath may be (and probably still is) enough to infect a similar amount of people as before.

And bear in mind also that most people get the virus eventually, so even if masks stop a few people getting it for a while, they'll still get it eventually, as Christina Pagel found. (I call this the 'Pagel Principle'.)

Even if there was, nonetheless, a small reduction in overall case numbers over a long-term period, say 2%, that doesn't result in a 2% reduction in deaths. Deaths are only a tiny fraction of cases. A 2% reduction in cases is likely to produce at most a 0.006% reduction in deaths (on an IFR of 3 in 1000), and probably far less, as the reduction in cases caused by you wearing your mask to a restaurant is unlikely to have a great effect on what happens in care homes and hospitals, where most Covid deaths happen. So the actual reduction would be even less than 0.006%, say 0.00006% (a hundredth of 0.006%).

Bear in mind that most Covid deaths are in people who would most likely have died soon anyway. This is why places like Sweden which never used masks (or lockdowns) have completely normal numbers of all-cause deaths. The average age of a Covid death is over 80, and care homes are where the highest number of Covid deaths take place. Physical frailty is the biggest predictor of a Covid death. So the number of instances where Covid actually killed someone healthy, with many years of life left, is very small, maybe a hundredth of all Covid deaths (it's probably far less). So that 0.00006% becomes a 0.0000006% reduction in deaths.

So even if there are 50,000 Covid-related deaths in the UK every year from now on (which is itself very unlikely), wearing masks will save about 0.0003 people a year. So we can expect to save one life every 3333 years by wearing masks. (Even if all this is out by a factor of one hundred, it would still take 33 years to save a life.) In the meantime, even by the UK government's own admission, ten thousand people or more could be dying every year from lockdowns measures.

Okay, so masks may not work, but they're a sign that you're concerned about Covid and you want to do your part.

They're a sign all right, a sign that you're participating in mass murder and the destruction of our freedoms.

You can diss masks all you like, I still don't feel safe without one, and I freak out if I see someone not wearing one.

Get a grip. A mask isn't going to help you, or them. If you're that afraid of getting Covid, stay inside and read up on the odds that you'll die from it.

C'mon, it's just a bit of cloth.

A blindfold is just a bit of cloth. A noose is just a bit of hemp. A knife is just a bit of metal. What the thing is made of is irrelevant. It's the use it's put to that matters. If I stuff a gag into your mouth it doesn't make it alright if I say 'It's just a bit of cloth'.

Part 2:
More face mask FAQs

.

Doesn't the 'precautionary principle' tell us to wear masks regardless of whether there's any good evidence that they work, because they might help, and it doesn't hurt to wear them?

Careless interpretations of what the 'precautionary principle' supposedly claims have caused immense damage in recent decades. There is no 'official' accepted description of the precautionary principle, and it is, in essence, nothing but the old adage 'better safe than sorry'. Various academics have tried and failed to spell out more clearly the details of what is involved in applying the principle.

The most important requirement for any fleshing out of the precautionary principle is that it must not recommend action in which the expected disutility of the proposed action exceeds expected utility, because that is by definition to act irrationally. Yet that is an issue that is routinely ignored by proponents of the precautionary principle. (I should note than in the years I spent studying the academic risk analysis literature I was shocked at the amount of authors who regularly attacked this requirement. That's right, *attacked*, not just ignored.)

If one ignores this requirement then any insane scheme can be recommended. For example, it is possible that unless we start crawling about on our hands and knees for the rest of our life, aliens will attack and destroy us. This is clearly irrational, but a simplistic interpretation of the precautionary principle will require us to do it. The reason it is irrational is that the expected utility vastly outweighs the expected disutility. The disutility lies in the harm that crawling about on our hands and knees will do to us and society. The expected utility is the gain we make by not being attacked by aliens, which is large, but weighted by the probability that crawling will achieve this, which is vanishingly small, thus making the expected utility tiny, and vastly outweighed by the expected disutility.

Moreover, this 'irrationalist' interpretation of the precautionary principle will mandate contradictory courses of action, for it is also possible that we can prevent alien attack by never going on our hands and knees, and always walking about on tiptoes, so we must do both this and the crawling, which is logically impossible.

So any acceptable version of the precautionary principle must obey what we can call standard 'risk-benefit analysis'. This is not the only requirement, by the way. There will be other requirements, such as that the precautionary principle cannot require us to perform immoral acts. For example, there might be a precautionary principle reason to slaughter everyone with red hair, but this is not morally justified, and so we should not do it, regardless of what the precautionary principle says. But conforming to standard risk-benefit analysis is a basic requirement for the precautionary principle.

It is not, enough, therefore, for mask proponents to merely say that the precautionary principle means we should wear masks. They need to make a case to show that the expected utilities outweigh the expected disutilities. This they almost never do. In fact, most mask proponents who fall back on the precautionary principle as their justification never talk about the disutilities of wearing masks; they regard mask-wearing as no big deal, and take it as obvious that the disutilities are zero. In fact, most such people never bother to say much at all about the whole issue, regarding an appeal to the precautionary principle as self-explanatory, when it is anything but.

Couldn't the precautionary principle be used against masks?

Yes. The sort of vague 'better safe than sorry' interpretation of the precautionary principle tells us we should never wear masks, because of all the possible harms that could come from doing so, and because we know that they do little to stop Covid. (Every non-pharmaceutical intervention could be blocked by this sort of simplistic application of the precautionary principle. In fact, any possible action can be, if you just go by the irrational applications of the principle that leftist behavioural scientists spout on breakfast TV.)

Asymptomatic spread is the real reason why we should wear masks.

Even if asymptomatic spread had been as bad as the scare-merchants said it wouldn't justify masks, because, as we have seen, masks don't work, and they have massive downsides. But I should in passing note that the early 2020 talk of Covid being a uniquely dangerous disease because it has this ability to be easily and frequently spread by asymptomatic people, unlike any other disease in history, was a massively over-hyped fear campaign which was used to frighten people into submission. You'll notice that you hardly ever hear about it now. That's because the evidence for it wasn't so good. Asymptomatic transmission, then, provides no good basis for mask wearing even if masks worked.

In 'Post-lockdown SARS-CoV-2 nucleic acid screening in nearly ten million residents of Wuhan, China' by Cao et al in *Nature Communications* 11, 5917 (2020), the authors found, out of ten million people who were tested, not a single case of asymptomatic transmission. Not one. Zero.

> Here, we describe a city-wide SARS-CoV-2 nucleic acid screening programme between May 14 and June 1, 2020 in Wuhan. All city residents aged six years or older were eligible and 9,899,828 (92.9%) participated. No new symptomatic cases and 300 asymptomatic cases (detection rate 0.303/10,000, 95% CI 0.270–0.339/10,000) were identified. There were no positive tests amongst 1,174 close contacts of asymptomatic cases.

No doubt it does happens, as it happens with all respiratory diseases, but it isn't as common as has been made out. Allyson Pollock, Professor of Public Health at Newcastle University, in an editorial in the *British Medical Journal* (371, 2020) titled 'Asymptomatic Transmission of Covid-19' says

> It's also unclear to what extent people with no symptoms transmit SARS-CoV-2. The only test for live virus is viral culture. PCR and lateral flow tests do not distinguish live virus. No test of infection or infectiousness is currently available for routine use. As things stand, a person who tests positive with any kind of test may or may not have an active infection with live virus, and may or may not be infectious. The relations between viral load, viral shedding, infection, infectiousness, and duration of infectiousness are not well understood.

Summing up, she says

> Searching for people who are asymptomatic yet infectious is like searching for needles that appear and reappear transiently in haystacks, particularly when rates are falling.

In a Dec 2020 meta-analysis by researchers from the University of Florida's Dept of Biostatistics titled 'Household Transmission of SARS-CoV-2: A Systematic Review and Meta-analysis' (by Madewell et al, in *JAMA Network Open* 2020, 3 (12)), it was found that the secondary attack rate (ie. the percentage of an infected person's contacts who got infected) for asymptomatic or presymptomatic transmission was close to zero (0.7%, but with confidence intervals of plus or minus 4.2%).

Mask wearing is effective, but only if everyone wears them (and you can only detect the effect if everyone wears them).

This sort of claim is often made by SAGE in its evidence reviews; for example:

> The population scale benefits of face coverings can only be realised if they are worn correctly and by sufficient people in a setting.

(From 'Considerations for potential impact of Plan B measures, 13 October 2021'.)

Why would this be true? It's strange to think that an intervention that is supposedly so effective as to warrant legal punishments for not complying somehow shows no detectable effect at all if even 80-90% of people wear them.

This claim, of course, provides the perfect excuse to explain away the failure of masks in any place (because nowhere will 100% of people wear masks). They didn't work in place X because not enough people wore them. They didn't work in place Y because not enough people wore them. And so on.

Amazing how just a few people not wearing a mask can be the difference between the disease spreading throughout the whole population, even though, say, 95% of that population are wearing a supposedly effective mask, and the disease disappearing in a few weeks or a couple of months at most. That is quite remarkable, and if you believe that I've got a bridge to sell you.

Do we need to wear a mask outside?

You don't need to wear a mask anywhere, but wearing one outside is particularly nuts, because hardly any Covid is caught outside. Even the scaremongering SAGE scientists, like Prof Calum Semple for instance, admit this:

> Speaking to Sky News, Professor Semple stressed: "First of all when you are outside there is ultra-violet light and there is good air change. So you don't catch the virus outside... that has got to be put to bed".

('"You DON'T catch Covid outside" Professor finally "puts to bed" outdoor transmission fears', by Hussey, *Daily Express*, 3 Jan 2022.)

As it's extremely difficult to catch Covid outside, why would you be insane enough to wear a mask outdoors?

But you don't really catch Covid anywhere other than care homes, hospitals and at home. There's not much transmission anywhere else. You sometimes see media stories hyping up, say, members of a church choir catching it, but catching it outside care homes, hospitals and at home really does not happen much.

How have children with autism and other learning difficulties coped with being forced to wear face masks?

It is very difficult for many autistic children to wear face masks, and many are being forced to wear masks regardless. I can barely touch on this issue, but the Organisation of Autism Research says in 'The Challenge of Face Masks' (12 Nov 2020) that

In Florida, a 12-year-old child was not allowed to attend school because he wasn't wearing a face mask, despite the fact that he is autistic and non-verbal and needs an in-person education, according to his mother. As reported on the News Channel 8 website, Ruby Rodriguez said she was told her son could come back to school only if she got a "district-issued mask exemption form signed by a doctor." Rodriguez tried to get a signature from her son's pediatrician, another pediatrician, and three walk-in clinics, as well as a facility for children with special needs and was unable to obtain an exemption.

Face masks in the classroom must make things very hard for deaf children?

Yes. The *Guardian* reports that

The National Deaf Children's Society (NDCS) surveyed more than 500 parents and found 27% of deaf children were being taught by teachers wearing masks, with the figures rising to 49% for students in sixth form or college, and 34% in secondary school.

The WHO says in their report 'Advice on the use of masks for children in the community in the context of COVID-19' (Aug 2020)

The wearing of masks by children with hearing loss or auditory problems may present learning barriers and further challenges, exacerbated by the need to adhere to the recommended physical distancing. These children may miss learning opportunities because of the degraded speech signal stemming from mask wearing, the elimination of lipreading and speaker expressions and physical distancing.

What are these mask protocols you mention?

Mask protocols are the things you should and shouldn't do with a mask. Governments and scientific bodies publish them, and companies that work in areas that require masks (eg. where there are a lot of small airborne objects such as wood or metal dust floating around) will usually also have their own protocols, although these are often somewhat different as they're not concerned with virus transmission, and there's no 'source control' to worry about. And mask companies themselves have their own recommendations. Here are some serious protocols that should apply if Covid really is a dangerous disease and a major public health threat. (These apply to the N95 and PPF2/3 masks as well.)

Your mask must cover your nose and chin as well as your mouth.

You must not touch your mask with your hands once it is on. This applies even if you've only been wearing it for a few minutes.

If you do touch your mask you must immediately discard it.

If you touch your mask then you must immediately wash your hands.

You must always remove your mask by the ear straps and not touch the mask itself.

You must replace your mask as soon as it gets wet.

You must replace your mask every hour, or two, or four (depending on the protocol), regardless. It should never be re-used.

You must fit the mask closely to your face so that air cannot go in or out the sides. [As I have explained, this is very difficult to achieve with most masks.]

You must never lay your used mask on a surface that someone may touch, such as a table.

Do not use masks with valves.

We should also note also that on packets of masks you will often see a warning that you should not wear them if your aim is to prevent virus transmission, as they aren't designed for this job and won't help. This is, shall we say, an extraordinary state of affairs. Most of the world is being forced to block their airways in order to do a job that even the manufacturers admit the things aren't designed for.

What are the WHO's particular protocols?

The WHO's current guidelines are short:

Clean your hands before you put your mask on, as well as before and after you take it off, and after you touch it at any time.

Make sure it covers both your nose, mouth and chin.

When you take off a mask, store it in a clean plastic bag, and every day either wash it if it's a fabric mask, or dispose of a medical mask in a trash bin.

Don't use masks with valves.

These guidelines are laughably watered-down, and this is because the WHO knows perfectly well that masks don't work and that Covid presents no great danger to society.

The WHO also has a 1-hour course – yes, one hour – that tells you 'when, where and how to wear a mask in community settings'.

Professor Raina Macintyre of UNSW (who is certainly no anti-masker) says

Despite more than half the world using cloth masks, global disease control guidelines, including those from the World Health Organisation, fail to clearly specify conditions of their use.

WHO's previous mask protocols, however, were more detailed (January 2020):

> If medical masks are worn, appropriate use and disposal is essential to ensure they are effective and to avoid any increase in risk of transmission associated with the incorrect use and disposal of masks.

> The following information on correct use of medical masks derives from the practices in health-care settings:

> - place mask carefully to cover mouth and nose and tie

> securely to minimise any gaps between the face and the mask;

> - while in use, avoid touching the mask;

> - remove the mask by using appropriate technique (i.e. do not touch the front but remove the lace from behind);

> - after removal or whenever you inadvertently touch a used mask, clean hands by using an alcohol-based hand rub or soap and water if visibly soiled

> - replace masks with a new clean, dry mask as soon as they become damp/humid;

> - do not re-use single-use masks;

> - discard single-use masks after each use and dispose of them immediately upon removal.

> Cloth (e.g. cotton or gauze) masks are not recommended under any circumstance.

Does the CDC publish mask protocols?

The CDC has a much longer but still dumbed-down, bozo-friendly list of protocols.

When selecting a mask, there are many choices. Here are some do's and don'ts.

DO choose masks that have 2 or more layers of washable, breathable fabric graphic.

DO choose masks that completely cover your nose and mouth.

DO choose masks that fit snugly against the sides of your face and don't have gaps.

DO choose masks that have a nose wire to prevent air from leaking out of the top of the mask.

DO NOT choose masks that are made of fabric that makes it hard to breathe, for example, vinyl.

DO NOT choose masks that have exhalation valves or vents which allow virus particles to escape.

DO NOT choose masks that are specially labeled "surgical" N95 respirators, as those should be prioritized for healthcare personnel

Special Considerations

Gaiters & face shields

Wear a gaiter with two layers, or fold it to make two layers.

Face shields are not recommended: Evaluation of face shields is ongoing, but effectiveness is unknown at this time.

Children

Find a mask that is made for children to help ensure proper fit.

Check to be sure the mask fits snugly over the nose and mouth and under the chin and that there are no gaps around the sides.

Do NOT put a mask on children younger than 2 years old.

Cold weather gear

Wear your scarf, ski mask or balaclava over your mask.

Scarves, ski masks and balaclavas are not substitutes for masks.

People with beards

Certain types of facial hair, like beards, can make mask fitting difficult. Masks that fit well protect you better. To have a better fit, people with beards can shave their beards or trim their beards close to the face.

Other ways to improve fit

Use a mask fitter or brace.

Wear one disposable mask underneath a cloth mask that has multiple layers of fabric. The second mask should push the edges of the inner mask against the face and beard.

For people with beards that are not trimmed close to the face, masks may fit loosely around the beard. However, people with beards should still wear a mask. Masks designed for people with beards are being evaluated, and information will be provided when it becomes available.

How to Wear

Wear a mask correctly and consistently for the best protection.

Be sure to wash your hands or use hand sanitizer before putting on a mask.

Do NOT touch the mask when wearing it. If you have to touch/adjust your mask often, it doesn't fit you properly, and you may need to find a different mask or make adjustments.

Do wear a mask that covers your nose and mouth and secure it under your chin, and fits snugly against the sides of your face.

How NOT to Wear a Mask

[Various pictures showing people that they should not wear a mask on their forehead, dangling from one ear, on their arm, only on their nose, on their chin, etc.]

How to take off a mask

Carefully, untie the strings behind your head or stretch the ear loops

Handle only by the ear loops or ties

Fold the outside corners together

Be careful not to touch your eyes, nose, and mouth when removing and wash hands immediately after removing

How to Clean

Reusable masks should be washed as soon as they become dirty, or at least once a day. If you have a disposable face mask, throw it away after wearing it once. Always and wash your hands after handling or touching a used mask.

Using a washing machine

Include your mask with your regular laundry.

Use regular laundry detergent and the appropriate settings according to the fabric label.

By hand

Wash your mask with tap water and laundry detergent or soap.

Rinse thoroughly with clean water to remove detergent or soap.

Dry your mask

Dry your mask completely in a warm or hot dryer

By hand

Hang your mask in direct sunlight to dry completely. If you cannot hang it in direct sunlight, hang or lay it flat and let it dry completely.

These guidelines, although much more thorough than WHO's, are still nothing but safety theatre. You can't 'choose a mask that doesn't have gaps' because every mask you can buy will let air out the sides. A nose wire provides nothing but the illusion of effectiveness.

Does the FDA publish its own set of mask protocols?

Yes. In it the FDA notes that respirators and surgical masks should not be used more than once, and should be discarded as soon as they become soiled.

Any other examples of mask protocols?

The Royal Society's report 'Face masks and coverings for the general public: Behavioural knowledge, effectiveness of cloth coverings and public messaging' listed these protocols on p. 29:

Employers should support their workers in using face coverings safely if they choose to wear one. This means telling workers:

Wash your hands thoroughly with soap and water for 20 seconds or use hand sanitiser before putting a face covering on, and before and after removing it.

When wearing a face covering, avoid touching your face or face covering, as you could contaminate them with germs from your hands.

Change your face covering if it becomes damp or if you've touched it.

Continue to wash your hands regularly.

Change and wash your face covering daily.

If the material is washable, wash in line with manufacturer's instructions. If it's not washable, dispose of it carefully in your usual waste.

Aren't some of the more 'serious' protocols a bit over-the-top?

If you really think Covid is very dangerous and one of the most important threats to society in history, and you genuinely think that masks are an answer rather than some safety theatre, then you should follow all the protocols I mention (and more) to give your mask a chance of working, and to make sure you don't end up spreading Covid yourself via your mask, by touching it, for example.

Face masks really do harbour virions – after all, they are supposed to catch them – so when you touch your face mask you are likely to be covering your fingers in them. A study titled 'Contamination by respiratory viruses on outer surface of medical masks used by hospital healthcare workers' by Chughtai, MacIntyre et al, in *BMC Infectious Diseases* (v.3 (19), June 2019, p.491) says

Respiratory pathogens on the outer surface of the used medical masks may result in self-contamination. The risk is higher with longer duration of mask use (> 6 h) and with higher rates of clinical contact. Protocols on duration of mask use should specify a maximum time of continuous use.

What's the situation for people with beards who want to wear a respirator?

Beards add a whole new layer of failure to respirator masks. Health authorities readily admit that your respirator mask won't work properly if you have facial hair.

The FDA says

> N95 respirators are not designed for children or people with facial hair. Because a proper fit cannot be achieved on children and people with facial hair, the N95 respirator may not provide full protection.

For an example of a media report on this, Dr Eric Cioe Peña, director of global health at Northwell Health in New Hyde Park, New York, told ABC News that

> hair under the edge of the mask breaks the seal and makes it useless.

Note the admission that without a good seal a respirator mask is useless.

Some hospitals now require medical staff to be clean-shaven for this reason, and you can find stories in the media about doctors and researchers who have shaved off their facial hair so they can wear their N95s. This one, accompanied by a before-and-after photos, tells us that

> Aerosol expert Donald Milton shaved his beard and donned a respirator when he started seeing Covid patients at the School of Public Health's research clinic.

(This is the same Donald Milton who will meet later on in the discussion of the Gesundheit-II studies in part 3.)

In 'To shave or not to shave: How do beards impact the effectiveness of face masks?' by Zuber, *CTV News*, 1 Dec 2020,

> Dr. Lisa Bryski, an emergency-room physician in Winnipeg, has seen many colleagues shave off their

beards in order to properly wear masks in the health-care field.

For cloth or surgical masks, a beard doesn't make any difference, because these aren't even intended to have a seal.

Should children ever wear respirators?

No. As we saw above, the FDA says 'N95 respirators are not designed for children or people with facial hair.'

The US's National Institute for Occupational Safety and Health also says children should not wear respirators:

NIOSH does not approve any type of respiratory protection for children.

The California Department of Public Health said of respirators (before Covid)

Children should not wear these masks – they do not fit properly and can impede breathing. If the air quality is poor enough that a child requires a mask, the child should remain indoors, in a safe place, and evacuation should be considered.

In a *Newsweek* article from 24 Jan 2022 called 'We're a Physician and Mathematician and a Data Scientist. N95s Won't Work for Kids', the authors say

Fit requirements and comfort issues are untenable in children who have small faces and are required to wear masks for six or more hours each day.

Shouldn't you wear a mask while listen to singing because the singer is hurling their infected air across a room?

No. This misunderstands how sound travels. When you hear a singer or an instrumentalist it isn't the air they expel that hits your ears. They send air out with a bit of force when they're belting it out, true, but this air doesn't travel that far before it is slowed down and then stopped by all the air in the way. The sound they produce, however, travels much further than their breath, because they're very different things. Sound is (or sound sensations are caused by, depending on how you look at it) very fast vibrations of air molecules. The singer's voice box vibrates the air molecules near it, which vibrates the air molecules next to them, and so on in a chain of effect. So you end up with fast-moving waves of vibrations in a large block of fairly static-but-vibrating air, where air molecules bump into the air molecules in front of and around them. (Or they bump into and vibrate solid matter like a wall, which then vibrates the air on the other side of it). This 'domino effect' continues on, further and further away from the singer. When the air next to your eardrum vibrates in the same way, so does your eardrum (this is what it has evolved to do). Your brain then turns this into aural sensations.

This is why you can hear someone singing or talking from another room even though it should be obvious that their expelled air molecules (and fine aerosols) are not reaching you. It's because a series of vibrations in the air has been created, which then vibrates the walls, floorboards, ceiling and joists, and that creates a series of similar vibrations in the air in your room. So each air molecule isn't moved very far by the voicebox, it just jiggles and bumps the air particles around it, back and forth, for a period.

If you're still not convinced, consider a solid object producing a sound by having vibrations induced in it (by hitting it, for example). The molecules in that object obviously stay pretty much where they are, but they do vibrate and produce a sound. They don't leap across the room to your ear. The same is true of the air, it stays pretty much where it is, while vibrating.

***Okay, but I heard that singing still sends more virus
particles out than normal breathing or talking in the area
close to the singer, so shouldn't I wear a mask when I sing
in my choir?***

Singing produces somewhat more virus than breathing, but
nowhere near as much as coughing. The amounts aren't
worth worrying about (see part 3.6), and you can't live your
life having your enjoyable activities ruined by an ineffective
method of trying to slightly reduce the already tiny chance
of getting a flu.

***What's this business about not being able to blow out a
candle supposed to show?***

There was an idea going around in 2020 that if you
couldn't blow out a candle with a mask on then that provide
the mask worked. Bill Nye, the Fake Science Guy, posted a
video on TikTok popularising this, and New York governor
Andrew Cuomo tweeted this video in July 2020 on Twitter.

This was further amplified by some academics:

> you want the flame to stay lit, says Amy Price, a senior
> research scientist at Stanford University's Anesthesia
> Informatics and Media Laboratory. Otherwise, it can be
> a sign that the mask isn't acting as a strong enough
> barrier. If you can blow out the flame easily while
> wearing a mask, she says, there's too much air exchange
> between you and the outside world.

This is incredibly dumb. It is certainly true that with some
higher-quality masks you can't blow candles out even if you
go up very close to them (I've tried it myself). This is a bad
thing, though. If the mask filter makes it difficult for your
breath to get through, then where does Amy Price and Bill
Nye think that breath is going to go? That's right, out the

sides of the mask. Precisely where it's not supposed to go. The point of any mask, and particularly a respirator, is that the breath goes through the mask's electret filter and comes out the front of the mask all cleansed of virions and bacteria, etc. Sending it out the sides defeats the whole point of the filter.

Also, making it difficult to breathe is not the point of a mask. But Bill Nye thinks it is. Several times in his video Nye talks about the importance of 'blocking the movement of air' 'It blocks the movement of air very effectively' is his high praise for the mask he claims works. Amy Price thinks this too, as she talks about a 'strong enough barrier', and complains that masks that let you blow out a candle allow 'too much air exchange between you and the outside world'.

But, of course, the point of a mask is not to block your breath but to filter it. Ideally a mask would allow you to breathe completely normally, and not reduce 'air exchange' in the slightest, while still removing pathogens and other harmful particles from your exhalations and inhalations. Making it harder to get air in and out of your lungs isn't in any way the aim. It is, in fact, very bad for you. Do I really need to spell this out to anyone, let alone supposed scientists? *Blocking your breath is bad for you.* Blocking your breath for more than a few minutes is not only extremely unpleasant, it's dangerous.

A less idiotic version of this view would admit that blocking your breath and making it harder to breathe is not, contra Nye and Price, the point, but rather that a difficulty to inhale or expel air (as demonstrated by an inability to blow a candle out) is an *indication* that the filter is working, because this is an unfortunate side effect of effective filters. But this is still an admission that breathing is difficult with a

respirator, and of course your breath will still go out the
sides.

What happens if you force all the air out through the filter by blocking the side gaps?

If you press down all the sides of your respirator against
your face so that not much air gets out the sides, but is
forced out the front through the filter, then you'll find that it
is difficult to breathe properly. If you try to blow that candle
out again, this time you can get it to flicker more, but it's
still very hard or even impossible to blow it out, which
shows that more of your breath is now going through the
filter rather than out the sides, but that breath is being
strongly impeded by the filter, which is why breathing in this
situation is so hard.

So in filtering our breath the respirator also impedes the
air's progress with its semi-solid nature. Yet for respirator
pushers the more air that goes through the filter the better.
This is the very situation they want, where all your breath is
forced through the filter, and you feel like you're slowly
suffocating, and you can feel yourself rebreathing in your
own hot exhalations. How is this in any way a sensible thing
to do for hours on end, every day? This is why anyone who
wears a respirator very soon adjusts it (even if only
unconsciously) so that the air flows in and out around the
sides of the mask.

(Some people have posted supposed refutations of Nye by
showing that they can blow out a candle wearing a
respirator, Needless to say, such 'refutations' completely
miss what is wrong with Nye's claim.)

Is there now a push in English-speaking countries to move people from cloth masks to N95s?

There does seem to be something like that happening in late 2021 and into 2022, with stories in the US media finally conceding that cloth masks don't work, and attempting to sow the seeds of a move to N95s (as has happened in Germany), now that the wearing of masks has gradually become normalised, and now that production has been ramped up so that shortages of respirators for the medical profession is less of an issue.

A 20 Dec 2020 CNN interview with one of their medical 'experts', Dr Leana Wen, got a lot of attention for its apparent belated concession that masks don't work, but in reality it was only a concession that cloth masks don't work. And that concession prepares the ground for governments and health institutions to require respirators instead.

> CNN's medical expert Dr. Leana Wen doubled down on her recent comments that cloth masks are nothing more "decorative" face-coverings and essentially useless against the coronavirus... "Cloth masks are not appropriate for this pandemic," Wen told CNN's John Berman on Christmas Eve. "It's not appropriate for Omicron, it was not appropriate for Delta, Alpha, or any of the previous variants either because we're dealing with something that's airborne. We're dealing with a virus that's extremely contagious".

But here's the sting in the tail:

> "And so at this point, what people should do is wear at least a 3-ply medical-grade, surgical mask," Wen stated. "Even better would be the N-95, K-N95, or KF94, the respirator masks".

(In 'CNN Medical Expert Doubles Down That Cloth Masks Were Never Appropriate For COVID-19' by Meads, *Daily Wire*, 18 Dec 2021.)

On 5 Jan 2022 ABC Eyewitness News ran a report titled 'Evidence emerging that cloth masks are not as effective as N95 masks against COVID':

> You better start stocking up on your surgical or N95 or KN95 masks. Studies are emerging that cloth masks are not as effective in preventing the spread of COVID. A study released in November by researchers at Yale University, Stanford University and others found that villages in Bangladesh where surgical masks were worn had 11% fewer cases of COVID than in villages where no masks were worn. In villages that wore cloth masks, infections were reduced by only 5%.

> The Mayo Clinic is now asking all of its patients and visitors to wear a surgical mask or other medical grade mask.

> "There is emerging evidence that a surgical mask or a hospital or a medical grade mask does a better job of preventing respiratory droplets carrying the virus to other people around you," said Dr. Adi Shah with the Mayo Clinic. Shah said evidence from smaller studies is also suggesting that a surgical mask offers better protection than a cloth mask.

Omicron is often used in these stories as a reason why cloth masks are no longer good enough. For example, consider this 5 Jan 2022 *USA Today* story:

> Your cloth face mask isn't protecting you against the coronavirus variant omicron, health officials say. As common as cloth face masks have become, health experts say, they do little to prevent tiny virus particles from getting into your nose or mouth and aren't effective

against the new variant. "Cloth masks are not going to cut it with omicron," says Linsey Marr, a researcher at Virginia Tech told NPR.

Notice that stunning admission about cloth masks:

They do little to prevent tiny virus particles from getting into your nose or mouth.

Suddenly the authorities decide it's time to admit this. Because they want to move on to the next rung on the ladder:

Health experts are urging the public to opt for three-ply surgical masks, KN95 masks or N95 masks, which offer more protection against the highly contagious variant.

In a 23 Dec 2021 NPR story titled 'With omicron, you need a mask that means business' (Dec 23 2021), it was said:

With the spread of omicron, experts say to wear high-filtration respirators in public indoor spaces for the best protection. With another coronavirus variant racing across the U.S., once again health authorities are urging people to mask up indoors... given how contagious omicron is, experts say, it's seriously time to upgrade to an N95 or similar high-filtration respirator when you're in public indoor spaces. "Cloth masks are not going to cut it with omicron," says Linsey Marr, a researcher at Virginia Tech who studies how viruses transmit in the air... True, a cloth mask can be a "marginally OK to maybe a decent filter," Marr says. But with something as highly transmissible as omicron, just "OK" isn't good enough.

'Ditch the cloth mask' said the *San Francisco Chronicle* on 5 Dec 2021. You can guess how the rest of the story goes.

In Britain the respirator push has been led by the country's chief frother-at-the-mouth, Trish Greenhalgh:

> It's time to rethink and upgrade masks for you and your family.

Slate said in 'CDC Updates Guidelines to Make Clear Cloth Masks Offer Least Protection Against COVID' (Jan 15 2022),

> Lots of experts had been saying it for a while but now the Centers for Disease Control and Prevention has made it official by revising is guidelines to recommend Americans wear "the most protective mask you can"… [the CDC] has made clear that certain masks offer better protection against the coronavirus than others… Although there had previously been concern about shortages of N95s and KN95s for healthcare workers that's no longer the case and people can now wear them without worry.

In fact the Biden government has been buying N95s in massive quantities – NBC News reported on 13 Jan 2022 ('Biden Details Federal 'Surge' of Medical Teams, Free COVID Tests & N95s to Fight Omicron') that

> The federal government has a stockpile of more than 750 million N95 masks, the White House said this week.

Why has it done this? Because the Biden government wants to start giving them out for free. From the same NBC News story:

> Biden also announced that for the first time his administration was planning to make high-quality N95 masks, which are most effective at preventing transmission of the virus, available for free.

Still think there's no push towards N95s?

If the mask fetishists can get people into respirators, and get them used to those by not insisting too much on a proper fit to start with, then their eventual next step will be to stop people being able to have side gaps, and so simply existing will become even more awful, not to mention our immune systems being ruined.

Who is Jeremy Howard?

Howard is one of the chief villains in the whole mask travesty. He's an Australian entrepreneur, self-promoter and big data guy, a former management consultant at McKinsey's, and one of WEF's Global Leaders. Some of his main projects involve developing digital medical services. In 2014 he started up and ran Enlitic, a company that specialised in disease diagnostics by AI. He has said in an interview that he got frustrated with Enlitic because he had grander visions about wanting to

> transform how diagnosis and treatment planning was
> done throughout medicine

and he couldn't get access to the data he wanted, so in 2018 he headed up a new institute called WAMRI, the Wicklow AI in Medicine Research Initiative, in the University of San Francisco's Data Institute. This unit is privately funded by Wicklow Capital, a company owned by multi-millionaire Dan Tierney, co-founder of the massive financial company GETCO (Global Electronic Trading Company), and a big money donor to the Democrats.

It's no doubt just a big coincidence that Howard's pushing of masks and other NPIs has played havoc with the traditional system of face-to-face medical appointments and consultations throughout the world, which is all to the benefit of those with grand visions of developing AI medical diagnostics and transforming medical treatment into a digital service.

In the early days of Covid, Howard co-founded and led the mask-advocacy group #Masks4All in partnership with some Czech scientists who had gone crazy for masks. #Masks4All had a brief moment of influence with an open letter they wrote urging governments around the world to mandate face masks. Over 100 scientists signed it. The first signature on the letter was Howard's, and Richard Horton (the hard-left editor of the *Lancet*) and Trish Greenhalgh also signed it, as well as the egregious Dr Eric Feigl-Ding.

The evidence cited as the basis for this call was a paper that Howard himself was lead author on, 'An evidence review of face masks against COVID-19', *Proceedings of the National Academy of Sciences* (v. 118 (4), Jan 2021), a mediocre piece of work that I take a look at in part 5.3.a.

#Masks4All soon faded after Howard had used it as a launchpad, and the claims it had made about the effectiveness of masks in the Czech Republic fell apart as Czech cases grew rapidly later in 2020. (#Masks4All's shouty website shows no signs of having been touched since April 2020.)

Howard used the attention gained to write gung-ho, ridiculous-but-influential pro-mask articles for media outlets such as the *Washington Post*, *The Guardian*, *The Atlantic*, and the *Sydney Morning Herald*, demanding governmental mask mandates.

In one media article he wrote, called 'Masks help stop the spread of coronavirus – the science is simple' (15 May 2020), he said

> Much to my surprise, I discovered that the evidence for wearing masks in public was very strong.

That's much to my surprise as well.

In a blog post written with Trish Greenhalgh, he and Greenhalgh say

> You can make one at home, from a t-shirt, handkerchief, or paper towel, or even just wrap a scarf or bandana around your face… There is no evidence that your mask needs to be made with any particular expertise or care to be effective for source control.

In his *Guardian* article he says

> But almost any kind of simple cloth covering over your mouth, such as a home-made mask, or even a bandanna, can stop the assassin in its tracks.

In January 2022 Howard finally admitted that cloth masks weren't much cop, and said we all had to wear respirators instead (so yes, another one who delayed admitting the truth until the respirator push was ready to go). He told Australia's ABC:

> "Ditch your cloth masks and also ditch your surgical masks."

We will, of course, wait in vain for an apology from him.

Trish Greenhalgh says cloth masks work because of…

It's no longer relevant what the cloth crank Trish Greenhalgh has previously said about cloth masks, because she has finally admitted, in a 17 Jan 2022 article in the *Conversation* called 'Time to upgrade from cloth and surgical masks to respirators? Your questions answered', that they don't work.

> In general, they [cloth masks] are poor filters of small airborne particles.

I notice that one of the co-authors on that Conversation article was Lisa M Brosseau. Her name rings a bell…

Yes, there's an amusing edge here. In a 2020 blog post Greenhalgh's mask-pushing colleague Jeremy Howard slagged off a popular article co-written by Dr Lisa M Brosseau, which recommended against cloth masks. Brosseau's article said

> We do not recommend requiring the general public who do not have symptoms of COVID-19-like illness to routinely wear cloth or surgical masks because there is no scientific evidence they are effective.

Howard said of this article that it was

> full of uncited claims, falsehoods, and misunderstandings, and wouldn't normally be something that would be taken seriously and need to be discussed in any detail.

Yet here is his old mask maniac collaborator Greenhalgh co-authoring an article with a certain Lisa M Brosseau which says that cloth masks don't work! Chalk that up as another Howard fail (as well as a Greenhalgh fail, although she'll never admit it).

It's also amusing that another of the authors on that *Conversation* article was Prof C. Raina Macintyre, who had said for years that cloth masks don't work. Greenhalgh owes the world an apology just as much as Howard does.

This popular mask expert called Joseph Allen says that side leakage isn't a problem: 'Yes, some aerosol escapes out the side, but direction of airflow matters. Reducing the plume in the speaker's cone of emissions as they directly interact with others is key'.

First of all, note that this is a total reinvention of what masks are supposed to do. The point of masks was supposed to be that they filtered the air going through the mask. This is why official government reports liked to cite filtering studies, often as their main evidence. This is why pro-maskers would point out that it was important to get a good fit even with cloth masks (because air was not supposed to go out the side). Their line on side leakage was generally that it didn't happen enough to be much of a worry. What Allen in engaging in here is a complete script rewrite.

We should also note that what he says assumes that all interactions involve two people standing face to face. Which isn't at all how people always interact. You often sit at tables side by side, or at an angle to each other. Children sit in classes all day with no-one facing them, the other students are all to the sides and behind them. Workers stand at production lines side-by-side.

Allen references the supposed benefit of the changed airflow direction in hospitals:

> when someone say [*sic*] surgical masks don't work in hospitals, they're ignoring the benefit of reducing the aerosol jet in front of the person.

But nurses very often interact closely with bed-ridden patients with the patient's face off to their side of the mask, such as when they are changing dressings on the patient's body.

Also, this is just another version of the line that 'Masks reduce transmission somewhat', with no consideration of whether the 'somewhat' outweighs the considerable harms caused by forced mask wearing.

Finally, I note that despite Allen claiming that side leaks are fine, he quickly goes on to say that 'fit is critical'. In fact, he published a whole article in *StatNews* on this topic

('Without training, N95 masks may not protect workers on the Covid-19 frontlines', 16 April 2020), in which he says

> an incorrectly worn mask will fail to protect the user from respiratory hazards like SARS-CoV-2... an improperly worn mask can give health care workers a false sense of security that they are being protected in a high-risk environment when they really aren't.

So we can take his claim that side leaks don't matter with a grain of salt.

Your anti-maskism must be misplaced, because Sweden didn't wear face masks much and they had enormous deaths.

No, Sweden's deaths have been entirely normal, as the graph below by Johan Hellstrom, using data from Sweden's official statistics agency, SCB Statistikmyndigheten, shows. (See also my article 'Sweden's figures DO show that lockdowns are a crime' on my website.)

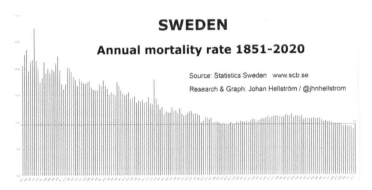

SWEDEN

Annual mortality rate 1851-2020

Source: Statistics Sweden www.scb.se
Research & Graph: Johan Hellström / @jhnhellstrom

Even if you just look at Covid deaths, Sweden has had fewer Covid deaths per head of population than the UK, as this graph from IanM makes clear.

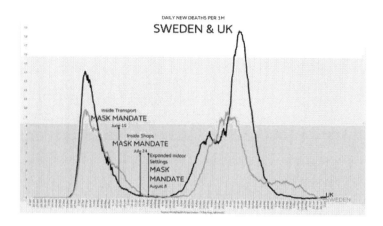

Didn't the Czech Republic achieve low Covid rates due to mask-wearing?

We met the mask advocacy group '#Masks4All', led by our friend Jeremy Howard, and various Czech scientists, earlier in this section. Early on in the Covid era they very loudly proclaimed that the Czech Republic had shown that masks worked.

Trish Greenhalgh also made this claim in a blog, and also in a paper called 'Face coverings for the public: Laying straw men to rest' in *Evaluation in Clinical Practice* (v. 26 (4), Aug 2020, pp.1070-7):

> Of note is the example of the Czech Republic and Austria, both of which introduced social distancing on the same day; the former also introduced compulsory face coverings. New covid-19 infections fell more quickly in the Czech Republic, and only began to fall in Austria after masks were made mandatory 2 weeks later.

The explanation of what happened in the Czech Republic was that most of Eastern Europe missed the first wave of Covid. But by winter 2020 the Czech Republic's rate started climbing dramatically, and soon overtook Austria, Germany,

Spain, Italy, Switzerland and the US. So masks didn't work there at all, and Greenhalgh and Howard were wrong once again.

Asian countries wore masks, and they had few cases.

Whatever the real reason for why some Asian countries initially had lower cases than the West, since then their cases have just got bigger and bigger. See, for example, this graph of Japan's cases, which went from a few dozen cases per day in spring/summer 2020, to over 26,000 a day in summer 2021. Then in early 2022 cases exploded, with over 100,000 cases a day in February 2022. So masks were not the reason why Japan did not have many cases back then.

Daily New Cases in Japan

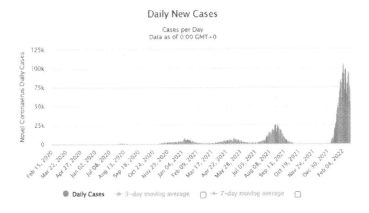

Or consider the Philippines, who have long been mask Nazis and were originally held up as a Covid success story. The picture there is similar to Japan.

Daily New Cases in the Philippines

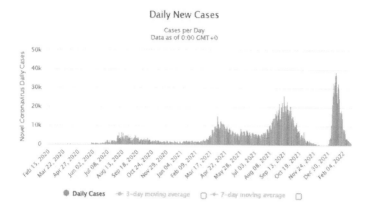

Daily New Cases

Cases per Day
Data as of 0:00 GMT+0

Flu disappeared in 2020/21, surely this is because of face masks?

No, because flu also disappeared in countries which didn't have much face mask use, so whatever the reason for that, it wasn't due to face masks.

Why did flu disappear then?

We're not entirely sure. One theory that has some credibility is that flu was displaced by Covid. This happens all the time, with some diseases 'displacing' others. This phenomenon is described in 'Virus–virus interactions impact the population dynamics of influenza and the common cold', by Nickbakhsh et al, in *Proceedings of the National Academy of Sciences* (v.116 (52), Dec 2019), who say

> When multiple pathogens cocirculate this can lead to competitive or cooperative forms of pathogen–pathogen interactions. It is believed that such interactions occur among cold and flu viruses, perhaps through broad-acting immunity, resulting in interlinked epidemiological patterns of infection... Our analyses provide strong

statistical support for the existence of interactions among respiratory viruses.

Some, on the other hand, have speculated that many flu cases have been misdiagnosed as Covid due to the limitations of testing. I don't know enough to pronounce on that, but flu has been coming back again recently, so that appears not to be the reason (although these days we should be sceptical of anything that involves testing.)

But Asians wear face masks and they never get the flu much.

False. Consider, for example, this UPI news report titled 'Millions in Japan affected as flu outbreak grips country' from February 2019.

> The worst flu outbreak on record in Japan has affected millions of people, with many patients hospitalized or in critical condition, according to reports. The total number of flu patients has surpassed 2.2 million across the country, and the infections have shown no signs of stopping, NHK reported Friday. According to Japan's ministry of health labor and welfare, more than 5,000 hospitals and clinics were on average reporting 57 flu patients per institution. The number is an increase from the previous winter, when hospitals were reporting an average of 54 patients per institution.

Does washing your cloth mask reduce its ability to trap the virus?

A 2019 study titled 'Optical microscopic study of surface morphology and filtering efficiency of face masks' by Neupane et al in *PeerJ* (v. 7 e7142. 26 Jun. 2019) said

> we found that efficiency dropped by 20% after the 4th washing and drying cycle. We observed a change in pore

size and shape and a decrease in microfibers within the pores after washing. Stretching of CM surface also altered the pore size and potentially decreased the filtering efficiency… This study showed that the filtering efficiency of cloth face masks were relatively lower, and washing and drying practices deteriorated the efficiency.

Here's a picture of the effect in action from Neupane et al – the mask in picture A is unwashed, and each letter after represents a further wash. (The short bar at the bottom of A represents 500 microns, and applies to all images.)

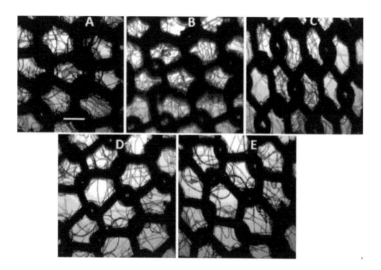

As cloth masks don't work anyway this isn't worth worrying about, and for the sake of hygiene you should regularly wash your cloth mask. For the sake of rationality you should put it away in a drawer (or the bin) and never wear it again.

Do masks get a build-up of bacteria and other pathogens on them after a while?

Any mask that can trap a virus will also trap bacteria and other pathogens, which are much larger than virions. And masks soon get wet, and so provide a damp and warm environment which is perfect for bacteria and mould to multiply. Some of these are likely to be breathed in, and some will be expelled out in greater quantities than would happen with someone who wasn't wearing a mask.

As this pro-mask writer admits (in *The Crimson White*, 20 Aug 2020):

> Candida Overgrowth is another perpetrator that reveals itself by leaving the skin raw, red, irritated, chapped, or rashy according to Everyday Health. Candida Overgrowth is basically a yeast infection on your mouth. This infection cannot solely be caused by wearing a mask, but the conditions a mask provides is perfect for the infection to grow.

Also:

> Microbiologist Sarah Lebeer (UAntwerp) confirms the link between wearing a mouth mask for a long time and complaints to the skin and the respiratory tract. "Our research shows that bacteria from the breath build up on the inside of a mask that you wear for a long time. Among them are many staphs, which are known to aggravate acne and sinusitis. On a mask that you wear for more than eight hours, those bacteria can even start to spread. In addition to the presence of bacteria, "not properly ventilating the sinuses" can also lead to complaints, says Lebeer. "Blocking the natural airflow with a mask can lead to headaches, nasal congestion, fatigue". In the weekly corona survey by the University of Antwerp last week, 16 percent of those surveyed

indicated that they suffered from acne due to wearing a mask. 7 percent reported sinus complaints. Eye pain and headaches were also common. "At the time of that survey, the schools hadn't even reopened".

How much of a build-up of bacteria and other pathogens can happen, though, and how dangerous could they be?

That's hard to say, because somehow, despite hundreds of billions, probably trillions, being spent on Covid measures, and trillions of masks having been worn, little large-scale quality research has been done on this issue.

You would be very unwise, however, to re-use a mask without sterilising it every day.

The *New York Post* talked to dentists who are worried: "We're seeing inflammation in people's gums that have been healthy forever, and cavities in people who have never had them before," says Dr. Rob Ramondi, a dentist and co-founder of One Manhattan Dental. "About 50% of our patients are being impacted by this".

That's not great, but at least it's only gum disease, which is not that serious.

Gum disease is serious:

"Gum disease — or periodontal disease — will eventually lead to strokes and an increased risk of heart attacks," says Dr. Marc Sclafani, another co-founder of One Manhattan Dental.

For more on the serious health risks from gum disease, read the AIER article 'What's Going On Under the Masks?' by Robert E. Wright (26 June 2021):

The subtitle of Stone's book, *Why the Lack of Proper Oral Care Is Killing Nursing Home Residents and How to Prevent It*, is much more poignant now than when the book appeared in 2015. Its warnings were largely ignored then though more seniors died of poor oral health than died with Covid, outside of the nursing home massacre states like New York and Michigan anyway.

What about that University of Florida study?

A lab at the University of Florida did detect some possibly harmful bacteria and pathogens on some masks that were sent in. This was first reported in a local newspaper:

A group of local parents sent 6 face masks to a lab at the University of Florida, requesting an analysis of contaminants found on the masks after they had been worn. The resulting report found that five masks were contaminated with bacteria, parasites, and fungi, including three with dangerous pathogenic and pneumonia-causing bacteria.

Something similar happened in Germany – a consumer magazine called *K-Tipp* did an examination of how hygienic used masks are. A German magazine called *Blick* described this as follows (I used Google Translate to translate the text into English).

20 used masks from commuters were examined in the laboratory. The result is sobering. The masks are full of bacteria and mould. The reason: masks act like filters, the air you breathe flows through the fibers of the tissue. This has consequences: bacteria and fungi get stuck. They multiply quickly in a warm, damp mask environment... 11 of the 20 masks tested contained more than 100,000 bacterial colonies. Three of them even more than a million... But that's not all: the microbiologists also found staphylococci. On 14 of the

20 masks. The bacteria can cause pneumonia and brain infections.

Is this good science?

The pro-maskers were quick to point out that the Florida findings cannot be taken too seriously, as some basic scientific criteria were not observed. There was no control group, for example. Not all bacteria and mould are harmful. We also need a baseline as it is likely that we normally have a lot of this on our skin to start with.

These are valid points (although having bacteria on your skin to start with is not so relevant, as you won't be breathing these bacteria in), but we should note the hypocrisy of these pro-maskers who dismiss such findings while aggressively pushing their own pet non-science-based interventions.

It is true that we should not put too much store on the findings from the Florida lab, but given that it is all too likely that masks will capture harmful contaminants over time, and given that most people are not regularly replacing or sterilising their masks, you would expect that the authorities would have urgently ordered a high-quality review into these sorts of dangers. They haven't, of course, and even after so much time they remain profoundly uninterested in the issue.

We should also note that the use of CPAP masks at night to help with sleep apnea has been known to cause serious cases of Legionella pneumonia, as well as Streptococcus infections, so it is not always true (as some have claimed) that bacteria and mould growth in masks is always harmless.

Any other cases of masks being infected?

In Switzerland 13 million masks had to be recalled because they had got mouldy. The following Euronews description of the situation was translated from German using Google Translate:

> The Swiss Confederation has recalled 13.5 million hygiene masks. But they weren't hygienic at all - the masks from old stocks are infested with mold. This is what tests at the University Hospital in Geneva have shown. Accordingly, there is a microbiological contamination with Aspergillus fumigatus... A 41-year-old employee of the Thun Hospital remembers in an interview with 20 minutes: "They smelled like a moldy bathroom ... Almost unbearable!" But despite complaints from the superiors, the mold masks had to be worn for up to nine hours in some cases. Hospital staff in Bern then complained of burning eyes and breathing problems.

Have any scientists researched the issue of mask contamination?

Some have, yes, although generally it's an issue that academics shy away from for political reasons. And the studies that have been done have received very little attention from the health authorities, or from the media.

A 2021 study called 'Cotton and Surgical Face Masks in Community Settings: Bacterial Contamination and Face Mask Hygiene' by Delanghe et al in *Frontiers of Medicine* (v.8 (732047), 3 Sep 2021) concludes that

> a considerable number of bacteria, including pathobionts and antibiotic resistant bacteria, accumulate on surgical and even more on cotton face masks after use. Based on

our results, face masks should be properly disposed of or sterilized after intensive use.

One 2018 study called 'Surgical masks as source of bacterial contamination during operative procedures' by Zhiqing et al in the *Journal of Orthopaedic Translation* (v.14, July 2018, pp.57-62) found that surgical masks used in operations contained significantly more bacteria than unworn control group masks that were in the same operating theatre.

A 2014 study in the *Oman Medical Journal* (v.29 (5), Sep 2014, pp.346–50) called 'Microbial Contamination on Used Surgical Masks among Hospital Personnel and Microbial Air Quality in their Working Wards: A Hospital in Bangkok' by Luksamijarulkul et al found

> High bacterial contamination on outside area of the used masks was demonstrated, and it showed a significant correlation with microbial air quality of working wards.

Science Daily said this of a *BMJ Open* study on cloth masks:

> The widespread use of cloth masks by healthcare workers may actually put them at increased risk of respiratory illness and viral infections and their global use should be discouraged, according to a UNSW study… The authors speculate that the cloth masks' moisture retention, their reuse and poor filtration may explain the increased risk of infection.

An April 2021 meta-analysis from Germany called 'Is a Mask That Covers the Mouth and Nose Free from Undesirable Side Effects in Everyday Use and Free of Potential Hazards?' by Kisielinski et al and published in the *International Journal of Environmental Research and Public Health* (v.18 (8), 20 April 2021) made the following points:

From an infection epidemiological point of view, masks in everyday use offer the risk of self-contamination by the wearer from both inside and outside, including via contaminated hands. In addition, masks are soaked by exhaled air, which potentially accumulates infectious agents from the nasopharynx and also from the ambient air on the outside and inside of the mask. In particular, serious infection-causing bacteria and fungi should be mentioned here, but also viruses.

These issues, by the way, have been known about for a long time, as exemplified by a story in the *Santa Barbara Daily News and the Independent* on November 16, 1918, entitled 'Mask is Chief Ally of "Flu", Physicians declare', which had the sub-heading

Average Person Doesn't Know How to Take Care of Mask and it Becomes Veritable Bacteria Incubator.

Bear in mind also that recent research has shown an association between lung cancer and oral bacteria entering the lungs (even bacteria that is harmless or beneficial). This bacteria can easily get into your mask, especially if you're one of those people who sneeze and cough into it, and then it can be breathed in from the mask into your lungs. There is obviously no long-term data on this, but it strongly suggests that wearing a mask is a very unwise thing to do.

See also 'Masks, false safety and real dangers, Part 2: Microbial challenges from masks' by Borovoy et al in *Primary Doctor Medical Journal* (9 Oct 2020) for a review of the issues.

What is the 'foegen effect'?

This is a hypothesis put forward by a German doctor, Zacharias Fögen, that masks may cause re-breathing in of virus particles trapped in the mask into deeper areas of the lungs, and to other areas where they would not normally go, like the olfactory nerve. I should stress that this hypothesis is entirely speculative and has not been studied, and the only presentation of it is in a non-peer-reviewed paper published by Fögen. It is still, however, a cause for concern and needs study (which of course hasn't happened).

Fögen's own explanation is as follows:

> The explanation for the increased RR [risk ratio] by masks is probably that virions that are breezed or coughed out in droplets are stopped in the facemask tissue, and after quick evaporation of the droplets, pure virions are reinhaled from a very short distance when breathing in. For further reference, I refer to this as the 'foegen effect' as I could not find this effect described earlier.

> By the 'foegen effect' the virions are not only spreading to other areas (like the olfactory nerve, causing loss of smell) but also (because of their smaller size) deeper into the respiratory tract. They bypass the bronchia and are inhaled deep into the alveoli, where they cause a pneumonia instead of a bronchitis, which would rather be typical for a virus infection. They also bypass the wall of multilayer squamous epithelium that they cannot pass in vitro and most likely cannot pass in vivo. Therefore, the only probable way for the virions to enter the blood vessels is through the alveoli.

> The 'foegen effect' also increases overall viral load, because virions that should have been removed from the respiratory tract are returned. The viral reproduction in vivo, including the reproduction of the returned virions, is exponential compared to the linear droplet reduction caused by the mask. Therefore, the number of exhaled or coughed out virions that pass through the facemask will

at some point exceed the number of virions shed without facemasks.

Did masks help with the 1918 influenza epidemic?

No. As the *Washington Post* reported, masks were useless in the USA during the 1918 influenza pandemic:

> During the influenza pandemic of 1918, officials often advised Americans to wear face masks in public. Doctors believed that masks could help prevent "spray infections," according to historian John M. Barry in his book, *The Great Influenza: The Story of the Deadliest Pandemic in History*. Enforced by local health officials, the facial coverings grew routine… "The masks worn by millions were useless as designed and could not prevent influenza," Barry wrote. "Only preventing exposure to the virus could".

Did masks make things worse with the 1918 influenza epidemic?

Possibly, and there has been speculation about this, but not much hard evidence.

Some say that most deaths in 1918-19 were actually from secondary pneumonia infection, rather than the flu itself. I have not looked into this issue in any detail, but note that this significant paper, co-authored by a certain Anthony Fauci, called 'Predominant Role of Bacterial Pneumonia as a Cause of Death in Pandemic Influenza: Implications for Pandemic Influenza Preparedness' makes this claim:

> Conclusions. The majority of deaths in the 1918–1919 influenza pandemic likely resulted directly from secondary bacterial pneumonia caused by common upper respiratory-tract bacteria. Less substantial data from the

subsequent 1957 and 1968 pandemics are consistent with these findings.

(From Morens, Taubenberger and Fauci, *The Journal of Infectious Diseases* v.198 (7), 1 Oct 2008, pp.962-70.)

However, I don't know of any research that says that the mask wearing of the time exacerbated this.

Is there an association between masks and headaches?

There is plenty of anecdotal evidence of an association, especially with respirator masks which make it difficult to breathe, but the scientific establishment has shown little interest in investigating any mask harms. But there have been a few findings.

One scientific study titled 'Headaches Associated With Personal Protective Equipment – A Cross-Sectional Study Among Frontline Healthcare Workers During COVID-19' by Ong et al in the journal *Headache* (v.60 (5), May 2020, pp.864-877), said

Conclusion: Most healthcare workers develop de novo PPE-associated headaches or exacerbation of their pre-existing headache disorders.

A German meta-analysis ('Is a Mask That Covers the Mouth and Nose Free from Undesirable Side Effects in Everyday Use and Free of Potential Hazards?' by Kisielinski et al, in the *International Journal of Environmental Research and Public Health*, v.18 (8), 20 April 2021), also found an increase in headaches:

In this paper, we refer to the psychological and physical deterioration as well as multiple symptoms described because of their consistent, recurrent and uniform presentation from different disciplines as a Mask-Induced Exhaustion Syndrome (MIES). We objectified evaluation evidenced changes in respiratory physiology of mask wearers with significant correlation of O2 drop and fatigue ($p < 0.05$), a clustered co-occurrence of respiratory impairment and O2 drop (67%), N95 mask and CO2 rise (82%), N95 mask and O2 drop (72%), N95 mask and headache (60%), respiratory impairment and temperature rise (88%), but also temperature rise and moisture (100%) under the masks. Extended mask-wearing by the general population could lead to relevant effects and consequences in many medical fields.

A 2009 randomised study in the *American Journal of Infection Control* (v.37 (5), June 2009, pp.417-9), titled 'Use of surgical face masks to reduce the incidence of the common cold among health care workers in Japan: a randomized controlled trial' by Jacobs et al, found that

subjects in the mask group were significantly more likely to experience headache during the study period.

In 'Headaches and the N95 face-mask amongst healthcare providers' by Lim et al in *Acta Neurologica Scandinavica* (113 (3), March 2006, pp. 199-202), the authors conclude

Healthcare providers may develop headaches following the use of the N95 face-mask. Shorter duration of face-mask wear may reduce the frequency and severity of these headaches.

In 'Is N95 face mask linked to dizziness and headache?' by Ipek et al in *International Archives of Occupational and Environmental Health* (v. 94 (7), Oct 2021, pp.1627-36), the authors say

Respiratory alkalosis and hypocarbia were detected after the use of N95. Acute respiratory alkalosis can cause headache, anxiety, tremor, muscle cramps. In this study, it was quantitatively shown that the participants' symptoms were due to respiratory alkalosis and hypocarbia.

In 'Effect of Wearing Face Masks on the Carbon Dioxide Concentration in the Breathing Zone' by Geiss, in a special issue of *Aerosol and Air Quality Research* on 'COVID-19 Aerosol Drivers, Impacts and Mitigation (X)' (v.21 (2), Feb 2021), author Otmar Geiss of the European Commission's Joint Research Centre in Ispra, Italy, found that

> concentrations [of carbon dioxide] in the detected range can cause undesirable symptoms, such as fatigue, headache, and loss of concentration.

Do masks really cause a carbon dioxide buildup/lack of oxygen?

It seems so, but serious research on this issue is somewhat lacking, so it's hard to be too confident about it. But you'd have to be mad to risk wearing a respirator properly – actually properly, with no side escape, so you can't breathe very easily – all day long. If you press down the sides of the mask against your face so that your breaths are forced through the front rather than escaping out the sides, then you can literally feel yourself re-breathing your own exhalations, and the inside of the mask become hot, as your warm exhalations can't escape very well.

(Note that if you apply the precautionary principle as liberally as mask proponents do then you should conclude that mask-wearing is not worth the risk.)

I take a look at the literature I have found on this issue in part 5.8.a. I should note that none of this research can ensure that the respirators involved are worn with a tight fit, and most likely they will not be, especially when anything strenuous is required. More dramatic results would probably be found if respirators were tightly attached to the face so that air cannot escape in and out the sides.

Is there a danger of breathing in fibres and other materials from a mask?

Yes, and this is especially worrying when artificial fibres are used, as they are with respirators and surgical masks, and most disposable masks. It is also more of a risk when respirator masks are used, as these require greater effort to breathe, and this causes more forceful breaths both in and out.

In a news report from Swansea University titled 'Nanoplastics and other harmful pollutants found within disposable face masks', it was reported on 4 May 2021 that a team of chemist and engineers from Swansea University researching nanoplastics within facemasks warned that

> There is also a need to understand the impact of such particle leaching on public health. One of the main concerns with these particles is that they were easily detached from face masks and leached into the water with no agitation, which suggests that these particles are mechanically unstable and readily available to be detached. 'Therefore, a full investigation is necessary to determine the quantities and potential impacts of these particles leaching into the environment, and the levels being inhaled by users during normal breathing. This is a significant concern, especially for health care professionals, key workers, and children who are required to wear masks for large proportions of the working or school day.

Ecotextile News in April 20201 reported that

> German scientists have found that wearing certain types of face masks for long periods of time could result in

potentially hazardous chemicals and harmful microplastics being inhaled deep into human lungs. Professor Michael Braungart, director at the Hamburg Environmental Institute and co-founder of the world-renowned Cradle to Cradle environmental standard has told Ecotextile News that mask wearers unwittingly run the risk of breathing in carcinogens, allergens and tiny synthetic microfibres by wearing both textile and nonwoven surgical masks for long periods of time.

And

His recent findings have been backed up by another leading industry textile chemist Dr. Dieter Sedlak, managing director and co-founder of Modern Testing Services Augsburg, Germany in partnership with Modern Testing Services Global, Hong Kong who found elevated concentrations of hazardous fluorocarbons, formaldehyde and other potentially carcinogenic substances on surgical face masks… textile chemical expert, Phil Patterson of Colour Connections, who also works with the highly respected ZDHC Foundation on chemical management. "In my opinion, textile masks do not begin to pass this most basic hazard test for kids, for whom the risks of COVID have been categorically demonstrated to be miniscule," he said.

In another interview, this time with the *Epoch Times*, Braungart said many masks

"are made of polyester and so you have a microplastic problem… You can clearly measure that. The microplastic is released through friction and is inhaled directly. Some masks contain chlorine compounds as a plastic layer". Many of the face masks would generally contain polyester. "When I have the mask in front of my face, then of course I breathe in the microplastic directly," explains Braungart. "It's like with the solvents. They are much more toxic when inhaled than when swallowed because the toxins go directly to the nervous system".

In an examination of loose mask fibres and debris (complete with microscopic images) in 'Masks, false safety and real dangers, Part 1: Friable mask particulate and lung vulnerability' by Borovoy et al (July 6, 2020), the authors said

> Masked individuals have measurably higher inspiratory flow than non-masked individuals. This study is of new masks removed from manufacturer packaging, as well as a laundered cloth mask, examined microscopically. Loose particulate was seen on each type of mask. Also, tight and loose fibers were seen on each type of mask. If every foreign particle and every fiber in every facemask is always secure and not detachable by airflow, then there should be no risk of inhalation of such particles and fibers. However, if even a small portion of mask fibers is detachable by inspiratory airflow, or if there is debris in mask manufacture or packaging or handling, then there is the possibility of not only entry of foreign material to the airways, but also entry to deep lung tissue, and potential pathological consequences of foreign bodies in the lungs.

The *South China Morning Post* reported on a paper published in the *Journal of Hazardous Materials* by a team from the Institute of Hydrobiology in Wuhan:

> Wearing a face mask has become a way of life during the coronavirus pandemic, but it can also cause us to inhale harmful plastic fibres, according to a new study by Chinese scientists. The researchers tested a wide range of mask products and found that nearly all would

increase the daily intake of microplastic fibres during wear because of their relatively fragile structure... Scientists first discovered microplastics in the lung tissue of some patients who died of lung cancer in the 1990s, and many other studies have since highlighted the potential damage to health caused by such materials. Plastic degrades slowly, so once in the lungs it tends to stay there and build up in volume. Some studies have found that the immune system can attack these foreign objects, causing prolonged inflammation that can lead to diseases such as cancer.

(Although the researchers admitted that 'the fibres could cause some health problems', they still recommended masks because they were under the impression that masks stop the Covid virus.)

In 'Need for assessing the inhalation of micro(nano)plastic debris shed from masks, respirators, and home-made face coverings during the COVID-19 pandemic' in *Environmental Pollution* by Han and He (Jan 1, 2021; 268), the authors say

By putting several top-selling medical face masks and N95 respirators under microscopes, however, we saw abundant loosely attached debris on their inner facings, some showing the morphology of fibers and others as particles, in the micron and sub-micron ranges.

The pictures the authors provided in their article (look at the 'Supplementary Data' section as well) vividly document the sort of things you will be breathing into your lungs with a face mask.

Does this issue with breathing in possibly harmful materials apply to cloth masks?

Han and He continue:

> For fabrics repurposed as face masks... debris is likely to be generated from cutting and tearing. Some fabrics, such as velvets, fleeces and towels, are known to shed microfibers when disturbed. Detergent residues and lint generated from machine laundering and tumble drying may also be present as inhalable contaminants in washed garments.

Has there ever been issues with workers in polypropylene factories having lung disease?

There have been some concerns about this, although there is no strong evidence for it being a major problem.

In 'The respiratory effects of occupational polypropylene flock exposure' by Atis et al in the *European Respiratory Journal* (v.25, 2005, pp.110-7) the authors said

> In conclusion, the present authors found exposure to polypropylene flock in the workplace to be associated with pulmonary functional impairment of a restrictive type and with reduced diffusing capacity.

It should be noted, though, that the correlation wasn't that strong.

In 'Pulmonary toxicity of inhaled polypropylene fibers in rats' by Hesterberg in *Fundamental and Applied Toxicology* (v.19 (3), Oct 1992, pp. 358-66), the authors found some mild, but reversible, lung effects in rats from exposure to polypropylene fibres:

> This study was initiated to assess the pulmonary toxicity of a polyolefin fiber composed of polypropylene in male Fischer 344 rats after 90 days of inhalation exposure...

Microscopic examination of the polypropylene fiber-exposed lungs revealed that, at all time points examined in the study, there was a dose-dependent increase in pulmonary macrophages. These minimal or mild increases in cellularity appeared to be reversible, especially at the lower doses 30 days post exposure. No fibrosis was observed in any of the groups. A strong correlation was found between the external exposure concentration, the time of exposure, and the lung fiber burden. The number of partially degraded (segmented) fibers within the lung increased with the exposure concentration and period of exposure, as well as with the period of recovery after termination of exposure at 90 days.

Nylon flock dust at a nylon production factory has previously been reported as causing lung issues, as described in 'Epidemiologic investigation of respiratory morbidity at a nylon flock plant' by Washko et al, in the *American Journal of Industrial Medicine* (v.38 (6), Dec 2000, pp. 628-38). The authors said

Findings of this study, along with those from studies reported elsewhere, implicate occupational exposure to flock-associated dust as a significant respiratory health hazard at this plant.

I've heard about graphene in masks being a danger. Is this a real thing?

Sort of. Health Canada issued a warning for one mask being used in daycare centres:

One model of mask distributed to Quebec schools and daycares may be dangerous for the lungs as they could contain a potentially toxic material, according to a directive sent out by the provincial government on

Friday... Health Canada warned of the potential for "early pulmonary toxicity" from the SNN200642 masks... Some daycare educators had been suspicious of these grey and blue masks for a while because they felt like they were swallowing cat hair while wearing them, Radio-Canada has learned. Health Canada conducted a preliminary risk assessment which revealed a potential for early lung damage associated with inhalation of microscopic graphene particles. Graphene is a strong, very thin material that is used in fabrication, but it can be harmful to lungs when inhaled and can cause long-term health problems.

However, Canada eventually cleared these masks as not dangerous. Still, would you want to wear a mask that makes you feel like you're swallowing cat hair while wearing it?

France recalled 60 million masks over similar concerns with graphene:

At least 60.5 million face masks rated as FFP2 and distributed to health workers should no longer be worn to protect against Covid, as inhaling their particles could be toxic for the lungs, health authority Santé publique France (SPF) has said. The masks, rated FFP2, contain "biomass graphene", and should no longer be worn as they can cause respiratory issues, the authority said. The masks are being recalled from use. They had been distributed for use in hospitals, pharmacies and other medical centres and situations.

Professor Andrew Maynard has researched 'nanomaterial risks and developing approaches to safe and responsible use for over 20 years'. He says that while there isn't a lot evidence that graphene presents any great risk to lungs (because it has barely been studied), nevertheless it seems highly irresponsible to include a material with unknown inhalation risks in a product that is intimately associated with inhalation. Especially when there are a growing number of face masks available that claim to use graphene.

What about fibreglass?

There are concerns that some older masks still contain fibreglass, which is very damaging to the lungs.

Are masks bad for the environment?

It seems so, even allowing for the usual environmentalist exaggeration. In 'An investigation into the leaching of micro and nano particles and chemical pollutants from disposal face masks linked to the COVID-19 pandemic' in *Water Research* (v.196, March 2021) by Sullivan, Delgado-Gallardo, Watson and Sarp (a team of chemists and engineers from Swansea University), the authors said

> This study focuses on the emission of pollutants from 7 DPF [disposable plastic facemasks] brands that were submerged in water to simulate environmental conditions if these DPFs were littered. The DPF leachates were filtered by inorganic membranes, and both particle-deposited organic membranes and the filtrates were characterized using techniques such as FTIR, SEM-EDX, Light Microscopy, ICP-MS and LC-MS. Micro and nano scale polymeric fibres, particles, siliceous fragments and leachable inorganic and organic chemicals were observed from all of the tested DPFs. Traces of concerning heavy metals (i.e. lead up to 6.79 µg/L) were detected in association with silicon containing fragments. ICP-MS also confirmed the presence of other leachable metals like cadmium (up to

1.92 µg/L), antimony (up to 393 µg/L) and copper (up to 4.17 µg/L). LC-MS analysis identified polar leachable organic species related to plastic additives and contaminants; polyamide-66 monomer and oligomers (nylon-66 synthesis), surfactant molecules, dye-like molecules and polyethylene glycol were all tentatively identified in the leachate. The toxicity of some of the chemicals found and the postulated risks of the rest of the present particles and molecules, raises the question of whether DPFs are safe to be used on a daily basis and what consequences are to be expected after their disposal into the environment.

In 'Covid-19 face masks: A potential source of microplastic fibers in the environment' by Fadare and Okoffoc, *Science of the Total Environment*, Oct 1 2020; 737, the authors say

> This demand has resulted in an unprecedented rise in the global production of face masks which are produced using polymeric materials... Disposable face masks (single use face masks) are produced from polymers such as polypropylene, polyurethane, polyacrylonitrile, polystyrene, polycarbonate, polyethylene, or polyester... Some of these materials are getting into waterways from where they reach the freshwater and marine environment adding to the presence of plastics in the aquatic medium.

Could these break down into microplastics?
Yes, Fadare and Okoffoc also add that

> Similarly, disposable face masks that get to the environment could be emerging new source of microplastic fibers, as they can degrade/fragment or break down into smaller size/pieces of particles under 5

mm known as microplastics under environmental conditions.

How often do respirator masks need to be replaced?

Respirators are supposed to be disposable, thrown away after every session of use, or whenever they get wet. The FDA says

> All FDA-cleared N95 respirators are labeled as "single-use," disposable devices. If your respirator is damaged or soiled, or if breathing becomes difficult, you should remove the respirator, discard it properly, and replace it with a new one.

It also says the same about surgical masks:

> Surgical masks are not intended to be used more than once. If your surgical mask is damaged or soiled, or if breathing through the mask becomes difficult, you should remove it, discard it safely, and replace it with a new one.

Why do they need to be replaced when they get wet? Do they really not work when they are wet?

I have found it surprisingly hard to get solid evidence on this issue, but Inglesby et al say in their 2006 review 'Disease Mitigation Measures in the Control of Pandemic Influenza', in *Biosecurity and Bioterrorism: Biodefense Strategy, Practice, and Science* (v.4 (4), 2006, p. 372), that

> the pores in the [surgical] mask become blocked by moisture from breathing, and the air stream simply diverts around the mask.

So you have to constantly throw away your masks and put on new ones, or at least use a new one every day?

Yes. People who work in industrial settings where masks really do help do follow these protocols, and they do put new masks on all the time. One guy I know who works in an engineering industry where he sometimes has to use masks says that he can go through eight to ten FFP2 masks in a day

Isn't that going to be extremely expensive? Especially seeing as respirator masks are expensive?

Yes. But you're the one who wants the masks, and goes around saying that any measure is justified 'if it saves just one life'.

Nine billion people wearing ten respirator masks a day requires the manufacture of ninety billion masks for every single day. Respirator prices have moved up and down greatly since March 2020, but if each mask costs $1 that's $90 billion a day, which adds up to over a trillion pounds within a fortnight.

Even if we just use one mask a day (because even most mask fanatics are going to change their masks more than that) that's still $9 billion a day.

Doesn't using disposable masks produce enormous and unsustainable amounts of masks that have to be disposed of (or which are thrown away into nature)?

Yes. To do it properly you'll have to dispose of 9 to 90 billion respirators every day, all over the world. Good luck with that.

Even the current amounts are enormous, and causing an incredible amount of litter. In 'COVID-19 Pandemic Repercussions on the Use and Management of Plastics' by Prata et al in *Environmental Science and Technology* (v.40

(30), June 2020), the authors estimate that the world was using, as of mid-2020, around 129 billion face masks and 65 billion disposable gloves per month. That means so far literally *trillions* of facemasks have been used.

(Some companies are making absolute fortunes out of this nonsense.)

MIT News claimed on July 20 2020 that 'the Covid-19 pandemic is estimated to generate up to 7,200 tons of medical waste every day, much of which is disposable masks'.

The *Times of India* reported on mask waste in its 5 July 2020 article 'Discarded surgical masks are adding to bio-hazard around Goa', saying that

the amount of waste it has generated is massive.

StudyFinds said on 26 March 2021 that

Recent studies are calling the millions of coronavirus face masks people throw away a ticking plastic bomb. Unfortunately, a new report from the Netherlands finds that bomb has already gone off when it comes to wildlife. A team of biologists is revealing the damage disposable COVID safety gear is having on the world's animal population.

(From 'COVID waste, discarded face masks are killing wildlife around the globe'.)

Generally the virtue-signalling middle classes who have pushed mask-wearing are the same ones who previously were furious with plastic pollution and recently angrily demanded that plastic straws be banned, but then, they were never bothered with consistency.

Are respirators made from biodegradable materials?

No, they're made from polypropylene plastic, and sometimes polyethylene terephthalate, thermoplastics which are not biodegradable. These materials take at least 20–30 years to disintegrate.

In 'The COVID-19 pandemic face mask waste: A blooming threat to the marine environment' by Dharmaraj et al, in *Chemosphere* (v.272, June 2021), the authors point out that

> Mostly, face masks are made of petroleum-based non-renewable polymers that are non-biodegradable, hazardous to the environment and create health issues.

Greens might want to note that polypropylene itself is made from petroleum fossil fuel hydrocarbons like crude oil, natural gas or shale gas.

Couldn't a respirator just be re-used?

Probably not, although there are different opinions.

A 7 Jan 2022 article in *Popular Mechanics* titled 'N95 Vs. KN95 Masks: What's the Difference?' by Linder suggests not, due to the decay of the crucial electrostatic charge. It quotes Jiaxing Huang, a materials scientist at Northwestern University, as saying

> When the charges are dissipated during usage or storage, the capability of stopping virus-sized particles diminishes. This is the main reason of not recommending the reuse of N95 masks.

On the other hand the inventor of the modern N95 filter, Peter Tsai, Emeritus Professor of Materials Science at the University of Tennessee, claims that an N95 can be worn one day and then again four days later (or maybe seven days later), as long as they have been kept in dry conditions, as any virus or bacteria on the mask will have died by then. He says that the electrostatic charge will last for years and will not be affected by use.

However, even if the virions and bacteria on the mask die after a few days, this won't necessarily apply to any mould or fungal growths on it, as we saw with the Swiss story about mould developing over time on masks.

And perhaps you can't be completely sure that all the virions and bacteria will die. A *Lancet Microbe* study called 'Stability of SARS-CoV-2 in different environmental conditions' by Chin et al (v.1 (1), E10, 1 May 2020) reported that

> a detectable level of infectious [SARS-CoV-2] virus could still be present on the outer layer of a surgical mask on day 7.

(It should also be said that the causal unconcern that Tsai and other scientists display about contamination of their respirators when discussing this matter greatly undermines the idea that Covid is a deadly disease that we should all be so frightened of that we have to ruin the world and our lives over it.)

So a better solution (if you take masks seriously) may be Tsai's alternative idea (which others have also had) that you can hang a mask in an oven (or put it in a thick paper bag in an oven) and heat it to 70 degrees Celsius for half an hour, which will kill the virions and bacteria on it. He claims that this will not affect the electrostatic charge much, or the filtration efficiency (he says he has tested this), as long as the mask does not touch any hot metal in the oven. Nor, he says, will any of these things affect the respirator's fit.

He says in a paper on cleaning N95s in the *Journal of Emergency Medicine* that steam-cleaning and boiling are not recommended because although they don't affect the electrostatic charge they can warp the mask's materials so that a good fit can no longer be obtained. Soap and water, and alcohol, should not be used at all as they will damage the charge. ('N95 Respirator Cleaning and Reuse Methods Proposed by the Inventor of the N95 Mask Material' by Junag and Tsai, *Journal of Emergency Medicine* v.58 (5), May 2020, pp.817–820.)

In 'Face masks against COVID-19: Standards, efficacy, testing and decontamination methods' by Ju et al in *Advances in colloid and interface science* (v.292, June 2021), the authors say

it should be noted that all N95 and surgical masks are designed for single-use, and all decontamination methods compromise mask integrity and filtration efficiency to a certain degree.

In 'Facial protection for healthcare workers during pandemics: a scoping review' by Godoy et al in *BMJ Global Health* (v. 5 (5), 2020), the authors say that decontamination methods

using microwave irradiation, microwave-generated steam and moist heat incubation can compromise the physical integrity of respirator components. Treatment with bleach results in residual odour, release of chlorine gas on exposure to moisture and, in one model, partial nose pad dissolution without an associated increase in aerosol penetration. Decontamination with hydrogen peroxide gas plasma, autoclave, 160°C dry heat, 70% isopropyl alcohol and soaking in soap and water may cause significant loss of filtration efficiency.

Although ultraviolet germicidal irradiation (UVGI) has previously been shown to inactivate SARS-CoV-1 and preserve N95 performance after three cycles of exposure (totalling 45 min at 1.8 mW/cm2), one study found that increasing UVGI doses could compromise the strength of N95 respirator material and straps. A recent analysis of N95 decontamination methods using Escherichia coli as a surrogate model for SARS-CoV-2 found that application of chlorine and alcohol-based methods led to a significant decrease in the efficiency of N95 filtration media due to loss of microfibre static charge.

The best methods, according to this review, were said to be

ultraviolet light, boiling water vapour and dry oven heating.

In 'COVID-19: Performance study of microplastic inhalation risk posed by wearing masks' by Li et al in *Journal of Hazardous Materials* (v. 411 (5), 5 June 2021), the authors say

Melt-blown fabric is fragile; washing with water, alcohol disinfection, and drying can damage its fiber structure and lead to the loss of its protective function.

In 2006 a Committee on the Development of Reusable Facemasks For Use During an Influenza Pandemic was convened by the US's National Academy of Sciences, Engineering and Medicine. The results were announced in a conference called 'Reusability of Facemasks During an Influenza Pandemic'. The committee found that

After considering all the testimony and other information we received, the committee concluded that there is currently no simple, reliable way to decontaminate these devices and enable people to use them safely more than once... Any method of decontaminating a disposable N95 filtering facepiece respirator or medical mask must remove the viral threat, be harmless to the user, and not compromise the integrity of the various parts of the device. The committee found no method of decontamination that met all three criteria.

In addition, the committee concluded that

there is no simple way to modify the manufacturing process or to dispense with fit-testing that would permit disposable N95 respirators to be reused.

Bear in mind that decontamination isn't the only issue. There is also the fact that as a mask is used and becomes soiled the pores will clog up with material, which will affect its ability to filter breath.

What about re-use results in the field?

When we look at real-world performance, the results of re-using respirators are not good.

In 'Failure Rates During Reuse of Disposable N95 Masks in Clinical Practice in the Emergency Department' by Check et al, in the *Western Journal of Emergency Medicine* (v.22 (3), May 2021, pp.547–51), the investigators found that N95s started failing qualitative fit tests after a couple of days, and after five days use around half failed:

Mask failure rate climbed after day 2 of use, with 33.3% of masks failing at day 3, 42.9% at day 4, and 50% at $\geq$ day 5'. They concluded that 'Disposable N95 masks have significant failure rates following reuse in clinical practice.

Does disinfecting a mask also increase the risk of microfibre and microplastic inhalation?

It may do, yes. In 'COVID-19: Performance study of microplastic inhalation risk posed by wearing masks' by Li et al in *Journal of Hazardous Materials* (v. 411 (5), 5 June

2021), the authors say that all methods of disinfection increased this risk:

> Common disinfection processes can damage the structure of masks and increase the risk of inhaling exogenous substances and microplastics generated from the masks.

For example:

> After treating via UV irradiation for 30 min, spherical-type microplastic inhalation risk posed by wearing masks for 2 h increased 1.33, 0.23, 3.72, 1.28, 4.84, 1.86, and 1.07 times for N95, surgical-A, cotton, fashion, nonwoven, surgical-B, and activated carbon masks, respectively.

Do we not really know how long the electrostatic charge lasts?

It appears so; at least, it's not an issue that much light has been cast upon. SciTechDaily said (in a 26 Dec 2020 story called 'This Anti-COVID Mask Breaks the Mold: Rechargeable N95 Mask With a Custom Fit'):

> N95 masks have their limits. Here's one report I have found: 'experts advise against reusing N95 masks, especially after wearing them the whole day. That's because when we exhale, we expel moisture from our mouth and lungs – and if we're wearing an N95 mask for long durations, that moisture eventually wears down the electrostatic charge on the virus-trapping fibers, Urban said.

(Urban being Jeff Urban, 'who directs the Inorganic Nanostructures Facility in Berkeley Lab's Molecular Foundry'.)

Part of the reason why it's hard to get information on this seems to be that it's very difficult to measure the electrostatic charge in mask fibres. In 'Experimental Study of Electrostatic Aerosol Filtration at Moderate Filter Face Velocity' by Sanchez et al, in *Aerosol Science and Technology* (v.47 (6), 2013) the authors say

> electrostatic fiber charge density is difficult to quantify.

(After this they say that

> measurements of aerosol collection efficiency are often used to calculate this fundamental parameter.

That is, filtration performance is often used to work out what the charge is likely to be, hardly an ideal situation.)

Could a rechargeable respirator be developed?

It's funny you should ask, because that's what Hossain et al are proposing in a paper in *Physics of Fluids* (32 (9), 8 Sep 2020), entitled 'Recharging and rejuvenation of decontaminated N95 masks'.

> We tested a technique by which the filter material maintains its charge and thus its filtration efficiency... Since the currents required are extremely small, a large battery is not required, and it is possible that a small compact and practical solution may be feasible.

It might enthuse the nerds, but it sounds like one step closer to biotyranny to me.

Is Peter Tsai really the inventor of the N95 respirator mask, as the media often claims?

Tsai didn't invent the N95 mask, but he did invent the particular filter design that is used in modern N95 masks (which was patented in 1995). N95s were first developed by 3M in the early 1970s (they were approved in 1972). 3M used the melt-blowing technology that they had used and developed previously for other products. N95s were originally used in industrial settings, but after the incorporation of Tsai's filter design they became used in healthcare settings as well (from 1996).

Apparently Tsai did not invent the idea of using an electrostatically charged filter in a mask made of artificial fibres – Wikipedia claims (in the 'N95 respirator' entry) that the Russians first came up with such a thing in the 1950s:

> Mass production of filtering facepieces was started in 1956 in the Soviet Union… The air was purified with nonwoven filtering material consisting of polymeric fibres carrying a strong electrostatic charge.

(I haven't managed to find further confirmation of this, though.)

Melt-blowing technology itself was invented at the Naval Research Laboratory by V. A. Wente in the 1950s, and then developed by other companies such as Exxon. (There are, of course, other methods of creating artificial fibres that go back to the 19th century.)

Some people say that there is a worry that masks 'nebulise' your infected droplets?

There are worries about this, although there doesn't seem to be much research on it. The idea is this. Larger droplets normally fall straight to the ground, where they are harmless. But when you wear a mask some of the larger droplets, instead of being trapped by your mask, get turned into finer aerosols by being sent, in effect, through a mesh, which is exactly how some nebulizers (literally called 'mesh nebulizers') work. These will be sprayed at the faces of the people you are facing, instead of just falling straight to the ground. And being fine aerosols they will also stay in the air for a longer period than they would have done as larger droplets, thus presenting more risk to the people nearby. They will also be much better at getting deeper into the lungs than large droplets, where they are more likely to cause an infection that leads to sickness.

One expert on Twitter, Dr Kevin McKernan, who says his career was spent on 'engineering emulsion PCR and Nebulization equipment for DNA and RNA shearing', has raised such concerns. He said

Do our masks stop large droplets or do they nebulize them into aerosols? From my emulsion days, best way to get a monodispersed emulsion is to force H_2O through a pore sized membrane that has a different phase (oil or air) on the other side of it.

And:

If you study the field you will see viral nebulization is a technique used to get higher infectivity of viruses. This is used with ventilator patients suffering from pseudomonas aeruginosa infections. Nebulize bacteriaphage to get deep into the lungs and kill bacteria.

In fact products exist on the marketplace to nebulize medicines because aerosols get deeper into the lungs than large droplets.

I should stress that McKernan was asking questions about some worries he has, not making any strong claims about this.

One paper that provides a small amount of evidence for this issue in relation to cloth masks is 'Low-cost measurement of face mask efficacy for filtering expelled droplets during speech' by Fischer et al in *Science Advances* (v.6 (36), 2 Sep 2020). The authors say

We noticed that speaking through some masks (particularly the neck gaiter) seemed to disperse the largest droplets into a multitude of smaller droplets (see fig. S5), which explains the apparent increase in droplet count relative to no mask in that case. Considering that smaller particles are airborne longer than large droplets (larger droplets sink faster), the use of such a mask might be counterproductive.

It should be noted that this was a quick and limited study which wasn't able to detect very fine aerosols; there may in fact be even more fine aerosols in reality.

Is this related to the concerns about 'aerosolised fomites'?

Related, yes. There is also a concern that masks can serve as source of SARS-CoV-2 transmission through tiny loose fibres and debris that are contaminated with SARS-CoV-2 being expelled by mask-wearers.

In 'Efficacy of masks and face coverings in controlling outward aerosol particle emission from expiratory activities' by Asadi et al, in *Scientific Reports* (v.10, 24 Sep 2020), the authors say

> non-respiratory particles aerosolized from virus-contaminated surfaces such as animal fur or paper tissues, can also carry influenza virus and infect susceptible animals. This observation raises the possibility that masks or other personal protective equipment (PPE), which have a higher likelihood of becoming contaminated with virus, might serve as sources of aerosolized fomites. Indeed, recent work by Liu et al. demonstrated that some of the highest counts of airborne SARS-CoV-2 (the virus responsible for COVID-19) occurred in hospital rooms where health care workers doffed their PPE, suggesting that virus was

potentially being aerosolized from virus-contaminated clothing or PPE, or resuspended from virus-contaminated dust on the floor... particle emission from homemade cloth masks—likely from shed fiber fragments—can substantially exceed emission when no mask is worn, a result that confounds assessment of their efficacy at blocking expiratory particle emission. Although no direct measurements of virus emission or infectivity were performed here, the results raise the possibility that shed fiber particulates from contaminated cotton masks might serve as sources of aerosolized fomites.

How many virions are required to infect someone with Covid? Or flu?

There appears to be no clear answer to this, at least I have not found any. This review in *Epidemiology and Infection* (v.149, 14 April 2021) says that the required dose is probably very low:

> the infective dose in humans for SARS-CoV-2 was estimated as 100 particles

although there are suggestions that it may have to take place over a period of at least twenty minutes. ('Review of infective dose, routes of transmission and outcome of COVID-19 caused by the SARS-COV-2: comparison with other respiratory viruses' by Karimzadeh et al.)

Former physics Professor Denis Rancourt is of the opinion, after his review of the evidence, that infection usually follows from a very small number of virions:

> All of this to say that: if anything gets through (and it always does, irrespective of the mask), then you are going to be infected. Masks cannot possibly work. It is not surprising, therefore, that no bias-free study has ever

found a benefit from wearing a mask or respirator in this application.

In 'Human Influenza Resulting from Aerosol Inhalation' by Alford et al in *Proceedings of the Society for Experimental Biology and Medicine* (v.122 (3), July 1 1966, pp.800-804), the authors say in their abstract that

> Volunteers were given A2 influenza virus in a small-particle aerosol. Infection and typical influenza resulted from low doses of virus administered in this manner. Low levels of serum neutralizing antibody were not completely effective in preventing infection and illness. The human infectious dose of this influenza strain when administered by aerosol to subjects free of serum neutralizing antibody was approximately 3 $TCID_{50}$.

This looks to be saying that only small amount of an influenza virus is needed to infect someone and make them ill, but I can't access the full text of this article.

(Disease research: here we have a field full of incredibly arrogant people who presume to constantly tell us what to do, and want us locked up if we don't do it, a field which has been given hundreds of billions of dollars, maybe trillions, over the last half-century, a field in which hundreds of thousands, maybe millions, of people have been employed, yet remarkably there has been very little progress in that time on basic questions like this.)

Do respirator masks stop gases?

No, they are not designed to do that. They are designed to catch tiny particles, but not gas. Which is just as well, as otherwise you wouldn't be able to breathe through one.

Is part of the reason for the failure with masks that the aerosols just follow the air flow through the gaps and around the fibres?

With 'mechanical' masks, that is, non-electret masks like cloth masks, this will be partly true – many aerosols will follow the air flow and go around the fibres, so it isn't just the gap size that matters. (With electret filters the electrostatic charge will pull many particles out of the air flow and towards the fibres, so this isn't such an issue with them.)

With mechanical masks there are still several factors that can cause particles to not follow an air flow and hit a fibre. The main three are called inertia impaction, interception, and diffusion. Inertial impaction refers to the situation when an aerosol (or particle in general) is heading towards a fibre and has too much inertia to be able to follow the air flow around the fibre in time, so it crashes into it instead. Interception is where a particle does follow the air flow around the fibre, but it's big enough that it scrapes against the fibre as it does so, and attaches to it. Diffusion refers to the situation I have previously described where very light particles like fine aerosols engage in Brownian motion, that is, they move about in a random, zig-zag way, because they are constantly buffeted about by the tiny air particles around them, so they can get knocked out of the air stream and go towards a fibre.

USA Today made much of these mechanisms in an article on 7 January 2022 called 'COVID mask guide for omicron surge: Why N95, KN95 masks are so much more effective than cloth' – yet another article from this time admitting that cloth masks are not up to the job – which did at least have some useful graphics illustrating these mechanisms.

What the article didn't say is that inertia impaction and interception generally operate on bigger particles (the ones too big to move out of the way), and diffusion on smaller ones (the ones that get buffeted about). In 'Performance of Mechanical Filters and Respirators for Capturing Nanoparticles – Limitations and Future Direction' by Mostofi et al in *Industrial Health* (v.48 (3), 2010, pp.296–304), the authors say:

> In general, diffusion is seen as the dominant collection mechanism for particles smaller than 0.2 μm, and interception and inertia impaction are dominant for the particles larger than 0.2 μm.

(If this is right it suggests that diffusion is not so important for the fine aerosols that carry Covid, which are generally around 0.7 to 1 micron, despite what many pro-mask defences claim, although possibly at that size, which is just slightly above 0.2 microns, both types of effect are operating somewhat weakly.)

There's also gravitational settling, aka gravity sedimentation, which is just the particles being pulled downwards by gravity, which seems to be only relevant for far larger particles.

Remember, though, that even N95s don't work very well with without their charge, so these mechanical methods only have a limited effect. Most aerosols are going to go around the fibres with the air flow (I can't put a figure on it, though).

Wouldn't respirators work less well when you breathe hard because the faster flow of air makes it harder for the electrostatic charge to pull the aerosols towards the fibres? And also the zig-zag motion will be less pronounced?

This happens to a small extent: electret masks have less filtering effect at higher flow rates, as confirmed by filtering studies. For example, in 'Filter performance of n99 and n95 facepiece respirators against viruses and ultrafine particles', by Eninger et al in *Annals of Occupational Hygiene* (v.52 (5), July 2008, pp.385-96), the authors say that

Inhalation airflow had a significant effect upon particle penetration through the tested respirator filters.

In 'Filtration Performance of FDA-Cleared Surgical Masks' by Rengasamy et al, *Journal of the International Society for Respiratory Protection* (v.26 (3), Spring-Summer 2009, pp.54-70), five surgical masks had their filtration tested at 30 and 85 litres a minute. The faster rate saw more particle penetration (that is, more particles got through the mask.)

This is relevant with respirators, as they make it much harder to breathe, and even harder still when the side gap escape route is minimised, so you have to push your breath faster. This will negate some of the electrostatic effects of the mask's filter, although probably by only a few percent.

The NIOSH testing standards require a N95 to be tested at a fast 85 litres per minute rate, which is equivalent to fairly hard exercise, so you'll still get a minimum 95% filtering effect whatever you're doing. In theory, anyway. (For those who are interested, the average resting breath rate, known as tidal breathing', is around six litres per minute.)

The penetration tests mainly use salt aerosols. How good are these simulating what happens with a coronavirus?

I can't really give any definitive answer, but this is an issue that has been looked at.

In 'Filter performance of n99 and n95 facepiece respirators against viruses and ultrafine particles' by Eninger et al in *Annals of Occupational Hygiene* (v.52 (5), July 2008, pp.385-96), the authors tested this issue and concluded

Filter penetration of the tested biological aerosols did not exceed that of inert NaCl aerosol. The results suggest that inert NaCl aerosols may generally be appropriate for modeling filter penetration of similarly sized virions.

In 'A comparison of facemask and respirator filtration test methods', by Rengasamy et al in the *Journal of Occupational and Environmental Hygiene* (v.14 (2), Feb 2017, pp.92-103), the authors say

The above results show that the NIOSH NaCl method is relatively conservative and is able to identify poorly performing filtration devices.

In 'Filtration performance of NIOSH-approved N95 and P100 filtering facepiece respirators against 4 to 30 nanometer-size nanoparticles' by Rengasamy et al in the *Journal of Occupational and Environmental Hygiene.* (v.5 (9), Sep 2008, pp.556-64), the authors say

The filtration data for 4-30 nm monodisperse particles supports previous studies that indicate NIOSH-approved air-purifying respirators provide expected levels of filtration protection against nanoparticles.

Didn't Dr Wu Lien-teh's work during the Manchurian plague in 1910-11 show that masks work?

Wu recommended mask use during this plague, and it may have helped. It's hard to be sure due to the lack of reliable records kept at the time, and Wu's name has had a halo attached to it by pro-maskers (for example, in 'Wisdom and western science: The work of Dr Wu Lien-The' by Goh et al, *Asia Pacific Journal of Public Health* v.1, 1987, pp.99–109, the authors say his work was 'a milestone in the systematic practice of epidemiological principles in disease control').

(Supposedly the tradition of Asian people wearing masks developed from Wu's intervention, although it's in more recent times that mask-wearing has become a fetish in Asia.)

The relevance of the Manchurian plague is doubtful, however, as it involved bacteria, not a virus, which may have been spread more by droplets than aerosols, which masks are more effective with. Also, the bacteria had a 99.9% fatality rate, which is completely the opposite to Covid.

It should also be noted that other very aggressive measures were taken at the same time in plague areas. Houses that had contained someone who was infected were burned to the ground. The bodies of victims were forcibly cremated. Harsh quarantine measures were strictly enforced, travel was stopped, and quarantine hospitals were set up.

In fact, the measures taken were not just aggressive, they were ruthless. Quarantine centres were set up in railway freight centres not only for people with the disease, but for anyone who was thought to have possibly come into contact with someone who had the disease, such as relatives or people in the fur-trapping and trading business, where the disease originated. People were locked in these cars together for five to ten days. If there was anyone in the freight car who did have the disease, then everyone in the car was likely to catch it from them and die.

As the influential DELVE report of 2020 says, 'Absence of evidence is not evidence of absence', and isn't that the situation with mask evidence?

This is a very wrong-headed response. The many randomized-controlled trials that have shown no effect of masks (see part 5.1) are evidence that masks don't work. The hundreds of countries and states that showed no effect whatsoever after they introduced mask mandates are evidence that masks don't work. This is not to say that we have completely overwhelming proof that masks don't work – many of the randomized-controlled trials, for instance, are not of the highest quality, and there are some other types of studies claiming to show they masks have some effect, though these are generally of low quality and reliability. But it is false to claim that there is 'no evidence of absence'.

Suppose it is claimed that there are ravens that are pink with green and orange spots. Suppose also that numerous searches have failed to find any ravens with this colouring. In that case we have evidence that there are no such ravens. It is not overwhelming proof, of course, and there is a small possibility that somewhere, hidden away from us, are such ravens, but we do have strong (if not conclusive) evidence to support the claim that no ravens are pink with green and orange spots, and clearly the probability that there are such ravens is very low.

In fact this analogy does not adequately convey the strength of the case against masks, because it is not being claimed that masks work occasionally in very specific circumstances in remote locations, but that masks generally work for everyone, in most circumstances, in all countries. Given that, and given that we now have widespread mask use all over the world, as well as having had high mask use in Asia for decades, it should be easy to show their effectiveness. So the situation isn't even akin to trying to find some unusually coloured ravens in a hidden valley somewhere remote, it's more akin to someone claiming that most ravens are pink with green and orange spots and they're all around us. In that case, the fact that we cannot see any no matter how hard we try is a very strong reason to think this claim is false. Similarly, if masks are effective against virus spread in general then the fact that so many mask studies fail to demonstrate this gives us a good reason to think that the evidence is (mostly) against masks.

For those who claim that masks have a small effect, the analogy would go like this. Some scientists claim – seemingly because they wish it to be true – that most ravens have small pink spots that are not easy to see from a distance. But close-up examination of numerous ravens fails to reveal any such spots. Occasionally one of these scientists excitedly claims to have seen a small pink spot on a raven in a situation where they didn't really get a good look, but a proper examination reveals that there was no pink spot. In this situation we once again have evidence of absence (of small pink spots on ravens), not just an absence of evidence.

Part 3:

The strange and deplorable case of the Gesundheit-II machine

Part 3 contents:

3.1: The Gesundheit-II machine

In this section I shall take a fairly in-depth look at a series of studies that all feature a contraption called the 'Gesundheit-II'. Yes, really. Despite the amusing name, this is a serious piece of scientific equipment, and it has been used in a number of studies that have been influential in changing the minds of governments and scientists about the effectiveness of face masks. We will find the closer look instructive.

The Gesundheit-II, also known as the 'G-II' for short, is an apparatus that is designed to collect large droplets and small aerosols from the breaths of test subjects, and keep them separate, so to allow them to be tested for infectedness separately. A description of the development of the machine can be found in 'Development and Performance Evaluation of an Exhaled-Breath Bioaerosol Collector for Influenza Virus' by McDevitt, Milton et al, *Aerosol Science and Technology* (v.47 (4), 2013, pp.444-51).

The Gesundheit-II has a cone at one end that the test subjects place their face into. The machine then collects moisture from the subject's breath, and it can catch the larger droplets and the fine aerosols separately.

> A conventional slit impactor collects particles greater than 5.0 μm. Condensation of water vapor is used to grow remaining particles, including fine particles, to a size large enough to be efficiently collected by a 1.0 μm slit impactor and be deposited into a buffer-containing collector.

The biological properties of the collected liquids are preserved, allowing for them to be tested for the presence of infectious agents.

The machine also involves a pump that creates a mild airflow that pulls breaths towards the collection area, to make sure that it gets collected from not only normal test subjects who aren't wearing a mask, but from test subjects who are wearing a mask and whose breath may be going out the side gaps. That's the claim, anyway.

(Interestingly one of the reasons why the Gesundheit-II was developed was because it was felt that mannequin studies were no good as they did not adequately simulate real-life conditions.)

It was named the 'Gesundheit-II' in honour of a similar apparatus from the 1960s that had the word 'Gesundheit' written on the side of the cone. This original contraption was invented by scientists from the U.S. Army Biological Center in Maryland, and the Institute of Allergy and Infectious Diseases, National Institutes of Health, also in Maryland.

The second Gesundheit machine was designed by a team from the Harvard Public School of Health: James J. McDevitt, Petros Koutrakis, Stephen T. Ferguson, Jack M. Wolfson, M. Patricia Fabian, Marco Martins, Jovan Pantelic and Donald K. Milton. It was announced to the scientific world in 2013.

Donald Milton (who has since moved from Harvard to the University of Maryland's School of Public Health) features in all of the studies discussed here. (He was, you may remember from part 1, one of the leading figures in the push to get aerosol spread recognised as the major way that Covid spreads.) McDevitt appears on the first two papers I examine. The first two papers also feature Benjamin Cowling from the University of Hong Kong, another prominent mask researcher and pro-masker (despite the fact that his own studies and meta-reviews have consistently failed to find any effect for them, despite his motivation to do so).

Milton boasts on his academic web page not only about his career success, but also about the public success and high-level establishment recognition that he has achieved by promoting face masks.

> His work also provided a key piece of the scientific basis for masks mandates that are now common throughout the world including the publication of a key paper April 1, 2020 that was downloaded over two million times during the first year of the pandemic… This work was cited by the National Academies in an April 1, 2020 letter to the White House as key evidence that face masks would make important contributions to controlling spread of COVID-19. In less than a year since publication, the paper has received significant attention with many citations (490 Scopus, 1039 Google Scholar, 198 Web of Science) and public and media attention (2.09 million downloads, Almetric score 20,848, 40,70 tweeters, 717 news outlets, 112 blogs, 69 Facebook pages and 22, video uploaders) making it the 6th highest ranked paper for online attention of 27,7972 papers tracked by Atmetric.

His bio also reveals that he is, as we would expect, being funded for his mask research by the NIH (whose director Francis Collins, and Anthony Fauci, the director of the National Institute of Allergy and Infectious Diseases, part of the NIH, were revealed to have conspired to smear the Great Barrington Declaration authors), the CDC, and, inevitably, the Bill Gates Foundation. He is also the Principal Investigator of the University of Maryland's 'Stop Covid' project. Not 'Investigate Covid', of course, but 'Stop Covid'. This gives you some idea of his incentives with Covid. There's not much money or prestige in being the scientist who says 'Covid isn't worth all this nonsense, let's just stop it all'. The academic groups at the heart of all this are serious money trains which depend on funding to keep them on the rails.

Milton has also published with Jonathan Van-Tam, the UK's Deputy Chief Medical Officer, and one of the chief architects of Britain's Covid power-grab, and Catherine Noakes, a SAGE member and Covid hysteric who says that Covid 'has reshaped science forever'. No doubt Noakes and Van-Tam will be very happy if this is true, as these previously unexceptionable scientists have now become well-known, powerful and influential, and both gave Royal Institution lectures at Christmas 2021, televised by the BBC, when previously this level of scientific rock stardom would never have happened for them.

So you see how someone like Milton is a part of the great 'Biomedical Industrial Complex' which is pushing for the biomedicalisation of society as totally normal. It's not that Milton is a mask fanatic like Trish Greenhalgh (he has stated that he thinks you don't need to wear masks if you know the people around you are vaccinated and healthy), but he wants everything in ordinary life to be filtered through the prism of his and his colleagues' assessment of the risks, and their solutions, whether they be masks, vaccines, or UV light machines (which he wants installed everywhere), or regular visual monitoring of air quality and CO_2 concentration, another of his ideas that he is pushing. This is more even more pernicious than what Greenhalgh does (although Milton, has inevitably, published with her as well), because at least her extreme-hypochondria-bordering-on-madness is publicly visible on her social media, whereas Milton comes across as so reasonable that before you know it we're being ruled by an international elite who have vapourised our freedoms on medical grounds.

3.2: The first Gesundheit-II study

The very first Gesundheit-II study was 'Influenza Virus Aerosols in Human Exhaled Breath: Particle Size, Culturability, and Effect of Surgical Masks' by Milton, Cowling, et al, in *PLoS Pathogens* (v.9 (3), 7 March 2013).

This study became influential in Covid times, and was used as a key piece of evidence in the influential DELVE report (discussed in part 4.1 below).

The study claimed that surgical masks were very effective at stopping large droplets from people infected with influenza A or B, but only mildly effective at stopping fine aerosols, although the authors spin this latter finding as significant, speculating that

> if one hypothesized that all transmission were due to aerosol particles <50 μm, and estimated a reproductive number of 1.5 for influenza (i.e. each infection generates 1.5 new infections on average at the start of the epidemic), then the use of surgical masks by every infected case could reduce the reproductive number below 1.

This is just our old friend 'Even a small effect from masks could be the difference between a virus dying out or spreading everywhere' that mask-lovers like to use, dressed up in slightly fancier language. Nothing in this study is offered to support it in regards to influenza, so it remains a pure fanciful hypothesis. (With Covid it seems almost certainly false, as no amount of non-pharmaceutical interventions has made any dent in its remorseless spread across the globe.)

There are some serious problems with this study. The first concerns coughing. Not only were maskless test subjects allowed to cough into the apparatus, they were actually *required* to cough *ten* times during the thirty minutes they sat there without a mask on (every three minutes). When they took their turn wearing the mask they were asked to cough ten times again (also every three minutes). We've been told constantly by the disease scientists in the media that coughing is very dangerous. If so, then of course there's going to be far more infectious particles picked up when the unmasked are tested than when the masked are tested if there is regular coughing. But this in no way mimics reality, because in the real world people mostly cover their coughs. So there is no way that this study can be said to have any application to the real world. The test should have specifically asked the subjects to cover their mouths when they coughed, as in real life. (Ideally they would have tested the subjects with and without coughing to see how much difference coughing actually made.)

Notably a later study (see next section) using the same apparatus which did not require participants to cough regularly, but allowed them to cough if they wanted to, found a much lower number of people whose aerosols and droplets tested positive for a virus. This strongly suggests that coughing produced a significant amount of the infected droplets and aerosols.

Another issue in the study as it relates to the current Covid situation is that it wasn't a test of asymptomatic people. They tested sick people because they wanted to see how much masks reduced the amount of the virus, but that means that the study has limited application to our current situation. Sick people aren't much of an issue as they stay at home, which is why the focus of pro-maskers has been on asymptomatic people. But the scare campaign over asymptomatic people has died down. It turns out that there really aren't that many asymptomatic people out there spreading the virus in large amounts. We also don't know whether asymptomatic people, the ones who do exist, emit much virus in their breaths. Seeing as most of the people in the study, people who were actually sick, didn't exhale much virus even with their masks off it's unlikely that the small number of asymptomatic people are much of a threat. (More on this issue when I look at the raw data.)

Another serious issue is how well does the apparatus work at collecting all the aerosols from the gaps at the side of the mask? Photos of the Gesundheit-II in action can be seen on some of the G-II articles, as well as on the web, and all of them show that only the front part of the subject's head is inside the cone, and it looks like breath could easily exit the side cheek gaps of the mask and not enter the cone at all.

The stated intention behind the design of the apparatus is to capture such emissions, and to that effect there is an air flow pulling air from the face end of the cone into the collection area. But there is quite a tight fit of the cone around the head, so it's not clear that all the exhaled breath is going to be pulled into the collection area – there doesn't look to be much of a gap for this air to be pulled back in. Besides, videos of people with masks on exhaling smoke or visible cold breath show that large plumes of breath quickly spread out to the sides of the head, above the head, and behind the head. It is hard to see how the cone's airflow can possibly capture all this flow, and some of the aerosols are likely to end up on the back and top of the subjects head, or on the outside of the cone, or else just to dissipate through the room.

The designers spend a lot of time talking about some of the intricate detail of the Gesundheit-II, and there is no doubt that some of it has been well-designed, but on these crucial matters there is very little explanation of how this problem would be overcome, and no evidence is provided of effectiveness. Even a simple video would help, showing how the apparatus captures smoke breathed out by a masked person.

It also seems entirely possible that aerosols from the breaths that come out of the gaps around the nose and chin, which go straight up or straight down, could deposit themselves onto the (inside) surface of the cone rather than making their way through the air to the collection area.

The results

Let us now look at the results. The results with droplets are fairly large and clear-cut, and in line with what we'd expect, and fairly irrelevant with regard to Covid spread, so I'm not going to bother quibbling with them. (This study actually helps the theory that droplets are not a significant part of virus spread because there was eight times as much virus in the fine aerosols as in the large droplets.)

The reduction in the amount of virus in fine aerosols with mask-wearers was nowhere near as pronounced as with the droplets.

> We detected viral RNA in 78% (29 of 37) of fine particle samples collected from volunteers when they were wearing a mask and in 92% (34 of 37) of samples collected when they were not wearing a mask... [this result was] borderline statistically significant.

In other words, masks reduced the number of people who exhaled infected breath from around nine in ten to eight in ten. So even if we took these figures as gospel (which we can't) they hardly show that mask-wearing is worth it.

We can't take this figures as gospel at all, though. For one thing, this result wasn't statistically significant: it had p=0.06, slightly outside the p=0.05 required for statistical significance, which they spin as 'borderline statistically significant'. The study was small. The confidence intervals were quite large, large enough that they can't really claim any effect here. (They also used a log-scaled Y-axis graphic to show the confidence intervals, which was highly misleading.)

(I should also note that a later and larger study that used the Gesundheit-II resulted in much lower percentages of symptomatic people having infected aerosols, even the non-mask-wearers.)

The authors, do, however, draw attention to the fact that there was a much larger reduction in the number of overall virus copies found in the aerosols (from all the subjects added together, that is):

The median number of viral copies in the fine particle fraction was 250 with masks and 560 without masks. The geometric mean copy number in the fine particle fraction without a facemask was 110 and the facemasks produced a 2.8 fold reduction in copy number.

It is very instructive to examine the raw aerosol data itself rather than relying on this general summary:

Subject	Masked	Unmasked
1	16	4
2	7	37
3	7	13
4	38	154
5	30	181
6	30	34
7	24,239	126,587
8	3	0
9	294	10
10	5	533
11	12,665	39,087
12	144	37
13	0	4
14	0	2
15	24	21
16	0	0
17	78	433
18	22	479
19	1640	2057
20	15	8
21	0	0
22	0	7
23	541	3888
24	8	895
25	245	672
26	10	32
27	454	787
28	0	11
29	761	230
30	319	666
31	181	556
32	711	5206
33	54	217
34	0	113
35	8	443
36	9	19
37	0	75

Note that there were six people, around a sixth of the 37 subjects, who had a *higher* number of virus copies with the mask than without (a result which the authors neglect to mention).

You will observe that just under 70% of all the virus copies come from one person, number 7. And 90% come from just two people (7 and 11). The great majority of the subjects produced very small amounts of virus copies in their fine aerosols relative to these two. These two people produced 126,587 and 39,087 virus copies respectively without their masks, whereas most of the other people produced numbers under 1000, mostly well under 1000 (eighteen people were under 100, and 26 were under 500).

The two subjects with the very high numbers had their numbers cut considerably when wearing masks, especially if we think in terms of percentages. (In reality it's most likely that these numbers were cut considerably by the fact that they were required to regularly cough when maskless, and the side gap issue, rather than the masks being effective in non-coughing periods, but let's ignore that for now.) But they still have far *higher* numbers *with* a mask than the majority of the other people had even without masks.

Now, we don't know what sort of virus copy number makes someone infectious. As another paper featuring Milton and Jonathan Van-Tam said,

> The infectious dose for airborne influenza and the infectious potential of cases infected by various modes are largely unknown.

('Influenza A (H3) illness and viral aerosol shedding from symptomatic naturally infected and experimentally infected cases' by de Mesquita et al in *Influenza and Other Respiratory Viruses*, v. 15 (1), Jan 2021, pp.154-63.)

But suppose you take the view that the only people with virus counts above, say, 1000 are potentially infectious. That means, though, that the two most infectious people are still very highly infectious even with masks, because they are still producing virus amounts in the tens of thousands, far more than anyone else. It is true that they are not producing as much as before, but they are still highly infectious despite the masks. In that case, wearing a mask isn't going to stop these two infecting people.

This position (that it's an aerosol virus count above 1000 that we have to worry about) also entails that the majority of even sick people are *not* infectious, because 87% of the subjects had less than 1000 virus copies in their aerosols. As sick people are a small majority of all people, that means that the vast majority of people at any point in time will not be infectious. But these people will still be forced to wear a mask by the pro-maskers. So an extremely unpleasant and damaging practice will be forced upon everyone, even though it will make no difference in at least 99% of cases. In fact, given that almost all the infectious people will be staying at home, because they are sick, almost every case of forced mask wearing in public will be pointless. And for the very few cases of people who are sick, yet who are walking around doing things and who are infectious (like number 7 and 11), wearing a mask won't stop them being very infectious. Similar points apply to asymptomatic people who have viral counts like numbers 7 and 11 – even if they are wearing masks when they are out and about it isn't going to stop them being very infectious. So masks are almost completely pointless on this position.

Suppose instead that a pro-masker took a different view on infectiousness and said that any amount of viral copies above zero makes someone potentially infectious, enough to justify forcing them to wear a mask. But then masks still aren't going to offer much protection. Take subject 27, whose count went down from 787 to 454 with a mask on.

He's still a danger with his mask on, even more than subject number 26 was *without* a mask (32 copies). Despite wearing his mask he's still a threat. How can he be allowed outside at all? Why would a frightened person who holds this view be assured by seeing people wearing masks when all these people are still infectious? And let's not forget the two biggest shedders (7 and 11) who are still massively infectious despite their masks, and practically guaranteed to infect people if it's true that any amount above zero is a danger. For the person who holds this view on infectiousness it would be rational to always remain at home no matter how many people wear masks.

So whichever position the mask proponent takes on the issue of what level of virus exhalation makes someone infectious, forced mask wearing makes little sense.

3.3. The Leung Gesundheit-II study

Another Gesundheit-II study that became very prominent just as Covid started was 'Respiratory virus shedding in exhaled breath and efficacy of face masks' by Leung, McDevitt, Cowling, Milton et al in *Nature Medicine* (v.26, pp.676–680, 3 April 2020). (Nancy Leung was a doctoral student of Milton and also Benjamin Cowling in Hong Kong.)

As Milton boasted in his University bio, this paper been very influential, and is often quoted as evidence for mask effectiveness (for example, by the DELVE report, see part 4.1). A closer look at it demonstrates that it in fact shows very little effectiveness for masks.

The study got 246 people with symptoms of ARI (acute respiratory illness) to breathe in the Gesundheit-II apparatus for thirty minutes while either wearing a surgical mask or not wearing a mask. (Most people did either one or the other, a few did both.) The machine collected large droplets and fine aerosols separately, and these were then tested for ordinary coronavirus (not Covid), influenza and rhinovirus, to see whether the masks made any difference.

Even ignoring the issues with the G-II, the results were a decidedly mixed bag:

Coronavirus (non-SARS-CoV-2)
Droplets: 3 out of 10 maskless coronavirus subjects' droplets tested positive (30%), whereas 0 out of 11 masked coronavirus subjects' droplets tested positive (0%). This difference was not statistically significant.
*Aerosols:*4 out of 10 maskless coronavirus subjects' aerosols tested positive (40%), whereas 0 out of 11 masked

coronavirus subjects' aerosols tested positive (0%). This difference was statistically significant.

Influenza
Droplets: 6 out of 23 maskless flu subjects' droplets tested positive (26%), whereas 1 out of 27 masked flu subjects' droplets tested positive (4%). This difference was statistically significant.
Aerosols: 8 out of 23 maskless flu subjects' aerosols tested positive (35%), whereas 6 out of 27 masked flu subjects' aerosols tested positive (22%). This difference was not statistically significant.

Rhinovirus
Droplets: 9 out of 32 maskless rhinovirus subjects' droplets tested positive (28%), whereas 6 out of 27 masked rhinovirus subjects' droplets tested positive (18.75%). This difference was not statistically significant.
Aerosols: 19 out of 32 maskless rhinovirus subjects' aerosols tested positive (56%) whereas 12 out of 27 masked rhinovirus subjects' aerosols tested positive (38%). This difference was not statistically significant.

So, three non-mask wearers (out of ten) had detectable coronavirus in their droplets, while none of the mask wearers did. For aerosols it was four non-mask wearers to zero mask wearers for coronavirus. For flu there was a reduction from 6 to 1 for droplets and 8 to 6 for aerosols. For rhinovirus the reduction was 9 to 6 for droplets and 19 to 12 for aerosols. Only two of the six results were statistically significant (coronavirus aerosols and influenza droplets).

It is hard to see any pattern here (assuming we take the study seriously). Masks seem to be effective against coronavirus in general, only effective with flu droplets, not flu aerosols, and the complete opposite for rhinovirus, effective against the aerosols but not the droplets. Given the tiny numbers involved it would seem prudent not to take these results too seriously.

The authors admit that

> Our findings indicate that surgical masks can efficaciously reduce the emission of influenza virus particles into the environment in respiratory droplets, but not in aerosols.

It may help the reader if we present the same data in simplified fashion, with droplets and aerosols in different sections (masked vs maskless):

Droplets
Coronavirus: 30% vs 0% (not SS).
Influenza: 26% vs 4% (SS.)
Rhinovirus: 28% vs 18.75% (not SS).

Aerosols
Coronavirus: 40% vs 0% (SS).
Influenza: 35% vs 22% (not SS).
Rhinovirus: 56% vs 38% (not SS).

It is worth noting that the great majority of the infected people (who had coronavirus, flu or rhinovirus confirmed by lab tests) didn't have *any* virus detected in either droplets or aerosols even when they didn't wear a mask. Only 30% of the maskless people with coronavirus had it show up in their droplets. (There were only ten such people anyway, making it a very underpowered test). Only 40% of them (ie. 4 out of the 10) had it show up in their aerosols. Only 26% of maskless people with flu had it show up in their droplets (8 out of 23), and only 35% in their aerosols (8 out of 23). For maskless people with rhinovirus it was 28% (9 out of 32) and 56% (19 out of 32). So, if we take these results seriously, we see that the great majority of people who are not only infected but ill don't shed any detectable virus at all even without a mask, and even given half an hour to do so, which makes mask-wearing even more pointless.

(This is also found in the Yan Gesundheit-II study which I look at in section 3.4, in which the authors say

> We recovered infectious virus from 52 (39%) of the fine aerosols.

The number of people who produce infected breath is notably less in this study than in the previous study where every participant was required to regularly cough into the apparatus, whereas in this one participants could cough if they liked, but weren't required to. (29% of participants didn't cough at all.) Most likely, then, coughing was the reason for the difference between the studies.

This is supported by the authors' admission that only a small number of non-coughers produced *any* infected droplets or particles:

> we identified virus RNA in a small number of participants who did not cough at all during the 30-min exhaled breath collection.

Unfortunately they decline to give us numbers or percentages, or the amount of virus particles produced by the coughers versus non-coughers, but this is enough to give us reason to think that coughing is playing a large role in these studies, in which case it is further reason to think that masks are pointless, because in real life people can simply cover their mouths.

It is also instructive to look at the 'absolute' percentage reduction, rather than the relative percentage reduction. When we do this the results look even less impressive. For example, to take one of the biggest differences, with influenza droplets, one could say that masks caused an 83% reduction in virus shedding, as it reduced the numbers from 6 to 1 (and 5 is 83% of 6), but it would be more revealing to say that masks reduced the percentage of shedders from 26% to 4%, a 22% absolute reduction. For influenza aerosols the reduction was from 35% to 22%, which could be described as 37% relative reduction (as 13 is 37% of 35), but the absolute reduction was a mere 13% (from 35% to 22%).

(These sorts of different ways of describing medical results was well-described in the book *Reckoning with Risk: Learning to Live with Uncertainty* by Gerd Gigerenzer, Penguin, 2003. Gigerenzer pointed out that presenting risk reductions in relative terms can give a misleading picture of an intervention. For example, suppose one says that spending billions on a treatment for X is worth it because it cuts deaths from X by seventy-five percent. But X could affect only 4 in every ten million people, and all this means is that the chance of anyone dying from X goes from 0.00004% to 0.00001%, an absolute reduction of 0.00003%, ie. three one-hundred thousandths of a percent. The first way of presenting the data makes the treatment look more like it is worth it, whereas the second makes clearer that the treatment isn't going to give you much for the money (even assuming that the promised reduction is real, which it may not be).)

So going back to the Leung study, even if the influenza aerosol reduction result was real (which it most likely isn't, and anyway it isn't a statistically significant result), and even if it also applied to Covid, would a 13% absolute reduction in the number of sick people who breathe out infected aerosols be worth the suffering and social damage caused by masks? Bearing in mind that a 13% reduction in the number of sick people who breathe out infectious virus isn't in any way the same thing as a 13% reduction in the number of people who get Covid, and certainly isn't the same thing as a 13% reduction in the number of people who die from Covid? Even if this result was real, it would be likely to make no difference at all to the number of people who get Covid (especially when we consider that the sick people who are the main spreaders will mostly stay at home).

We can also reasonably surmise that coughing produces a far higher number of infected aerosols (and droplets), and is responsible for the cases of high viral copies produced by some people in the previous study. (We will see further reason to think that in the next section on the Yan G-II paper.)

It's suspicious that little is made of the viral load numbers in the Leung study, when in the previous Gesundheit-II study (Milton et al) this was their main selling point. The authors present this data in the paper in the form of medians (with the interquartile range), which is not very informative. Only two of the six results are statistically significant (the same ones as above: coronavirus aerosols and flu droplets). It may have been instructive to look at the raw data of the viral load numbers like we did in the last study, but most unfortunately the authors have not provided the raw data in the form of a list of numbers like the previous G-II study did (which is hardly in the spirit of 'open science' standards).

They have instead presented the data in a very unsatisfactory and inexact graphical manner.

There's no point looking at the coronavirus results, because there's so few of them, but here's the flu results (from Fig. 1 in the paper).

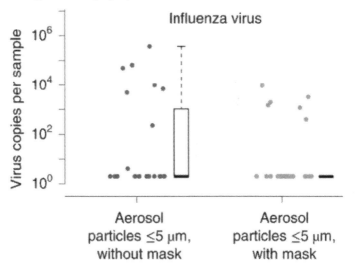

Each dot represents a test subject, and its height on the Y-axis indicates the number of virus particles found in that subject's fine aerosols.

The first thing to note is the one very low maskless result (at the bottom of the unmasked column on the left-hand side). This result is barely above 0, so the reduction in numbers from 8 people to 6 people here doesn't tell the whole story, it's more like 7 to 6. But getting back to viral load numbers, note that there isn't that much difference between the masked and maskless results. We have to be careful because we're dealing with a log-scale Y (vertical) axis, where the numbers increase rapidly as you go up, so the three top unmasked dots are much greater than the middle dots than you might think. But almost all of the subjects who produced infected breath without a mask are still producing infected breath with a mask, at around the 5000–10,000 mark, around the middle of the unmasked range. And the number of people producing no virions is almost the same. The main difference is that the masked people don't have the three very high results that the maskless did, but other than that things are pretty similar. The difference, the authors note in their analysis using medians, is not statistically significant (and not even close to it, with p=0.26 – p needs to be 0.05 to be statistically significant).

So looking at viral load in this paper doesn't help convince us that masks work for flu, in fact it convinces us that masks don't make much difference. It would be more convincing if not only was there a huge difference between the number of people with infected breath (say 90% versus 10%), but if the masked people with infected breath all had tiny readings. As I said in the previous section, we don't really know what level of infected breath is likely to infect someone, but it is clear that all these six masked people are still pumping out plenty of virus *despite* wearing masks, at a typical level that a maskless person does.

I should point out that one review of the evidence of how much is required to infect someone, titled 'Review of infective dose, routes of transmission and outcome of COVID-19 caused by the SARS-COV-2: comparison with other respiratory viruses' by Karimzadeh et al in *Epidemiology and Infection* (v.149, 14 April 2021), says

> the infective dose in humans for SARS-CoV-2 was estimated as 100 particles.

If this is right then mask-wearing is completely pointless even if masks are effective to some degree.

You may want to take an opposite view to Karimzadeh et al and hold that only people with enormously high viral loads like a hundreds of thousands (per half hour) are potentially infectious, but in that case, as well as having to defend that, you're admitting that even most sick people are not infectious even if they don't wear a mask (assuming Leung's results are credible, which of course they may not be.)

If we look at rhinovirus (see the graph on the next page), we get a similar story. The masked results are cluttered around the same vertical area where most of the maskless results are. A few of the much higher maskless dots have disappeared, and there's a few less cases overall, but it's a fairly similar picture in both scenarios. Most of the maskless people with rhinovirus are breathing out the same amount of virions as most of the masked ones, and the authors acknowledge that the viral load difference is not statistically significant (nor is the reduction in the number of people with infected breath). Even this by itself, without considering the coughing and side-gap issues, combined with the fact that these are sick people, not healthy people, shows that masks are useless for aerosols.

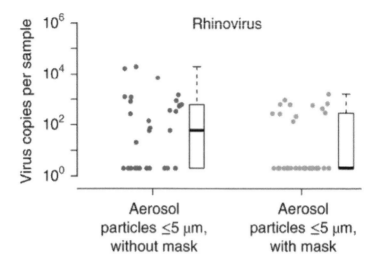

Overall, it is difficult to see how any positive conclusions about masks can be drawn from Leung's results, even the statistically significant ones, especially given the small numbers, but the authors shamelessly spin the situation in their abstract, saying 'Our results indicate that surgical face masks could prevent transmission of human coronaviruses and influenza viruses from symptomatic individuals'. No wonder the mask pushers loved this article. Given the political incentives of the time (the paper came out in April 2020), it appears that the presentation of the paper was spun to suit the circumstances.

3.4. The Yan Gesundheit-II study

In 2018 Yan, de Mesquita, Milton, and others, published a G-II paper titled 'Infectious virus in exhaled breath of symptomatic seasonal influenza cases from a college community', in *Proceedings of the National Academy of Sciences* (v.115 (5), 30 Jan 2018, pp.1081-1086).

This paper is mainly of interest because of its findings about coughing. The authors found vastly more virions in fine aerosols produced by regular coughing than not coughing – around 100,000 on average compared to around a thousand (see graph H in Fig. 2).

They also claimed to have found an association of fine-aerosol copy number with cough frequency:

> viral RNA copy number in fine aerosols was moderately well correlated with cough frequency... In regression analyses, cough frequency was significantly associated with increased fine- and coarse-aerosol shedding.

They also pronounced on sneezing:

> The few sneezes observed were not associated with greater RNA copy numbers in either coarse or fine aerosols... sneezing does not appear to make an important contribution to influenza virus shedding in aerosols.

However, they also admit that the G-II fails to collect many large droplets produced by sneezing:

> sneezes generate considerable amounts of large-droplet spray composed of many ballistic droplets not collected by our sampler.

Frankly, this makes you wonder whether any of these G-II results mean much at all.

3.5. The Coleman Gesundheit-II study

The third study to be looked at is 'Viral Load of Severe Acute Respiratory Syndrome Coronavirus 2 (SARS-CoV-2) in Respiratory Aerosols Emitted by Patients With Coronavirus Disease 2019 (COVID-19) While Breathing, Talking, and Singing', by Coleman, et al (including Milton), *Clinical Infectious Diseases*, 2021 ciab691). I will call this the 'Coleman paper'.

It doesn't look at masks at all, but it is still relevant, as will be shown.

Twenty-two participants were recruited in Singapore, all with diagnosed Covid infection. Table 3 from the paper presents the aggregate numbers of virus particles produced by those people.

Table 3. Sum total of Viral RNA Loads Emitted in Coarse and Fine Respiratory Aerosols, for a Subgroup of Patients With COVID-19 With Detectable SARS-COV2 in Respiratory Aerosols

	Coarse	**Fine**	**Total**
Breathing	897	1062	1959.3
Talking	868	11,787	12,655.9
Singing	2762	13,653	16,415.5
All three	4527	26,503	31,030.3

These numbers won't mean much to most people, but to those of us who've laboured through the previous two Gesundheit-II papers, they're staggering. Breathing for half an hour in the previous studies always produced a few people with viral copies in the tens of thousands to hundreds of thousands ranges, but here the sum total of 23 people only comes to 1,062 (for fine aerosols). That's an average of 46 for each person, and no one person could have produced more than 1,062.

Unfortunately we don't have a breakdown of the amount of viral copies in fine aerosols for each person (another breach of open science standards), but we do have a breakdown of how many viral copies each person produced in droplets and fine aerosols combined, in Table 1, presented over the page. Seeing as Table 3 above tells us that aerosols accounted for a bit over half of the viral copies with breathing, Table 1 gives us a guide as to the probable amount of virus particles emitted through fine aerosols. The highest number of viral copies any person produced through half an hour of breathing was 550 (subject number 18), so the amount produced by this person through fine aerosols alone was probably around 300.

(Table 1 also shows us that only 7 people out of 22 produced any viral copies at all in either aerosols or droplets, from breathing, while 13 did when talking and singing were added in.)

Table 1

SARS-CoV-2 in Respiratory Aerosols Emitted by Patients With COVID-19 in Singapore, February–April 2021

Aerosolized SARS-CoV-2 RNA Copies Emitted

Subject	Breathing	Talking	Singing	Total
1	0	0	0	0
2	0	0	0	0
3	0	0	0	0
4	0	417	0	417
5	0	234	135	369
6	0	79	713	793
7	0	0	0	0
8	0	0	0	0
9	0	908	0	908
10	63	310	1811	2186
11	0	0	154	154
12	227	4336	4277	8841
13	140	733	0	874
14	0	0	0	0
15	442	1356	978	2777
16	224	1373	5821	7419
17	0	0	143	143
18	550	477	1216	2244
19	0	0	0	0
20	0	0	0	0
21	310	2428	1162	3901
22	0	0	0	0

Why are these numbers so much smaller than in the previous studies?

It could be that SARS-CoV-2 is produced in much smaller amounts than the diseases in those studies, but this seems unlikely. We might reasonably suspect the answer has to do with coughing, and what the authors say seems to show that this is the case:

> No patients were observed to have sneezed during sample collection; however, 2 participants were observed to be coughing.

So unlike the previous studies which contained a lot of coughing (regular forced coughing in the case of the first Gesundheit-II study), this one contained hardly any, so it's a reasonable bet that this was the difference.

Note that the Coleman study authors say that

> Participant 4, who emitted 417 RNA copies in fine speech aerosols, was coughing during talking and singing. Participant 22 coughed frequently during all 3 activities but did not emit detectable viral RNA.

This shows that coughing doesn't necessarily produce virions from everyone, but we already knew that, because lots of people in the previous studies coughed regularly but still produced little or no virus copies. But that doesn't mean that coughing can't be the reason why the previous studies produced so many more virus copies than this one, the previous studies contained a small proportion of people who produced very large amounts of viral copies, so only they needed to do this via coughing.

If this is right, and coughing is the main source of the large numbers of viral copies produced in those studies, then those earlier studies are discredited in regard to what they supposedly say about masks. The coughing produced most of the virus copies, but then that makes the comparison with masks pointless, because most people (especially most sick people) don't just cough at the people around them, they cover their mouths (and they usually stay at home as well, but even asymptomatic people will mostly cover their mouths). The comparison should have been between masked people and maskless people who didn't cough into the Gesundheit-II.

(There is still also the issue of the capturing side gaps to be settled.)

I don't claim any great strength for these conclusions, but it's up to the authors of these studies to convince us of their worth, not for me to provide a definitive analysis. My main interest in them anyway is the way the results have been manipulated and hyped. I'm even yet to be convinced that the Gesundheit-II studies are worth anything at all, and the correct attitude may be just to take them with a pinch of salt.

(One thing I can agree with is that the Gesundheit-II studies have shown that fine aerosols are a far more important, method of transmission than larger droplets, and Milton has made much of this. But as it was modern disease transmission scientists who had previously told us to change our minds and to accept that normal breathing was not involved in respiratory virus spread, only droplets, that's no great victory for the modern practitioners of the field.)

3.6. Singing and talking

The Coleman study scaremongers about singing and talking, claiming that they are dangerous activities which need to be controlled:

> Fine aerosols produced by talking and singing contain more SARS-CoV-2 copies than coarse aerosols and may play a significant role in SARS-CoV-2 transmission… these expiratory activities are hypothesized to play a crucial role in virus transmission… in singing situations, safe distancing among singers and averting and filtering airflow from choir to audience (eg, by deploying air curtains) are important considerations. For situations involving talking, determining airflow patterns and minimizing exposure through seating and furniture configurations, distancing, and air-movement alteration (such as fans, including desk fans) would be practical options… Reducing airborne transmission by altering or averting direct airflow exposure in singing and speech situations indoors may be important practical options to adopt.

(Remember what I said about people like Milton wanting all of ordinary life to become viewed through a biomedical frame, run, of course, by people like him?)

Milton's University (Maryland) released a news report on Aug 13 titled 'Researchers Continue to Zero in on How COVID-19 Spreads: New Public Health Study Shows Singing, Talking Emit More Virus', which said

> The new study published in Clinical Infectious Diseases last week found that 94% of the virus measured in the experiment was emitted while participants used their voices.

This is a misleading and totally unnecessary way of putting it, especially when there is so much hysteria about Covid.

This is all relatively sober scientific language, but outside the constraints of a scientific paper or a University press release the shrieking madness of those who are freaking out about talking and singing becomes more plain. Trish Greenhalgh, for example, tweeted on 5 December 2021

> I think they key behavioural change we need is SILENCE while unmasked for eating/drinking, since it's vocalising that releases virus.

Many pro-maskers have started recently pushing this mad and inhuman idea that we need to stop people talking in pubs and restaurants, and that live singing performances should be stopped, or take place behind 'air curtains'. All this is a part of their push to insert themselves into every enjoyable private activity. It's safety Nazism taken to a new level. It's weaponised hypochondria.

Despite the claims the authors of the Coleman paper make about singing and talking being dangerous, the amount of viral copies produced is quite small compared to the amounts produced in previous studies which involved coughing. Singing produced 16,415 copies between 23 people, which is 713 per person for fifteen minutes. This would equate to 1,426 per person for half an hour. Seeing as some people apparently produced no viral copies, the average for those who did would have been higher, but these numbers are still nothing special in the context of the last two studies. Talking produced even less virus than singing. We're supposed to be frightened of them just because they're have a bit more virus than breathing. For those people who already frightened of breathing, this makes sense, but for those of us who think the whole Covid scare campaign is lunacy, this is just more nonsense.

The attempt to portray singing and talking as dangerous activities is reprehensible, and the people involved should be ashamed of themselves. It's just another example of how ordinary life is being co-opted and disrupted by the biomedical security state through their exaggerated claims in order to increase their own power, and we'd better off without these people being given truckloads of money to produce research which is used to hold the rest of us captive. The world would have been immeasurably better off had these nerds been middle managers in factories or working in bookstores.

3.7. The Adenaiye Gesundheit-II study

In 'Infectious Severe Acute Respiratory Syndrome
Coronavirus 2 (SARS-CoV-2) in Exhaled Aerosols and
Efficacy of Masks During Early Mild Infection' by
Adenaiye et al (including Coleman and Milton), *Clinical
Infectious Diseases* (14 Sep 2021), the authors conclude in
their abstract that

> SARS-CoV-2 is evolving toward more efficient
> aerosol generation and loose-fitting masks provide
> significant but only modest source control. Therefore,
> until vaccination rates are very high, continued
> layered controls and tight-fitting masks and respirators
> will be necessary.

The use of 'therefore' indicates that a course in logic is
required; their conclusion doesn't follow at all from their
premises, even assuming both premises are true, nor does it
even provide much probabilistic support. There is a an
enormous amount of extra argument required here to show
that the conclusion follows.

The Adenaiye study itself is somewhat similar to Leung's,
and it also fails to provide a list of the number of viral copies
produced by each participant, not even in the Supplementary
Data, another dreadful lapse in modern Open Science
standards. The numerical data they do show is again
presented in an unhelpful, unclear and inexact graphic form,
even worse than in Leung's paper. Dots near lines are very
hard to make out, as are the dots at the bottom.

Here are the fine aerosol results.

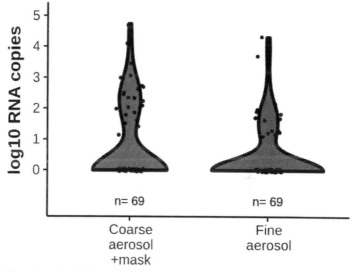

The data is difficult to make out with any precision, but we can see that almost all the results are under 1000 virus copies for every participant, even without a mask, most well under, with only three (out of 69 participants) producing more – as far as I can tell, one subject produced a bit over a thousand, one around 10,000, and one about 60-70,000 (note that coughs were allowed). Yet in the original Milton G-II paper we were told that masks were a great success in reducing viral particle numbers, even though this was mainly due to a large reduction with one participant, whose viral particle count with a mask on was 24,239. So why are we worrying about the participants in this study, almost all of whom produce far fewer viral particles without a mask on than that person in the original study did with a mask? If this person was no threat when breathing out 24,239 particles, why bother with a mask for these people? For consistency's sake, either you say that masks are not necessary here, or you admit that the original G-II paper failed to make its case for mask use.

Most of the subjects in the Adenaiye study have had their virion count reduced from a few hundred to around one hundred or just under by wearing a mask. Why a reduction of a few hundred particles over half an hour counts as a success – and such a tremendous success that the authors make it the main conclusion of their influential paper – is not explained.

Perhaps it could be argued that, using Karimzadeh 2021 from section 3.3 as a guide, that the important thing is to get the count to under one hundred, because one hundred particles is enough to infect someone. But anyone producing under a thousand particles over the course of half an hour is unlikely to infect anyone, because the vast majority of their particles are not going to end up in someone else's lungs – unless, perhaps, they are both hiding away together in a small broom closet.

Anyway, the two highest counts are still very high, and they are the people who were most likely to infect someone else. The 60,000-70,00 participant is still producing about 20,000 particles after putting a mask on, and the participant who produced about 10,000 without a mask comes down to about 6000-7000 with a mask. So the people who are most likely to be infecting others are still going to be doing so even with a mask on.

(I note again the suspicion that many of the aerosols from masked subjects are leaving side gaps and not being detected by the machine. But even if this were not so, the results here don't provide any reason to think that masks will be an effective intervention that is worth the long-term pain and damage they cause.)

3.8. Is the Gesundheit-II machine only getting a fraction of the viral copies?

It turns out that we have reason to think that the Gesundheit-II machine is only catching a fraction of the viral copies. In 'Development of an efficient viral aerosol collector for higher sampling flow rate' by Lin et al in *Environmental Science and Pollution Research* (v.25, 2018, pp.3884–3893), the authors say

> Gesundheit II (G-II) is inefficient for collecting aerosol smaller than 50 nm. However, many viral aerosols have sizes smaller than 50 nm. Therefore, when using G-II for sampling coughed influenza virus, the system has a high physical collection efficiency, but a low viability preservation (10%).

And Milton and some colleagues themselves seem admit something like this when they say, in a November 2021 Medrxiv preprint titled 'Intrahost-diversity of influenza A virus in upper and lower respiratory tract derived samples from a college community' (by Sapoval, Milton et al)

> This is further exacerbated by the varying viral load in different sample types, potential issues with amplification and sequencing, and previously outlined challenges in the intrahost variant calling. Although use of a Gesundheit-II bioaerosol sampler allows for direct collection of viral aerosols from human sources, the viral load detected in these samples is dependent on when samples were collected during the course of infection and individual characteristics of infected study participants (Yan et al. 2018). Compared with NPS [nasopharyngeal swab] data the geometric means and maxima for fine and coarse aerosols were 3-4

log10 RNA copies lower. Advancements in bioaerosol collection and recovery that could provide larger samples of aerosolized viruses could potentially lead to improvements in both RNA detection and depth of sequence coverage.

And in the Adenaiye 2021 study, it was said that

The shedding rates detected using the G-II in both studies, however, were lower than those reported by Ma et al using a sampler that requires subjects to blow through a narrow straw.

If the Gesundheit-II is only collecting some fraction of the actual viral copies, then the results will have been further distorted. There could well be in reality a greater percentage of mask wearers who do produce infected breath, and most likely the number of viral copies produced by mask-wearers would turn out to be even greater, perhaps far greater, in reality, and so the idea that masks are effective at stopping the virus would be even more battered.

This will also be amplified if it is true that some of the aerosols escaping from mask side-gaps are not being detected by the machine. If only, say, half of the mask wearer's aerosols are going into the machine, and then only, say, 10% of those are being registered, then only 5% of the viral copies of the mask-wearers are being registered.

There are other Gesundheit-II studies (although these are the main ones), and of course there are many complexities involved that one could spend months, or years, going through. But it is up to these pro-mask authors to convince us. It is not our job to spend even more time looking at their little area of research, especially when it has been unconvincing so far, and when we can already see from a general overview of the field that masking is all downside and no upside, and is just being used as part of a power grab.

Part 4:

The influential UK face mask reviews: DELVE, Royal Society, and the January 2022 UK Government Evidence Summary

Part 4 contents:

4.1. The DELVE April 2020 report on face masks

DELVE produced the first quasi-official report on masks in the UK, which was fed into SAGE in April 2020. It was reported to have been very influential in persuading SAGE and the UK government to recommend masks a few month later.

Who or what is DELVE? 'DELVE' stands for 'Data Evaluation and Learning for Viral Epidemics', and it describes itself as follows:

> a multi-disciplinary group, convened by the Royal Society, to support a data-driven approach to learning from the different approaches countries are taking to managing the pandemic. This effort has been discussed with and welcomed by Government, who have arranged for it to provide input through SAGE, its scientific advisory group for emergencies.

(The other report that also influenced the UK government to force masks on the population was done by another team, although that team was also convened by... the Royal Society. The same Royal Society that went deeply political a few years back.)

DELVE's people

Amongst DELVE's people were five people from Imperial College (the academic epicentre of Covid scaremongering), Devi Sridhar, the well-known WEF Covid nut who has driven the Scottish lunacy in her role as advisor to Nicola Sturgeon, two people who work with Sridhar, four people who work in institutes that have the word 'Global' in the name (any institute that has 'Global' in its name can be assumed to be political), five nerds from DeepMind, which is a Google-owned company (including its boss Demis Hassabis, who is also on SAGE), Nicholas Stern, previously known for producing a famously bad climate change economics report, three other climate change people, a black American woman whose research interests are 'Racial and Ethnic Health Disparities, Critical Race Theory, and Black Family Studies', and an Asian-American doing an Ecology PhD in America (plus a lot of young woke researchers who no doubt did the bulk of the 'work').

Also on DELVE is Venki Ramakrishnan, the Indian-American president of the Royal Society, who also just happens to be on SAGE, in case you were wondering how independent DELVE is. Ramakrishnan himself is very much a globalist climate-change type who thinks the WHO should be given real political power.

He appeared on BBC Radio 4's Today programme in July 2020 to advocate compulsory mask-wearing, and was reported to have sneered at "inappropriate randomized-controlled trials "as "methodological fetishism". He was also reported as saying that

> Not wearing a face covering outside the home should be considered as "anti-social" as drink-driving, or failing to wear a seat belt

which doesn't leave you in any doubt as to his view on masks. And the *Financial Times* reported him as trying to shame the UK on mask-wearing with the old we're-falling-behind-other-countries trick:

> The UK is way behind many countries in terms of wearing masks.

The first report

Let's take a look at the initial DELVE report that so influenced SAGE. The first thing to be said is that the scientific review of the evidence in it is very thin. It consists of around six very shallow pages that barely skim the surface of the issue. The rest of the report is padded out using the old trick of adding a lot of irrelevant technical-looking material on other matters, such as what's happening with masks in other parts of the world, material that most politicians and civil servants are not going to bother looking at, as they will just read the overall summary. This is hardly an in-depth look at the evidence.

There are two, and only two, main claims advanced to underpin the mask recommendation. The first is a wild claim about asymptomatic transmission:

> Asymptomatic (including presymptomatic) infected individuals are infectious. Without mitigation, the current estimate is that 40%-80% of infections occur from individuals without symptoms.

Any sensible scientist with knowledge of the history of diseases would have realised that this is exactly the sort of claim made in the early stages of a new disease that so often turns out to be a massive exaggeration. But there was no-one on DELVE like that, and sensationalism was the flavour of the day. Needless to say these extreme claims about asymptomatic transmission have collapsed over the last year, which is why you rarely hear about it any more, when it used to be that you couldn't go two minutes without people shrieking about it. Covid turns out to have been like any other respiratory disease: asymptomatic spread may play a part (we don't really know precisely), but it's probably a minor player, and probably happens to the same sort of degree that it does with other diseases.

The second claim used to underpin the mask recommendation is that large droplets are a major source of transmission, so we need to use masks because they stop droplets.

The 'Key Points'

These claims are described in the three 'Key Points' from the report (p. 1).

Key points

1. Asymptomatic (including presymptomatic) infected individuals are infectious. Without mitigation, the current estimate is that 40%-80% of infections occur from individuals without symptoms...

2. Droplets from infected individuals are a major mode of transmission [WHO]. This understanding is the basis of the recommendations for physical distancing, and for surgical masks to be adequate protection for HCWs in most settings [PHE]. Droplets do not only come from coughing or sneezing: in a-/pre-symptomatic individuals, droplets are generated via talking and breathing [Anfinrud, NEJM, 2020]

3. Face masks reduce droplet dispersal. Cloth-based face masks reduce emission of particles by variable amounts, for example [Anfinrud, NEJM 2020] showed that they are almost completely eliminated. [Davies, Dis Med Pub Pre 2013] showed that they filtered viral particles during coughing at about 50 to 100% of the filtration efficiency of surgical masks, depending on fabric, with absolute filtration efficiencies of 50-70%, and about 70-80% for oral bacteria. [van der Sande, Plos One 2008] showed 50% filtering efficiency for airborne particles.

This evidence supports the conclusion that more widespread risk based face mask adoption can help to control the Covid-19 epidemic by reducing the shedding of droplets into the environment from asymptomatic individuals.

So, from their own mouths, it is clear what the basis of DELVE's mask recommendations are: Covid is mainly spread by asymptomatic people, and is spread mainly by droplets. Neither of these things turned out to be true. (Even if they had been true, it wouldn't have justified mask mandates, but they aren't even true.) So the DELVE report is a complete irrelevance.

Despite this, the report infected the British establishment with pro-mask thinking that has never gone away. DELVE has never acknowledged that their report got things completely wrong.

Note that in key point 3 our old friend 'coughing' comes back into play: it is claimed that face masks 'filtered viral particles during coughing'. But as we have seen, what happens in coughing is irrelevant, as you don't need a mask to cover your coughs.

Note also that in point 3, three references are given (the first of which is also the only reference given for point 2 other than WHO and PHE). The quality of these gives us an indication of the quality of the review itself.

The Anfinrud paper

The first, 'Visualizing Speech-Generated Oral Fluid Droplets with Laser Light Scattering', by Anfinrud et al, *New England Journal of Medicine* (v.382, 21 May, 2020, pp. 2061-3) is not a peer-reviewed article but a short letter to the editor outlining the use of a laser light sheet to show some droplets that are emitted when someone talks, and to show that these are stopped by masks. These are large droplets only, though, all bigger than twenty microns.

(Jeremy Howard was very enthusiastic about this study, and said

> The light-scattering experiment cannot see "micro-droplets" that are smaller than 5 microns and could contain some viral particles. But experts don't think that these are responsible for much COVID-19 transmission.

Oops.)

The Davies paper

The second paper, 'Testing the Efficacy of Homemade Masks: Would They Protect in an Influenza Pandemic?' by Davies et al, in *Disaster Medicine and Public Health Preparedness* (v.7 (4), 22 May 2013, pp.413-8), was a tiny-sized, low-quality study done by some PHE (Public Health England) people. It has the feel of a backyard study done on the weekend with the some gear they bought home from work. The study looked at bacteria, not virions, and guess what? It was entirely based on our tiresome old friend, the cough, so again it has no application to the real world. It is noteworthy mainly because all the participants said, when asked, that they would not wear a mask all the time, and because the authors admit that

> if as a mask it does not fit well around the nose and mouth, or the material freely allows infectious aerosols to pass through it, then it will be of no benefit.

Anyway, the results are hardly a ringing endorsement of homemade or cloth masks. Homemade masks performed three times worse than surgical masks (they couldn't even stop coughs very well), and the authors say that even against droplets they should only be considered as a 'last resort'. As for aerosols, forget it:

these masks would provide the wearers little protection from microorganisms from others persons who are infected with respiratory diseases. As a result, we would not recommend the use of homemade face masks as a method of reducing transmission of infection from aerosols.

Some evidence.

The van der Sande paper

The third is 'Professional and Home-Made Face Masks Reduce Exposure to Respiratory Infections among the General Population', by van der Sande et al, *PLoS One* (v.3 (7), 9 July 2008). This was a somewhat more serious study than the first two, but it was not a real-life study, and the 'outward protection' test, that is, the test of how well masks blocked particles from exhalations, which is what DELVE was concerned with, was performed by a mannequin.

The DELVE authors seriously misrepresent this study. They say that cloth masks

showed 50% filtering efficiency for airborne particles

but this was in fact the (rough) result for inhalations, not exhalations. For exhalations, which is what DELVE was concerned with, with their focus on masks as source control, cloth masks did very little. Van der Sande and co say, in regards to exhalations, that

The home-made masks only provided marginal protection... Home made masks, and to a lesser degree surgical masks, are unlikely to confer much protection against transmission of small particles like droplet nuclei.

They qualify this by saying these masks will be more effective if 'transmission is predominantly carried by larger droplets', that is, they'll be more effective if larger droplets rather than fine aerosols are the major method of transmission. As they aren't, the masks will in fact be far less effective in reality.

It is also of interest to note the appearance here, immediately after this statement, an old pro-mask chestnut:

> but as the reproduction number of influenza may not be very high a small reduction in transmissibility of the virus may be sufficient for reducing the reproduction number to a value smaller than 1 and thus extinguishing the epidemic.

How did so many academics produce such a poor report?

As Covid is not spread much by droplets my criticisms of these papers is unnecessary, but I wanted you to get an idea of the poor quality of the DELVE report. It's hard to believe that some of the more respectable scientists on DELVE signed off on this, although whether any of the scientists involved can be considered serious is debatable (with the notable exception of Ramakrishnan, who, for all his politicking, is a heavyweight biochemist with a Nobel Prize to his name).

There are 68 academics listed as being part of DELVE, either on the Action Team, The Working Group and the Steering Committee. That is an enormous amount of academics to produce a report as dire as this one, which reads like it was cobbled together by a few dim postgrads over a weekend.

The Gesundheit studies

The report's discussions of the evidence base also leans heavily on two other studies (see p, 5), and these are the first two Gesundheit-II studies I analysed in some depth earlier in part 3. As we saw there, these studies have serious questions surrounding them. The DELVE report doesn't bother to spend any time looking at these studies, but then it didn't do that with any of the studies it cited.

Some criticisms from other academics

On May 4th 2020 the Science Media Centre issued some responses to the DELVE report from various experts. Here are some of the critical responses.

Dr Ben Killingley, Consultant in Acute Medicine (Clinical Lead) and Infectious Diseases, University College London Hospital, said:

> Regarding the analysis of the evidence base – the report is overly optimistic about the value of face coverings and it is incorrect to conclude that the evidence shows that face covering can reduce viral transmission in the community. There is in fact no good evidence that face coverings achieve this.

Dr Antonio Lazzarino, Department of Epidemiology and Public Health, UCL, dismissed the review as non-science:

> That is not a piece of research. That is a non-systematic review of anecdotal and non-clinical studies. The evidence we need before we implement public interventions involving billions of people, must come ideally from randomised controlled trials at population level or at least from observational follow-up studies with comparison groups. This will allow us to quantify the positive and negative effects of wearing masks. Based on what we now know about the dynamics of transmission and the pathophysiology of covid-19, the negative effects of wearing masks outweigh the positive.

Dr Simon Clarke, Associate Professor in Cellular Microbiology, University of Reading, also dismissed the study as any sort of science:

> This report from the Royal Society, while interesting, represents a set of valid opinions rather than any conceptual advance in our understanding of the usefulness of face-masks or coverings. It falls short of delivering new evidence and too casually dismisses precautionary principle when addressing the possibility that masks and coverings could have negative effects on people's behaviours. Until more evidence is delivered in either direction, that's all advice can be based on – opinions.

4.2. DELVE report update

The last update to the DELVE report happened on 7th July 2020.

The two authors

Despite the long list of 68 academics on DELVE's website (what do they actually do in DELVE?), this was credited to just two people, Prof Lalita Ramakrishnan, who is the sister of the prominent DELVE member, Royal Society President, and mask 'enthusiast' Venki Ramakrishnan (who we met earlier in part 4.1), and Prof Paul Edelstein, an American from the University of Pennsylvania, who doesn't half talk a lot of nonsense – Sky News reports him as saying

> The evidence for the benefit of wearing face coverings in protecting others from infection is becoming clearer all the time.

Nope.

> In fact, we have now identified convincing decades-old and apparently forgotten evidence, from the time when surgical masks were made of cloth and were reusable, showing that they help to prevent transmission of airborne infectious agents.

You really didn't.

> There is now even some evidence that masks might directly benefit the wearer.

What a pity, then, that no such evidence appeared in what you produced.

Aerosol spread quietly added in

In the update there was no acknowledgement at all of the failures of the first report. Instead of explicitly reporting that there was increasing evidence that aerosols were the most important method of transmission, not droplets as the original report assumed, the update instead just quietly and dishonestly added aerosols to droplets as the major methods of transmission. Instead of pointing out that there was considerable doubt about the ability of masks to block aerosols, the update claimed that there was evidence that masks worked against them (no good evidence was given for this).

Seven new studies that supposedly support mask wearing

The update listed seven new studies that supposedly support mask use. Three of these are modelling studies. Modelling studies are generally worthless as evidence, and, bizarrely, the authors themselves criticise these three studies both on the grounds that they are modelling studies, and so will have 'assumed parameters that may or may not be correct', and also on other grounds. In fact, for one of them they say

> the conclusions of this study are not supported by the presented evidence, as summarized by a number of scientists requesting a retraction by the authors.

Given these criticisms, it is hard to see why these studies were included in the list of relevant new studies, other than as a way of filling up space and making it look like some proper research has been done.

The Payne paper

Four observational studies were referenced as providing support for masks. One was titled 'SARS-CoV-2 Infections and Serologic Responses from a Sample of U.S. Navy Service Members — USS Theodore Roosevelt, April 2020' by Payne et al, in the CDC's *Morbidity and Mortality Weekly Report* (MMWR), June 12, 2020 v. 69 (23), June 12 2020, pp.714–721. This study concerned a Covid outbreak on board a US Navy ship. However, if you go to the actual study itself you will see that face masks were just one of a range of preventative measures that were mixed together, and so there was no real way of determining the effect masks had.

The Wang paper

Also cited was a Chinese study titled 'Reduction of secondary transmission of SARS-CoV-2 in households by face mask use, disinfection and social distancing: a cohort study in Beijing, China' by Wang et al (*BMJ Global Health*, v. 5 (5), 2020). This had the same problem. It claimed that secondary transmission was reduced by mask-wearing, but the families that reported no secondary cases also engaged in far more other possible relevant behaviours than the families that did report secondary cases.

The Cheng paper

Another study cited was 'The role of community-wide wearing of face mask for control of coronavirus disease 2019 (COVID-19) epidemic due to SARS-CoV-2' by Cheng et al in *Journal of Infection* (v.81 (1), 2020, pp. 107-114). This was a weak, speculative article that suggested that Hong Kong had less cases than other countries because of the very high level of mask wearing in public. No strong reason was given to think that masks were the reason rather than anything else (such as Hong Kong's previous widespread exposure to SARS-1 in 2003), and Cheng's article relied on an appeal to the precautionary principle:

> we believe that it is still advisable to encourage people to wear face masks in the public based on the precautionary principles.

Unlike almost all of the other Asian countries, Hong Kong's case counts stayed low until the last week of February 2022, when they increased dramatically to over 8,000 a day, and their hospitals became overwhelmed. As Hong Kong has one of the most draconian mask mandates in the world, which the government strongly enforces, and mask compliance is at 98%, one might reasonably doubt the claim that it was masks that kept Covid at bay in Hong Kong until then. (The same has happened in South Korea, which also had low case counts all along, but at the time of writing had over 171,000 cases a day in late February.)

Weirdly, another reference is given by the DELVE update at this point to support the claim that Hong Kong shows that masks work, and this is a reference to an Asthma UK webpage about what people with asthma can do to prevent getting coronavirus, which contains no evidence whatsoever for the effectiveness of masks, or anything about Hong Kong. The best interpretation of this irrelevant link is that it was a mistake, but that doesn't say much for the report's attention to detail, nor does it say much for those people who supposedly read the report and acted on it, for that footnote is still there eighteen months later.

The Mitze paper

The last paper cited is an article called 'Face Masks Considerably Reduce COVID-19 Cases in Germany: A Synthetic Control Method Approach' by Mitze et al. This is another weak paper, which has not been published in a peer-reviewed journal, that looked mainly at the mask mandate introduced in Jena in Germany, and claimed that it showed that mask mandates result in a massive reduction in infections:

> Assessing the credibility of the various estimates, we conclude that face masks reduce the daily growth rate of reported infections by around 40%.

Like all such studies they couldn't really untangle other possible factors.

The long-term stats for Thuringia (Jena's state)

Have cases in Jena stayed low since that paper was released? It doesn't appear that they have. I have been unable to find Covid stats purely for Jena, but the long-term stats for Thuringia, the German state where Jena is located, saw cases remain low until the end of 2020, after which they rose greatly, flattened out over summer 2021, and then rose sharply.

Thuringia compared to the rest of Germany

But how does Thuringia compare to the rest of Germany, you might ask? According to the *New York Times*, Thuringia has had one of the highest overall incidences in Germany.

So if the same happened in Jena as the rest of Thuringia in this time, we can conclude that whatever the reason for Jena having few cases early on, it was nothing to do with masks.

Jena vs the rest of Thuringia

Was Jena the same as the rest of Thuringia? Most likely, given the following bits of circumstantial evidence.

First of all we have a German newspaper story on Covid cases in autumn 2021 (20 Oct), which reported that the eastern states of Thuringia and Saxony have seen their own infection rates rise dramatically… [Thuringia was] the eastern state [with] by far the highest incidence in the country.

It doesn't say anything about Jena being any different to the rest of the state, which you would expect it to notice if it had been, because this same newspaper (*The Local de*) ran a glowing story previously on Mitze's report about Jena, with sub-headlines like 'So why were masks so successful in Jena?, and quotes from Witze like 'Jena is a pioneer city'.

According to the Robert Kock Institute's Covid page, Jena has had the same level of Covid cases in the first week of January 2002 as most of the rest of Thuringia.

So probably Jena's cases have been very high like the rest of Thuringia, despite the fact that they have mandated mask use throughout this period. Masks, then, didn't protect Jena after all. Mitze's study, was, as I said, weak, and should have never have been cited as evidence.

Germany wasn't leading the world at all

Of course, the whole of Germany, with some of the toughest and most viciously enforced mask requirements in the world, is a living, breathing – well, breathing with difficulty – refutation of the effectiveness of masks. (And in general it's a living refutation of the uselessness of non-pharmaceutical interventions). So it's amusing to look back on these authors who were so convinced that places in Germany like Jena were showing the world how to do it.

Overall verdict on the DELVE update

Overall we can conclude that the DELVE July 2020 update is, like the original report, junk.

4.3. The Royal Society's June 2020 face mask report

The other strongly influential review (along with DELVE) in the UK in 2020 was a rapid review titled 'Face masks and coverings for the general public: Behavioural knowledge, effectiveness of cloth coverings and public messaging' released on 26 June 2020. This was presented as a joint effort from the Royal Society's Science in Emergencies Tasking – Covid-19 (SET-C) group and the British Academy, although it was mainly written by three academics from Oxford's Leverhulme Centre for Demographic Science, including Prof Melinda Mills, and the Centre was keen to claim it as its own.

Also included in the list of authors on p. 33 is a certain Prof Roy Anderson, a key figure in the early colonisation of the UK governments scientific advisory panels by cynical scaremongers. (He's also on the Royal Society's SET-C steering committee).

Like the DELVE report, and all the other UK government and health institution face mask reports, this report was not peer-reviewed, which the authors acknowledge:

> This paper is a pre-print and has not been subject to formal peer-review.

(Even calling it a 'pre-print' is misleading, because with pre-prints the intention is that they will go through peer review, whereas these reports never do.)

Soon after this report was released the UK government announced a mask mandate.

> Face coverings in shops will be made compulsory from 24 July, and the prohibition may be extended to other

indoor spaces. The move follows last week's COVID-19 face coverings study from Oxford's Leverhulme Centre for Demographic Science on behalf of the Royal Society and British Academy.

Oxford's Leverhulme Centre for Demographic Science

The reader should be aware that Oxford's Leverhulme Centre for Demographic Science is an explicitly activist department made up of woke left-wingers. The Centre's own description says they intend to

> disrupt, realign and raise the value of demography in science and society... Producing real-time nowcasting of demographic processes – with a focus on inequality – diversity and environmental context, will revolutionize the discipline of demography.

Their research topics include 'Environmental context, demography and climate change', 'Inequality and diversity', 'Sociogenomics: nature and nurture', 'global sustainability', and 'Ethics, truth and trust'. These are, of course, all key progressive buzzwords and phrases, so we should be very careful about accepting any of the Centre's output at face value.

If you take a look at their faculty list it's the usual collection of sociologists and geographers, the sort who would have been vicars a few hundred years ago, all of them over-promoted and over-funded. Just the first line of the faculty bios gives you research interests like diversity, environmental measures, social epidemiology, gender, power and sexual decision-making, urban poverty, inequality issues among Africans in the diaspora, etc.

And how independent was the report from SAGE? Well, the lead author, Melinda Mills, is a member of SAGE's SPI-B committee, the behavioural science arm of SAGE, that is, the arm of SAGE that advises the government on how to manipulate the public's behaviour, so the answers to this question will range from 'not much' to 'not at all'. There is a large degree of coordination going behind the scenes with everything COVID-related that the public is not aware of, and which the media determinedly ignores.

Melinda Mills

Melinda Mills is a Canadian-Dutch sociologist who has published a paper claiming that vaccine passports increase vaccine uptake, and has chaired a government review into them, and is favour of them. She's a member of a 'High Level' European Commission Group which advises the EC's Economic Commissioner (and former Italian PM) Paolo Gentiloni on

> the main economic and social challenges the European economy will face in the post-COVID environment.

She's on various other government and official bodies, as well as international ones like Population Europe (she's a member of its Council of Advisors). She has an MBE, she's a Fellow of the British Academy, she's one of the governors of Nuffield College Oxford, she's a member of the European Academy of Sociology, she's on the Executive Council of the Economic and Social Research Council. She's also listed on the front page of the John Snow Memorandum as one of their most prominent supporters. The John Snow Memorandum is a sickening, pro-lockdown misinformation campaign filled with many of the hard-left maniacs from Independent SAGE. She's also a vaccine fascist, who believes that anti-vaccine talk should be criminalised. Not exactly the most independent and disinterested 'expert', then. In fact, she's about as establishment-entrenched as you can get.

Shabby tricks: The Royal Society report and the Chinese-language study

Onto the Royal Society report itself. You won't be surprised to hear that it's execrable. It starts with some complaints about the existing mask meta-analyses, noting that some of the studies were under-powered, set in non-community settings (like healthcare), and didn't look at cloth masks (almost all RCTs have been on respirators and surgical masks). Although they weren't very clear about it, the point of the RS review seemed to be that they were instead going to look at cloth masks studies instead of the surgical and respirator RCTs... even though most such studies were under-powered, not randomised, and were in non-community settings like healthcare (and one of the four studies chosen didn't even deal with cloth masks).

Remarkably, their whole meta-analysis on whether masks provide protection for the wearer was based on four non-RCT Chinese studies (one also involved Hong Kong). These were:

'Factors Associated with Household Transmission of Pandemic (H1N1) 2009 among Self-Quarantined Patients in Beijing, China' by Zhang et al, *PLoS One* (v.8 (10), Oct 18 2013).

'Risk factors for SARS infection among hospital healthcare workers in Beijing: a case control study', by Liu et al, in *Tropical Medicine and International Health* (v.4 supp.1, Nov 2009, pp. 52-9).

'Effectiveness of precautions against droplets and contact in prevention of nosocomial transmission of severe acute respiratory syndrome (SARS)' by Seto et al, *Lancet* (v.361 (9368), May 2003, pp.1519–1520).

'Effectiveness of personal protective measures in prevention of nosocomial transmission of severe acute respiratory syndrome', by Yin et al, *Zhonghua liuxingbingxue zazhi* (v.25 (1), Jan 2004, pp.18-22). (The journal's title appears to translate to 'Chinese Journal of Epidemiology'.)

They conveniently managed to exclude the only randomized-controlled trial on cloth masks, Macintyre's 2015 *BMJ Open* study (see part 5.1.c):

> due to the absence of a clear control group (i.e., they lacked a 'no mask' control group and compared only medical versus cloth masks).

So the Royal Society authors junked the only half-decent study on cloth masks, done by someone with a lot of experience in testing masks, in favour of some lesser quality studies instead, from China.

The RS report's own analysis of these papers was extremely thin, consisting of around one page of shallow analysis, plus a table of results, plus another table at the start listing the studies chosen.

Two of the included studies showed a small effect for cloth masks, while one (Zhang's) showed that cloth masks made things a bit worse. But one of the included studies, Yin's 2004 study, showed an enormous effect: 80% of non-maskers got sick, while only 22.8% of cloth mask-wearers did. This is so out kilter with every other mask study ever done that it has to be considered dubious. *It was this one outlying study that got them the result they wanted*, because its extreme results so heavily outweighed the other studies when they added them all in together.

Note that three of the studies that showed a protective effect, including Yin's, were looking at SARS, a very different disease to Covid in terms of its transmission and infection fatality rate. Also, Yin's abstract made it clear that it was concerned with droplet spread only, not aerosol spread:

Nosocomial infection of SARS can be prevented effectively by precautions against droplets.

The other study, by Zhang et al, was on bird flu, which is much more akin to Covid, and this was the one study that showed that, if anything, cloth masks made things worse.

What's more, Yin's study concerned hospital staff who were participating

in direct first aid for severe SARS patients.

Not walking down a supermarket aisle. Not sitting in a classroom. Doing first aid on a patient severely ill with a serious disease in hospital.

Shall we have a read of Yin's study then? No, unfortunately we won't be able to do that, for amazingly enough, this study was *written in Chinese only*, so we can't even begin to analyse it, except for the abstract which is in English. The report's authors had a translation done, but you won't be surprised to hear that we are not privy to it.

The other studies were in decent journals: *PLOS One*, *Lancet*, and *Tropical Medicine and International Health* (which all have either high or respectable impact factors, not that that makes them good studies). But our deciding study, Yin's, was in what appears to be the *Chinese Journal of Epidemiology* (which doesn't even have an impact factor). And although it may not be polite to say it, China hasn't always had the most rigorous approach to scientific practice, so one would be a fool to take a study like this at face value.

Even from the abstract alone we can tell that the paper is terrible. The study is not randomised. The staff were interviewed after the infected ones had become infected, and were asked about their protective habits, and this provides a lot of scope for their recollections to be coloured by whether they were infected or not (eg. infected people may decide that they didn't wear their mask enough, while someone who didn't get infected may decide that they did, even if both wore their mask the same amount).

There were many other protective factors at play:

> Univariate analysis showed that mask, gown, gloves, goggles, footwear, "hand-washing and disinfecting", gargle, "membrane protection", "taking shower and changing clothing after work", "avoid from eating and drinking in ward", oseltamivir phospha tall [*sic*] had protective effects.

('Oseltamivir phosphate', aka Tamiflu, is an anti-viral medicine.)

So there was a lot of potential for the other factors to muddy the waters. The confidence intervals for masks were large. This does not look like a study that would pass muster in a serious Western scientific journal, or even as an undergraduate project, even just going by the abstract. Yet this was the study that resulted in the British people, including school children, spending many of the days in the next year and a half with rags over their mouths and noses.

None of the affiliations of the authors in Yin's study are listed, except Yin himself, whose affiliation is given as 'Chinese Field Epidemiology Training Program, Chinese Center for Disease Control and Prevention'. This could mean he was a student, and this was a student project, which hardly fills one with confidence, or it could mean that he was one of the CCDCP's instructors, which means he's a

Chinese state employee, which also gives me little confidence. Not much comes up on a Google search for Yin, and judging by a ResearchGate search the small amount of other scientific work he has done is all as a minor co-author. We know very little about this incredibly influential-but-obscure Chinese scientist whose low-quality research from years ago in a low-quality journal has changed the course of the United Kingdom.

Call me old-fashioned, but I'm not crazy about everyone in Britain being forcibly muzzled on the basis of a single worthless non-randomized paper with loads of confounds from almost two decades ago with wide confidence intervals in a no-reputation Chinese journal on a disease with very different characteristics and which is not even in English and has incredible results that have never been seen before or since, and which was performed by either a student or a Chinese state employee, and which has been filtered through and spun by an activist University department who I wouldn't trust to go to the store without them radically changing the shopping list based on their political beliefs. No thanks.

A look at two of the other Asian studies

I should note a few things about two of the other cited papers which supposedly showed a small effect of masks. First of all, the Liu study in *Tropical Medicine and International Health*. This was not performed in a community setting, but in a hospital on the frontline of SARS (a disease with very different characteristics to Covid), with doctors and nurses who were in very close contact with SARS patients, and often performing emergency procedures on them.

Also, it was retrospective recall study, which relied on patients correctly remembering whether they had worn masks or not, along with a whole heap of other possible protective and risk factors, and after they knew whether they had got SARS or not, which might have affected their recall. They had to give a yes or no answer to whether they wore a mask or not. This has the problem that a subject who wore the mask some of the time and who didn't get SARS is liable to answer yes to the question of whether they wore a mask, whereas someone who wore it the same amount of time but who did get SARS is liable to say no to the question, as they attribute their infection to not wearing a mask enough.

If we take the study seriously, then we can also note (from Table 2 in the study) that wearing eye glasses, performing nose washes, and taking prophylactic anti-viral medication also apparently reduced infection, yet no-one in the Covid hysteria complex is recommending these actions. We should also note that, according to this study, wearing disposable masks slightly increased one's risk of getting SARS, and wearing one mask layer almost doubled one's risk of infection. So maybe it isn't a good idea to take this study seriously, especially when we note that there were so many possible confounding factors, such as in which section of the hospital a subject worked, which had a big effect.

The Seto *Lancet* study is a short paper with a tiny number of infected subjects (13). Like the Liu study this was a hospital study, not a community study, and was a retrospective recall study. It also concerned SARS. It didn't have any cloth masks, but looked at N95s, surgical masks and paper masks.

Staff were asked to answer 'Yes', 'Most of the time', or 'No' as to their mask use. The paper reports that

> These levels of response were to ensure that No
> indicated a definite lapse in practice.

This, however, makes the possible bias clear. If saying you didn't wear a mask was an actual 'lapse in practice', then staff are more likely to answer Yes or Most of the time (which the study counts as a Yes) than No, even if their mask-wearing was not most of the time and they should have answered No. You may say that this problem would affect the infected and non-infected groups equally, but someone in the infected group is less likely to say Yes or Most of the Time when they shouldn't as they may feel that it was their fault for getting infected as they didn't always wear their mask and so they should admit that, whereas in the non-infected group someone who should really answer No may feel that there is no point admitting that they didn't always adhere to practice as no bad consequences came from it, so they don't say No. (The point isn't that anything like this definitely did occur, just that there is some probability that it may have occurred, and the study didn't have any way of preventing it.)

This study concluded that

> the association for gloves was not significant.

This completely contrasts with the previous study, which found that gloves were massively significant. But with such a small number of infected people and so many problems and confounders it is really best not to draw any conclusions from this paper, and to toss it in the bin (along with the other ones).

Interestingly the paper itself was negative about paper masks, even though the paper mask result was what the RS report highlighted about this paper. The study said

The finding that paper masks did not significantly reduce the risk is not unexpected. Such masks, being easily wet with saliva, are never recommended as a precaution against droplets.

The RS report didn't mention this. In fact, it's hard to see how the RS report could have regarded this study as relevant seeing as it didn't look at cloth masks at all, and the RS report explicitly stated that it was about cloth masks (which was in the title). So even forgetting all the other faults with the paper, it should never have been included in the first place.

The second part of the Royal Society report, which was one based on a single study

Let's now move on to look at the second part of the Royal Society report, which looked at source control, that is, whether masks stopped the wearer passing infection on (the first part concerned whether masks protected the wearer). The conclusions reached in the report in regard to this issue were based on... one study. That's right. One single study. And not even a study that looked at the real world. Certainly not a randomized-controlled trial. Not even a study that looked at mask wearing by actual people.

The study was called 'Aerosol Filtration Efficiency of Common Fabrics Used in Respiratory Cloth Masks' by Konda et al, in *ACS Nano* (v.14 (5), 24 April 2020, pp.6339–47).

It used salt aerosols which were sent through various materials, and combinations of materials, to determine their filtering effectiveness. It was claimed that cotton, chiffon, flannel and silk were good at filtering, in these artificial conditions. And that's it. That's the entire basis of the RS report's decision to recommend that the whole country should wear masks as source control to stop people spreading Covid.

The RS report says of this study that

> The authors [ie. the authors of the *ACS Nano* study] therefore conclude from this study that combinations of various commonly available fabrics used in cloth masks and face coverings can provide significant protection against the transmission of aerosol particles.

This entire topic was disposed of in the RS report in three shallow paragraphs, along with a picture of the filtering results from the fabrics. There was no discussion of the vital importance of the air gaps in cloth masks, of which the *ACD Nano* study at least acknowledged:

> Our studies also imply that gaps (as caused by an improper fit of the mask) can result in over a 60% decrease in the filtration efficiency, implying the need for future cloth mask design studies to take into account issues of "fit" and leakage, while allowing the exhaled air to vent efficiently.

The RS report briefly mentioned this issue in passing, but made nothing of it, except to vapidly add 'suggesting the importance of proper fit and usage'. For cloth masks there is, of course, no 'proper fit and usage' that will prevent most of your breath escaping out the sides of a mask. There was no discussion of whether reducing the level of virions that go through a cloth mask (assume we ignore the side gap issue) will have any effect on reducing infections. There was no discussion of the harms of wearing a mask (and the lead author, Melinda Mills, was still refusing to acknowledge the existence of such harms in a TV interview in December 2021.) There was no discussion of... well, there was no discussion of anything, not even much discussion of the *ACS*

Nano study itself. It was enough to know that some material will filter out some salt aerosols, and that is all we needed to know, it seems.

As a contrast to the Konda *ACS Nano* study, compare this 2021 study from a team at the University of Waterloo who tested the filtration ability of cloth and surgical masks and found disastrous results, as reported in 'Experimental investigation of indoor aerosol dispersion and accumulation in the context of COVID-19: Effects of masks and ventilation' by Shah et al, in *Physics of Fluids* (v.33, 17 May 2021):

> The results show that a standard surgical and three-ply cloth masks, which see current widespread use, filter at apparent efficiencies of only 12.4% and 9.8%, respectively.

How did they fill up the report when the evidence review was so thin?

You may be wondering how the authors of the Royal Society report filled up 37 pages when their case for masks took so few pages. The answer is that, like DELVE, they used the old trick of filling up the report with other material that had no relevance to their justification of face masks, including discussions of international face mask policies, behavioural factors related to face mask adherence, public understanding of virus transmission, risk perception, supply concerns, public adherence to face coverings, importance of clear and consistent public messaging, etc.

There were also numerous complaints made in the report along the following lines:

> We note there have also been no clinical trials of handwashing, coughing into your elbow, social

distancing and quarantine, yet these measures have been widely adopted and are considered as effective.

In other words, 'We got some other repressive stuff through without having to provide evidence, so why should we have to provide evidence for face masks which is the same sort of thing?' Nor do they acknowledge that forcing people to wear masks for hours on end day after day hardly compares to asking people to wash their hands more, or cough into their elbows, nor that hand-washing has long been established scientifically as effective at killing virus particles and bacteria.

The crucial footnoting errors

I will end this section by drawing attention to two horrendous footnoting mistakes in the Royal Society report, which occur at crucial points. The reference to Yin's vital Chinese paper was completely wrong; I only managed to eventually locate it because there was another reference to it later.

The second section, on source control, was entirely based, as I have said, on just one paper, Konda's *ACS Nano* paper. Yet the RS report's authors didn't even bother to name it, or its journal, or its author, just its date, and there was no footnote for it, and there was nothing in the reference section anywhere about it. After some dogged internet sleuthing using the date I finally found the paper (it had the same date, discussed the same materials, and had the same results).

Convenient as these mistakes/omissions were to stop anyone taking a more critical look at the report, I shall assume they were innocent mistakes. The first may have been caused by the relevant reference in the References section having its number changed in the course of editing, without the changed number being updated in the main text, which can happen, but it is indicative of extreme carelessness, no matter what the time pressure, as this was one of the two most crucial references in the whole report. The other crucial reference just wasn't there at all. That is dreadfully poor. How did no-one on the long list of authors not notice this? Even if not at the time, surely afterwards?

But, astonishingly enough, those footnoting errors are still there, after 18 months (as of the start of 2022). That tells you that the number of people – including scientists, policy-makers, journalists, politicians, academics, other interested parties, concerned members of the public, and the report's own supposed authors – who have checked the vital references that the report depends upon is probably (not counting me) around zero.

4.4. The UK government's 'Evidence Summary' for the decision to remask children in schools in January 2022

On Monday 3rd January 2022 the UK government mandated masks in high schools again in England. (Strictly speaking they didn't make it law, but every high school in the country toed the line.) This was on top of the rules introduced in December 2021 requiring masks in indoor spaces and public transport again. Despite promising to release the evidence the decision was based on, they only released, through the Department for Education (DfE) on Wednesday 5th January 2022, an 'Evidence Summary'.

As a scientific document and evidence review the Summary is worthless, and contains what pro-lockdown propagandists like to call 'misinformation'. For example, on p. 5, in the second paragraph of the first section to deal with providing evidence, it says

> Person-to-person transmission of COVID-19 can occur by direct transmission of droplets (respiratory particles with ballistic trajectory that directly deposit on mucous membranes such as the lining of the mouth and nose), by airborne transmission of aerosols (smaller respiratory particles that remain suspended in the air and can be inhaled), or by touching the eyes, nose or mouth after direct contact with surfaces on which these virus-carrying particles have deposited.

So even in 2022 the government scientists are still downplaying the fact that fine aerosols are the most likely the main method of transmission, and bigging up droplets transmission, even though it's now known that this is far less important.

Note also that the paragraph goes on to say

> The effectiveness of face coverings stems mostly from
> reducing the emission of these virus-carrying particles
> when worn by an infected person (source control). They
> may provide a small amount of protection to an
> uninfected wearer; however, this is not their primary
> intended purpose.

In other words, the old government line, that stemmed
from the days when droplets were the worry, that face masks
are all about source control and thus are about protecting
others, is still being maintained. But it's interesting to note
that the government scientists involved (who, by the way,
aren't named) are now openly admitting that masks are
pretty much useless at protecting the wearer.

It's also interesting that in the Introduction it is admitted
that children are at very little risk, but no clear rationale is
given for why they are being forced to wear masks again,
other than some vague handwaving about 'balancing risks'.
(We all know why, of course, it's because the rabid teaching
unions, full of bedwetters and authoritarians who like
restrictions, have, in conjunction with the activist scientists,
pushed the government into taking this action).

Here's some more foolishness:

> SAGE has advised that there are preliminary indications
> that Omicron might show more airborne transmission;
> this would make the use of face coverings, alongside
> mitigations such as ventilation, even more important
> than for Delta.

More airborne transmission will, of course, make masks
even more pointless, because as we have seen over and over
again, masks mainly stop (if anything) large droplets, not
fine aerosols. (The idea that Omicron is more airborne than

Delta is perhaps overblown, but as it's not really relevant here I won't bother looking at it.)

The report says that it looked at drawbacks of masks in the classrooms, 'making this a balanced judgement', because it took these harms into account. It did actually describe some of the drawbacks, for example

> Research into the effect of mask wearing on communication has found that concealing a speaker's lips led to lower performance, lower confidence scores, and increased perceived effort on the part of the listener. Moreover, meta-cognitive monitoring was worse when listening in these conditions compared with listening to an unmasked talker.

But there's no explanation of how these very serious issues were taken into account, and no indication that they affected the judgement at all.

We also have a convenient footnote problem here again, as two of the surveys that the report draws upon for mask drawbacks (and which I would like to examine), have broken links.

The masked vs non-masked schools comparison

Let's now look at the evidence offered by this review.

The main piece of original evidence offered is the comparison of masked schools versus unmasked schools presented in 'Annex A – preliminary DfE analysis on the use of face coverings in secondary schools' (p. 11). The results are extraordinary – in that they show absolutely nothing of interest and it is a complete mystery why the government scientists, civil servants and ministers involved thought they in any way supported their decision.

The results were that schools that decided to mandate masks saw a fall in Covid-related absences from 5.3% on 1

October 2021 to 3.0% in the third week of October, whereas schools that did not mandate masks saw a smaller fall, from 5.3% to 3.6%, over the same period. (There were 123 masked schools, and 1192 non-masked/control schools, in the study.)

> This suggests that COVID-19 absence fell by 0.6 percentage points more (an 11% relative difference) in secondary schools that used face masks compared to similar schools that did not over a 2–3-week period.

This is rub-your-eyes-in-astonishment stuff. A tiny 0.6% difference, over a period that is clearly too short to allow any confident pronouncements, is being held up as a reason why our children have to be muzzled again, and suffer all the downsides that the report went into and claimed to take into account? Moreover, the Covid absence rates in non-masked schools actually fell during this period. The difference isn't even statistically significant, as the authors – who are conveniently anonymous – admit. Nor is it peer-reviewed, as they also admit.

Even if we accepted these results as gospel all they would show is that masks make hardly any difference (slightly less kids miss a week of school), and so given the awfulness of masks, and the harm they are doing to the children themselves and their education, these results, if they were real (not that they are), should actually result in masks being banished from the classroom forever.

The raw data

But wait, it gets worse. It turns out these weren't even the real results. No, these were the 'weighted' results, which were derived from applying some dubious transformations on the unweighted, ie, raw, data. What were the 'unweighted' (real) results then? They were very different to what the report presented. The non-masked schools started at 2.8%, not 5.3%, and they barely changed over that period, ending up at 2.9%. The masked schools' raw data was the same, it started at 5.3% and fell to 3.0%.

So the raw data shows that the unmasked schools had a slightly *lower* rate of absence than the masked schools! No wonder the authors were keen to do some adjustments. Both types of school ended up at virtually the same point.

The other misleading thing about this 'weighted' data is that it hides the very important and relevant fact that the masked and unmasked schools did not, in fact, coincidentally start off with the exact same number of Covid absences, 5.3%, but very different absence numbers, 5.3% versus 2.8%. So the schools that decided to mask up had far more children off at that stage with Covid, almost twice as many. This raises the definite possibility that those schools were influenced to mask up by their higher rates of absences. It also strongly suggests that those schools were suffering from local Covid outbreaks at the time, and what we saw over the next three weeks in the figures going down is not anything to do with masks, but simply a regression to the mean, that is, the inevitable return to normal.

In fact, it is hard to see any reason other than local outbreaks to explain why those schools had higher absence rates to start with. After all, there was almost ten times the number of schools in the control group than in the masked group, so (in the absence of evidence to the contrary) the control group's absence rate of 2.8% is more likely to be closer to the general absence rate across the whole country at that time than the far smaller intervention group's rate, in which case the intervention group's much higher rate is most likely to be explained by higher levels of Covid in their local areas. (If there is another credible explanation the review chose to cover it up rather than report it.)

If those higher absence rates were down to local outbreaks, then regression to the mean is the most likely explanation of why they went down (as the local outbreaks subsided). It also explains why the study thought that if the non-masked schools had started at 5.3% their rates would also have come down over that period, despite them not wearing masks.

Really we should have had a country-wide map of the schools in the study, and information about the general Covid rates at the time in the areas that the schools are in to give us a clearer picture of what was going on, rather than just simple overall numbers. As I have shown in part 3, it is always better to have the detailed data to look at, rather than relying on general summaries. Never rely on simple overall numbers, especially when it's a highly political issue and the numbers have been provided to you by a government with a vested interest in defending their decisions.

It would also have helped if the authors had separated out those schools in the masked intervention group that had rates much closer to the control group (if any), and then checked to see if they went down much, and whether the decrease in the overall average in the intervention group was driven by a smaller subgroup of schools with very high absence rates that went down considerably, because that is far more indicative of regression to the mean (due to local outbreaks dying out), than masks.

One way to show that regression to the mean was probably not the explanation would be to find two schools in the same area with the same starting absence rate, one of which adopted mask mandates, and the other didn't, and show that the absence rate declined far more in the masked school than the other. And then do this over and over again for numerous schools so that you have a decent-sized sample. But nothing like has been done. (It's unlikely that this could have happened to any great degree with these results anyway.)

'Weighting' results

We also don't know anything about how the weighting was achieved. The report says it used some new and obscure statistical method called 'entropy balancing', and it waffles on about this for three pages (pp. 16-18), but nothing specific is revealed about what it did in this study.

Let me say a little about weighting or adjusting results to allow for differences between groups. This is usually fine in standard circumstances. For example, suppose you are looking at an intervention that purports to reduce skin cancer by comparing an intervention group and a control group, and one of those groups has a younger population, or lives in a sunnier clime, or has a darker skin which is less prone naturally to get skin cancer. In that situation weighting the results makes sense, and the process of doing so is usually straightforward (although it's still not ideal to be using such different populations, and the more you have to adjust the data the less confident you can be about your results).

However, weighting can be used to distort or doctor results, especially seeing as science never used to insist very much that scientists reveal exactly how they performed these sorts of transformations. In fact many scientists would never even reveal their raw results, only the transformed results. This was never a satisfactory state of affairs, but it became a raging controversy as scientists began to turn their fields into political weapons, especially climate change. Many influential studies claiming to show the existence of anthropogenic global warming came under suspicion because the authors refused to reveal their raw data despite many requests to do so.

The scientific establishment mainly took the side of the climate change activist scientists (because they were all on the same side politically), but the pressure continued to grow, and at the same time a movement was emerging (especially popular on the left) which sought to make all scientific results and data available to everyone. This was partly because of philanthropic reasons ('make science available to everyone everywhere in the world'), but also because there were suspicions that some results were being manipulated (ironically, in those not-so-long-ago days, there used to be many suspicions about drug company research – funny how things so quickly change).

Eventually the 'open science' ideal became widely adopted, and it's now seen as a fairly standard practice to make all your data and results available. (This also became easier to do, and easier to check up on, as journals moved to the internet). Some researchers still try to ignore it, though, particularly in dubious fields like climate change.

The researchers in the January 2022 Evidence Summary have not explained in any way at all how they have transformed their results, so what they did can't be examined. The authors seem to have gone far beyond standard straightforward data corrections, and we can reasonably suspect their changes are based on assumptions which are tenuous and speculative, and quite possibly biased. This isn't just straightforward statistics, it's educated guesswork presented as statistics. So there's no reason to accept it.

For instance, they say

After applying the weighting, the initial COVID-19 absence rate for the control group increases to match the initial rate of the treatment group. This allows us to assess what the change in absence in the control group would likely have been had the control group started with the same initial absence rate as the treatment group; if both groups were to start at the same initial absence rate, it is likely the absence rate in both groups would decrease across the treatment period, but the absence rate would decrease more for the treatment group.

On what basis, though, do they decide that if the absence rate in the unmasked schools was higher then it's likely those absences would have decreased, only not as much as in the mask schools? What makes it likely? What would have changed to make the starting rates higher? One possible story you could tell is to suppose that the unmasked schools had been in areas that had local outbreaks, in which case it is not at all unlikely that those schools would have had higher absence rates than they in reality, and it would make sense then that their rates would drop as the local outbreaks died down. But that would be, in effect, to admit that most of the decrease in the intervention group is being driven by the same thing and so most of its decrease has nothing to do with masks. (And the question would remain as to what justifies the conclusion that the absence rates in the masked schools would drop more than in the unmasked schools?)

My point here is that you can't just say 'Let's suppose they had the same starting rates' and leave it at that. You have to specify the conditions that hold under which this would occur. Those conditions then need to be taken into account in your reconstruction (because this is in fact a reconstruction, in a somewhat different possible world). They can't just be discarded when it suits you. You're dealing with a different set of circumstances and your hypotheses about what happens in these circumstances needs to be justified (which is not at all easy to do when you're dealing with a counterfactual scenario). This also means that you are moving away from straightforward statistics and into the realm of speculation and modelling and assumptions. That's not just maths.

Also, the more your possible world differs from the actual world then the more tentative your hypotheses become, and this applies double when you're dealing with matters that are not already well-studied. You're not dealing with just one simple change like supposing that a population has more younger members than it actually has, and looking at the effect this is likely to have on skin cancer, making use of the considerable data that already exists on the correlation between skin cancer and age. We don't have an established and highly relevant data set here that we can just straightforwardly apply to this situation.

Is the question being begged?

The other worry here is that the question is being begged. 'Begging the question' doesn't mean 'raises the question' (as many assume), but 'assuming your conclusion as a premise'. That is, are the researchers already assuming that masks work when they weight the data in such a way that they achieve the result that the absences decreased more in the masked classes than the unmasked classes? There is not just one set of transformations that could be applied in a case like this, you can tweak your weights and apply different weights in different combinations to get very different results, and this will be true of 'entropy balancing' just as it is true of any other method. (Such problems are familiar in modelling.)

So on what basis did these researchers set up their weighting so that they got these results? Did they do so on the assumption that masks have an effect? If so, it would be begging the question to then claim that these results show that masks are effective. (This is a constant issue in climate science models.) If not, what justified the use of those weights? What justified the use of weights that resulted in the mask group having a greater decrease than the unmasked group? The raw data alone didn't show this. So what did? There is no answer in the text. Open science demands an explanation of the rationale behind each transformation, especially unusual ones, otherwise all we have is opinion dressed up as science.

'Entropy balancing'

As I briefly mentioned above, the authors talk about using a process called 'entropy balancing', which seems to be an experimental and very non-standard statistical method proposed by one statistician ten years ago that hasn't had much acceptance in the field. (There seems to be only one main paper on this, 'Entropy Balancing for Causal Effects: A Multivariate Reweighting Method to Produce Balanced Samples in Observational Studies' by Hainmueller in *Political Analysis*, v.20, 2012, pp.25–46, which is highly technical). However, the discussion of entropy balancing in the DfE report is very unenlightening, and the authors provide no assurances that they have not exceeded the limitations of the technique that Hainmueller himself identified on pp. 34-5 of his paper.

Lack of detail about what happened in the three-week period

I also should also point out that the review is very vague about what happened during the relevant three week period in October. Did all the schools in the control group all require masks at the start of this period, or just at some stage during it? Did any of these schools have mask requirements in place beforehand? These sorts of questions are just neglected.

It's still an uninteresting result

As I said earlier, though, even the weighted results don't tell us anything interesting, so all this is irrelevant anyway. We still have nothing that supports mask use even with the dubious 'weighted' results. Besides, to outweigh the terrible downsides of masking school children you don't just need a possible small effect, you need extremely strong results (and even then it's unlikely that masking school children would be justified). Yet far from having extremely strong results here we have nothing, nothing at all.

The SAGE maze

What other evidence does the DfE report rely upon?

E1

The very first piece of mask-related evidence that the review relies upon, when it claims on p. 5 that 'wearing face coverings in as many indoor environments as is practicable will help to reduce transmission', was a paper called 'Non-Pharmaceutical Interventions (NPIs) in the context of Omicron'. This is not, as you might expect, a serious, published, peer-reviewed, incontrovertibly strong piece of research, but merely a report prepared by two SAGE sub-groups: the EMG (the Environmental Modelling Group), and SPI-B (the Scientific Pandemic Insights Group on Behaviours, who deal with psy-ops.) Let's call this paper 'E1'. This isn't exactly an independent confirmation. I wouldn't trust any of the SAGE subgroups, and particularly

SPI-B or either of the modelling groups, to help a blind man across the road, let alone marking their own homework.

And the only relevant thing this 'paper' says about masks is

> Wearing face coverings in as many indoor environments as is practicable will help to reduce transmission. There is clear evidence from studies with individuals that face coverings can substantially reduce emission of the virus and can provide some protection to others, and higher quality, better fitting face coverings are more likely to be effective. This is detailed in a paper discussed at SAGE 96 [footnote 1].

The first sentence here states the conclusion, and thus forms no part of the premises. The second sentence, however, is merely is a statement of opinion, not a scientific evidence base.

E2

But maybe the 'footnote 1' at the end of the third sentence will lead us to a proper evidence base? Think again. That merely takes you to a paper, which I label 'E2', called 'Considerations for potential impact of Plan B measures, 13 October 2021'.

Which was written by... wait for it... the EMG and SPI-B again, this time with SPI-M (the Scientific Pandemic Influenza Group on Modelling, a different group who do similar things to the EMG, and who have done much damage to the country with their ridiculous modelling).

Moreover, this professes itself to merely be a minor updating of an earlier report:

> We have not been able to undertake a comprehensive review due to the tight timescales involved, so this paper draws on previous work alongside more recent studies.

E3

That earlier report was by the EMG, from January 2021, a year earlier than the January 2022 Evidence Summary. I label it 'E3', and it was called 'Application of physical distancing and fabric face coverings in mitigating the B117 variant SARS-CoV-2 virus in public, workplace and community, 13 January 2021'.

Ever get the feeling you're being fobbed off?

No wonder nothing much seems to have changed with the British government and their mask recommendations, they're mostly just recycling their earlier inadequate analyses over and over.

Another look at E2

Before we look at that even earlier (Jan 2021) E3 paper, note that the section of E2 that deals with the evidence base for masks merely has some short, shallow, misleading reviews – I say 'reviews', but probably 'brief mentions' would be more accurate – of some poor-quality evidence, such as the terrible Bangladesh study (see part 5.1.d) which is cited as good evidence (on p. 18). It also cites three studies that use the Gesundheit-II apparatus I discussed earlier. There isn't, of course, any discussion of the issues with the Gesundheit-II (as discussed earlier in part 3), but then there isn't really any discussion at all of any of the papers cited, there are just footnotes given to papers which supposedly support the very general and sweeping claims that are made about masks. The papers cited are mainly observational studies, mechanistic studies of filtration characteristics, meta-analyses that suit the authors, and other government documents which are much the same as this one. No published randomized-controlled trials or other high-quality evidence are cited.

E2 is bigger on making grand, ex-cathedra announcements than it is on providing a proper evidence review. Announcements like

> Face coverings are likely to reduce transmission through all routes by partially reducing emission of and/or exposure to the full range of aerosol and droplets that carry the virus, including those that deposit on surfaces (high confidence).

Note that this statement, while apparently strong at a brief glance, is actually very vague: all is says about transmissions is that they are 'reduced'. That could mean anything from slightly reduced to strongly reduced (though anyone who reads a little closer will see a clue in the form of the words 'partially reducing emissions', itself a somewhat imprecise phrase, but not words they would have chosen had they thought there was a strong reduction in emissions).

We should also recall that E1 said (my italics)

> There is clear evidence from studies with individuals that face coverings can *substantially* reduce emission of the virus

yet E1 just nods us off to E2, and E2, as we just saw, did not say anything like 'substantially' (and E3, which E2 relies upon, is, as we shall see, far less bullish).

Also of interest with E2 is that buried deep within it is the admission that

> viral emissions may be more likely to be in smaller aerosols than previously thought... There is a greater confidence that face coverings reduce emission and inhalation of large droplets than fine aerosols.

Another thing to note about E2 is the following claim, which these sorts of evidence reviews often make:

> The population scale benefits of face coverings can only be realised if they are worn correctly and by sufficient people in a setting.

When this sort of thing is said in the face mask literature it usually turn out to mean that the difference that masks make can only be detected if almost everyone wears them, almost of the time (which provides a nice excuse why population-level effects can never be detected – it's because not enough people wear them). And even then the effect will be small. Which basically tells you that they are useless, or at least not worth the cost of them.

E4

E2 also says that it should be read in conjunction with yet another paper, 'Behavioural considerations for maintaining or reintroducing behavioural interventions and introducing new measures in Autumn 2021' by SPI_B. Call this E4.

This is, however, just the same sort of thing again. It concludes that

> A large body of evidence demonstrates the effectiveness of face coverings in reducing transmission and, to a lesser extent, protecting the wearer (see EMG Consensus statement, SAGE 96).

E5

The main reference in E4 is yet again to another SAGE paper, which they call 'EMG Consensus statement, SAGE 96', which I call E5. This is like playing with Russian dolls. E4 did cite some other papers, but these were generally low quality, including the Bangladesh study, and another paper from the talking-in-a-restaurant-has-to-stop loons, and none were analysed in the paper, only cited. The only other non-SAGE paper that was discussed at all, and briefly, was a convoluted, data-torturing study by Melinda Mills and two others from the Leverhulme Centre for Demographic Science which was based on the ONS Covid-19 Infection Survey and which had small results. It admitted that

Participation in the study is voluntary and thus self-selection bias may affect the results.

What we are seeing is the scientific equivalent of opera buffa, with comically convoluted and implausible plots, with appearances from absurdly over-confident comic buffoons who pop up and make pompous and ridiculous pronouncements that bear no relation to reality. And characters who often appear in disguise pretending to be someone else.

I decided to go further into the maze and look at E5, the 'EMG Consensus statement, SAGE 96' paper. No link to this was given, though, and when I tried to find it, there was nothing called exactly that. There were two things with similar names associated with SAGE meeting 96, and these were 'EMRG: Consensus statement on COVID-19, 6 October 2021', and 'EMG and NERVTAG: Update on transmission and environmental and behavioural mitigation strategies, including in the context of Delta, 13 October 2021'. The latter was the only one relevant to masks, so I'll assume that's the one.

This short paper (which contains only four and two-thirds pages on an evidence review, much of which did not concern masks), says

Promoting high levels of wearing face coverings or face masks can potentially reduce transmission through all transmission routes, especially via close range and long-range airborne transmission (high confidence). This is covered separately in the SAGE Plan B paper [A].

E2 again

So we get fobbed off onto yet another SAGE-related paper. That paper turns out to be 'Considerations for potential impact of Plan B measures, 13 October 2021', which, although you've probably forgotten by now, was one of the papers that we were directed to earlier, and which got us nowhere, ie. E2 on my list. The very one which said

> We have not been able to undertake a comprehensive review due to the tight timescales involved, so this paper draws on previous work alongside more recent studies.

We're going in circles now. E2 said it was to be read in conjunction with E4, and E4 depends greatly on E5, but E5 takes us back to E2. There's just a series of inadequate papers that disguise their inadequacy by sending the reader further and further back to almost identical papers with different names, and eventually you come back to where you started.

E3 again

And *another* SAGE paper is cited as evidence in E5, and this turns out to be... E3.

Back to E5

There were a few other non-SAGE sources of evidence cited in E5. Two of them were the problematic Coleman and Adenaiye Gesundheit-II studies, which we looked at part 3. But there was also some discussion of some situations that were described as evidence. These were appallingly bad. For example:

> An outbreak in a school in the US reported transmission from a symptomatic teacher over 2 days to 50% of children in a class, with higher numbers in the front row nearest to the teacher. Six-foot distancing between desks and mask mandates were in place for pupils and teacher, but the teacher removed her mask to read out loud. The investigation reports that windows/doors were open and a HEPA air filter was present, but there is no data on effectiveness of these measures.

This is their idea of high-quality evidence. Two other similar stories are told.

E3 in some depth

Let's now take a look at E3, the earlier 13th January 2021 paper that some of these other papers relied on, which was called 'Application of physical distancing and fabric face coverings in mitigating the B117 variant SARS-CoV-2 virus in public, workplace and community'. This paper has many of the faults of the other papers. There is not much evidence cited, it engages in very little analysis of the evidence, and it makes outdated claims like

> the larger the respiratory particle the more likely it will contain viral particles.

The interesting thing about it, though, is that it doesn't make the strong claims that the later papers make, it's far more circumspect. For example, after mentioning some pro-mask studies it warns

> These figures should be treated with caution as it is not possible to establish the specific role of face coverings compared to other interventions in place at the same time

or how transferable cases from other countries are transferable to the UK.

It warns against modelling studies:

Several modelling studies are reported within a recent systematic review (Howard et al, 2020) that also suggest substantial impacts on the value of R in a population, but are based on idealised assumptions around the efficacy and adherence to wearing face coverings.

It says there isn't good evidence of masks protecting the wearer:

Public use of face coverings may provide some protection to the wearer, however this is not their intended purpose and there is insufficient evidence to assume that they can provide effective protection when used for this purpose.

It admits that masks in the real world are very different from masks in an idealised laboratory setting:

The real-world effectiveness of face coverings depends on multiple factors including the materials used, the fit of the face covering and the behaviour of the wearer.

It admits that any (supposed) effect of face coverings is difficult to untangle from other factors:

However, the PHE review concludes that within ecological studies it is difficult to identify the mechanisms by which face coverings reduce transmission or their effect in isolation from other interventions and behaviours.

The study admits that masks are not so good at coping with fine aerosols even in the laboratory, let alone the real world:

Mechanistic evidence from laboratory and controlled participant studies suggests most face coverings are likely to be effective at blocking the emission of droplets and larger (nasopharyngeal) aerosol particles but are less effective at limiting the emission of smaller (thoracic and respirable) aerosols.

It admits that cloth masks aren't very good:

some tests have shown that single layer materials used for face coverings can have filtration efficiencies as low as 5%, and recommend multi-layer construction which is substantially better.

And that in the real world masks are even more rubbish.

It is likely that this efficiency, especially for smaller aerosols, may be reduced where face coverings are poorly fitting or incorrectly worn.

Yet this paper is supposed to be a key reason why masks were introduced in Britain.

The HSA review

Let's go back to the January 2022 DfE Evidence Summary and see if there are any other important pieces of evidence used, so we can get away from these awful government scientist propaganda papers. It turns out there is one more piece of evidence which the 2022 report strongly relies on. This is a November 2021 review called 'The effectiveness of face coverings to reduce transmission of COVID-19 in community settings', by the... UK Health Security Agency. Oh. It's another governmental body review. (The HSA is what replaced PHE, Public Health England, in 2021.)

Note also the subtitle: 'A rapid review'. So it's not even a proper review. It's funny how the UK government and the governmental health agencies, with their huge amounts of staff and money, have somehow never found the time to do a proper review, despite Covid having been around for well over two years now.

It purports to be a proper meta-analysis, and to be fair, it is in some ways superior (or apparently superior) to the SAGE papers we looked at above – those come across like initial rough notes which are to form the basis of a proper analysis later (an analysis which never comes), whereas this review at least spends some time analysing studies rather than just gesturing at them, attempts to put them in some context, and tries to draw some general conclusions from a wide body of literature. That's as far as the good points go, though. The analyses are generally shallow, but, more importantly, the quality of the evidence included is terrible. 25 papers were included. Guess how many were randomized-controlled trials (RCTs)? Just two. In fact, not even two, because one of those was the Bangladesh study, which doesn't count as a proper study.

23 of the 25 studies were observational studies. So 92% of the studies were of a type that can't be trusted to provide objective results.

But wait, it gets even worse. Eleven of the observational studies – almost half of them – were not even published in peer-reviewed journals (they were preprints and reports).

Also, a majority of the papers in the analysis were explicitly rated by the HSA report's authors themselves as 'low quality', and the analysis is full of endless qualifications about how the poor quality of the materials should be grounds for considerable scepticism about their results. The authors rate the Bangladesh study as 'medium quality', so you can imagine how bad the 'low quality' studies are.

For one of the summer camp studies that was included the authors made the extraordinary admission that

> one further study (preprint, rated as low quality) was included but unable to provide evidence due to its design.

Why on Earth was a study that couldn't provide any evidence be listed as a part of the analysis? This is a joke.

Only one 'high quality' paper

There was only one included paper they rated as 'high quality', which was a 'technical article' put on the web as part of the ONS's Covid-19 Infection Survey.

This survey has been asking people about face mask use as well as recording their test status. This 'technical article' is not my idea of a high quality research, and it's not peer-reviewed, published research. There is a high risk of bias with this survey, because it relies on voluntary responses from the sort of people willing to engage with it. (Melinda Mills' paper that was mentioned a few pages back also made use of the data in this survey.)

There are also some unusual results in this ONS study. Those who wore masks just 'Sometimes' had almost the same results as those who wore masks 'Always', which rather goes against the usual idea that masks only work if we wear them all the time. Is 'sometimes' okay then? And people who never wore masks had almost exactly the same results as people in the 'Not needed' category. What does 'Not needed' mean?

> 'not needed' refers to individuals reporting not leaving their home (for example, shielding) and so face coverings were not needed.

So going outside, amongst people, without a mask on, was virtually the same as staying inside without a mask? These results should give one some pause before accepting the study's results at face value.

We should also remember a couple of important things here. Firstly, the data is merely listing 'cases', ie. people who record a positive PCR test, which is not at all the same thing as being sick (most PCR positive cases are not from people who are ill, and this is especially so with people who test themselves often).

Also, people who always wear masks are more likely to be people who hide away from others generally, and this may be the reason why their test figures are going to be lower in that period. (But we should also remember the 'Pagel Principle': such people are still likely to end up getting Covid at some stage anyway.)

The HSA 's sub-conclusions

When we look at the conclusions of each subsection of the HSA analysis they're nothing for pro-maskers to get excited about. (Thankfully there isn't any attempt at 'pooling' numbers.)

RCTs:

One RCT provides direct evidence that face coverings (surgical and cloth face coverings) can be effective at reducing COVID-19 transmission... Another RCT was inconclusive, reporting a non-significant reduction.

Schools and summer camp studies:

Three studies set in schools and a summer camp had mixed results, with 2 studies suggesting face coverings were associated with reduced COVID-19 transmission and 1 study suggesting no statistically significant effect.

Observational studies:

Eleven observational association studies had mixed results, with 6 studies suggesting face coverings were associated with reduced COVID-19 transmission and 5 suggesting no statistically significant association.

None of this provides any good reason to declare that masks are effective, particularly given the low quality of evidence, and given that that the one RCT that supported masks was the terrible Bangladesh study. So why did their overall conclusion say

Evidence from 2 RCTs and 23 observational studies predominantly suggest that face coverings can reduce the spread of COVID-19 in the community, through both source control and wearer protection, as well as universal masking.

The 'contact tracing' studies seemed to have tipped the balance for them:

All 8 contact tracing studies suggested that contacts of primary cases were less likely to develop COVID-19 if either the primary case or the close contact, or both, wore a face covering.

Note that five of these contact-tracing studies were rated as low quality, and three medium quality. Here are some of the author's own comments about some of these studies so you get the idea of their quality:

Many contacts (34%) could not be reached, and data collection on face covering use was collected via telephone interviews more than 1 month after the contact events, which may have affected the results in either direction...

Many contacts (43%) were not included in the analysis as they did not have data for both face covering use and

RT-PCR testing, which may have affected the results in either direction…

Liu et al assessed face covering use through online surveys, which may have reduced the reliability of the assessment, and Galow et al did not report their data collection method.

Yet the authors decided, on the basis of this rubbish, to say that the studies that they analysed in their report

predominantly suggest that face coverings can reduce the spread of COVID-19 in the community.

That is absolute bollocks, and everyone involved should be fired.

The MMWR review

What other evidence does the DfE January 2022 Evidence Summary rely on? Not a lot else, and hardly any non-government evidence is cited, and one of the papers cited is a modelling study.

One non-modelling and non-government paper they do refer to is 'Pediatric COVID-19 Cases in Counties With and Without School Mask Requirements — United States, July 1–September 4, 2021', by Budzyn et al, in *Morbidity and Mortality Weekly Report* (v.70, 2021, pp.1377–1378). This very short paper claims to find that a sample of US counties with mask mandates had lower rates of infection than a sample of counties without mask mandates.

This is another over-hyped piece of nothing. Even the authors themselves admit that the study is very limited:

this was an ecologic study, and causation cannot be inferred… Third, county-level teacher vaccination rate and school testing data were not controlled for in the analyses… Finally, because of the small sample size of counties selected for the analysis, the findings might not be generalizable.

So it can't be taken seriously. But even if you do want to take it seriously, note that the differences are tiny, even though the authors shamelessly try to spin them as far bigger than they are, with a graph carefully designed to make the differences look huge, and they present the results linguistically in the following fashion:

The average change from week −1 (1–7 days before the start of school) to week 1 (7–13 days after the start of school) for counties with school mask requirements (16.32 cases per 100,000 children and adolescents aged <18 years per day) was 18.53 cases per 100,000 per day lower than the average change for counties without school mask requirements (34.85 per 100,000 per day) (p<0.001).

This way of presenting the difference can make it seem bigger than it is ('Look, it's less than half – 18 compared to 34!'). A less misleading presentation would say that we're talking about an increase of 0.035% for that period for non-mask schools compared to a 0.016% increase in that period for masked schools, a difference of 0.019%, just under one fiftieth of one percent. Big deal.

This study has also been criticised for other faults (as well as these ones). *Red State* said

The real story is that the CDC cherry-picked a time period from July 1st-September 4th, meaning that children weren't even in school for the vast majority of the study. In fact, in some of the counties covered, children were only in school for a week or so by the time the study concluded. The study also cherry-picked some counties that already had rising infection rates prior to school beginning, with no control for testing so as to compare counties with similar case trends.

What's the point of masks in schools even if they do make a small difference?

Before I finish this section on the DfE Evidence Summary I should make the following point. Suppose we accept, for the sake of argument, that masks do reduce Covid spread in schools to some small or even medium degree. So what? This doesn't make Covid disappear (and it most definitely has not disappeared from the many US schools that have required children to wear masks for well over a year and a half). Covid still hangs around and spreads, only possibly slower than before. So most children will still get it at some stage, and most teachers will as well. All the masks would be doing, if they worked, is to help prolong the epidemic period, and help prolong the awful period when children are abused by the people and institutions which are supposed to be helping them.

Children are being sacrificed again, not for their own benefit, because Covid doesn't threaten them, but because some older adults are irrationally frightened of children, but still insist on getting the paycheck they want for working with them.

Which is the worst report?

If I had to choose which was the worst report out of DELVE report, the DELVE update, the Royal Society report, the HSA November 2021 rapid review, and the DfE Evidence Summary, it would be very hard to pick, as they're all shockingly bad. It would be hard to go past the pointless twisting of the data in the DfE report, but possibly the Royal

Society reports just pips it for its outrageous and cynical use of the Chinese-language study.

Part 5:

A look at the face mask literature

Part 5 contents:

In part 5 I look at the scientific literature on face mask use. I look at a lot of studies, but I am not undertaking an exhaustive review of all mask studies, which is an impossible task. However, I *do* review all the randomized controlled trials, which are the most credible trials. After that I look at a selection of the better trials and meta-analyses. I do focus more on those papers that conclude that there is little or no benefit to mask wearing. I have done this because academia, governments, health institutions and the media are currently giving such an appallingly one-sided view that a corrective is needed.

Also, many of the studies that pro-maskers refer to are not credible, or are not relevant to the real world, and a better evidence base is required.

Bear in mind, as statistician William Briggs says,

> The burden of proof is entirely on those who make masklessness a crime: they are imposing, we are not. I have no obligation, none whatsoever, to show masks do not work. But, we have more than enough evidence they do not.

I also refer the reader to *City Journal's* 'Do Masks Work? A Review of the Evidence', which demolishes some poor studies, including ones that the CDC has pushed. For example, the CDC has especially promoted an incredibly weak observational study which

> focused on two Covid-positive hairstylists at a beauty salon in Missouri. The two stylists, who were masked, provided services for 139 people, who were mostly masked, for several days after developing Covid-19 symptoms. The 67 customers who subsequently chose to get tested for the coronavirus tested negative, and none of the 72 others reported symptoms.

The CDC's spin was reported uncritically in media such as the *New York Times*.

'This study', the *City Journal* article went on,

has major limitations. For starters, any number of the 72 untested customers could have had Covid-19 but been asymptomatic, or else had symptoms that they chose not to report to the Greene County Health Department, the entity doing the asking. The apparent lack of spread of Covid-19 could have been a result of good ventilation, good hand hygiene, minimal coughing by the stylists, or the fact that stylists generally, as the researchers note, "cut hair while clients are facing away from them." The researchers also observe that "viral shedding" of the coronavirus "is at its highest during the 2 to 3 days before symptom onset." Yet no customers who saw the stylists when they were at their most contagious were tested for Covid-19 or asked about symptoms. Most importantly, this study does not have a control group. Nobody has any idea how many people, if any, would have been infected had no masks been worn in the salon. Late last year, at a gym in Virginia in which people apparently did not wear masks most of the time, a trainer tested positive for the coronavirus. As CNN reported, the gym contacted everyone whom the trainer had coached before getting sick—50 members in all—"but not one member developed symptoms." Clearly, this doesn't prove that not wearing masks prevents transmission.

5.1: The effectiveness of face masks: randomized-controlled trials

Part 5.1 contents

5.1.a. The Danish randomized-controlled trial (DANMASK)

5.1.b. Other randomized controlled trials

5.1.c. The only cloth mask randomized-controlled trial

5.1.d. An attempt at a new randomized controlled trial (the 'Bangladesh study')

The first question to ask is, where are all the randomised controlled trials looking at face masks and Covid-19? There's only one, the Danish mask study (see below). As Prof Vinay Prasad of the University of California at San Francisco, who co-wrote a 25,000 word review of mask evidence for the Cato Institute, says:

> The truth is we should have run several cluster RCTs in western, high income nations. For kids, adults, in different settings, with variation in masking strategies. We didn't do it for the same reason people RT the *Guardian* headline. Faith outpaced evidence when it comes to masks.

We can be sure that if masks worked, health bodies such as the CDC would have leaped at the chance to show this by funding a plethora of randomized controlled trials. The fact that they have ignored the chance to do so tells you what they know they'd find if they did any proper studies.

One other worry is worth mentioning here (amongst many worries). It is clear that many of the scientists in this field, even the ones who have performed semi-decent RCTs, are really mask activists, who try to spin their negative results to make them sound as pro-mask as they can. You should always have that in mind when you read any study in this field. (I make some relevant comments on this sort of thing in the sections below as I go through the articles.) Objectivity cannot be taken for granted, as this is a highly politicised area, and some scientists are, shall we say, less than scrupulous.

In the rest of section 5.1 I look at all the peer-reviewed published randomized controlled trials (sixteen in all) that have tested the effectiveness of masks in reducing the transmission of respiratory viruses, as well as a more recent (and failed) attempt at producing a quality randomized-controlled trial in Bangladesh.

5.1.a. The Danish randomized-controlled trial (DANMASK)

The only randomized controlled trial to ever study face mask effectiveness against Covid-19 (and the only one to take place after March 2020) is the DANMASK 'Danish' mask study. Surgical, not cloth masks or respirators, were tested. It's called 'Effectiveness of Adding a Mask Recommendation to Other Public Health Measures to Prevent SARS-CoV-2 Infection in Danish Mask Wearers: A Randomized Controlled Trial' by Bundgaard et al, and was published in *Annals of Internal Medicine* (March 2021). The results were that very slightly more (2.1%) maskless people got Covid or tested positive (or had antibodies) than mask wearers (1.8%). This difference of 0.3% was not only tiny, it was 'not statistically significant'.

The American Institute for Economic Research (in 'Masking: A Careful Review of the Evidence', by Paul E. Alexander, 11 Feb 2021) noted that

> Interestingly, these results emerged in a setting where social distancing and other public health measures were in effect, except for mask-wearing.

(Some pro-maskers have tried to make out that this paper merely failed to show a 50% reduction in infection, which was the stated intention of the paper, leaving readers with the idea that maybe it showed a 40% infection, or something similar. In fact it found no statistically significant difference between the masked and maskless groups.)

Note that the authors were reportedly forced to water down their findings, which it seems were even more negative than what appears in print, in order to get published.

The authors were not at all anti-maskers, or, at least, they were content to still push masks in their paper (possibly under editorial direction) on the grounds that their study tested whether masks protected the wearer, but didn't study whether masks worked as source control:

> The findings, however, should not be used to conclude that a recommendation for everyone to wear masks in the community would not be effective in reducing SARS-CoV-2 infections, because the trial did not test the role of masks in source control of SARS-CoV-2 infection.

Some editors of the journal that reluctantly published the paper have made the amazing claim that the paper actually supports mask use. The *Los Angeles Times* reports that

A trio of editors of *Annals of Internal Medicine*, the
journal that published the study, went further. "Masks
likely need to be worn by most if not all people to reduce
community infection rates," they wrote. "The results of
this trial should motivate widespread mask wearing to
protect our communities and thereby ourselves".

So the story that the paper was watered down by editors of
the *Annals* would appear to be all too plausible.

The biased media treatment of this paper is worth noting.
Whereas poor quality papers that supported mask-wearing
had received ecstatic and uncritical coverage in most media
outlets, this one was attacked and undermined and held to
completely different standards, despite the fact that this was
the one that that agreed with the previous randomised
controlled trials. For example, the *New York Times*, which
had the month before ran a puff piece for a sensationalist
paper by the IHME which simply assumed that mask
wearing worked, published a piece (on 18 Nov 2020)
undermining the Danish study on shoddy grounds.

Critics were quick to note the study's limitations…
Other experts were unconvinced. The incidence of
infections in Denmark was lower than it is today in many
places, meaning the effectiveness of masks for wearers
may have been harder to detect, they noted. "There is
absolutely no doubt that masks work as source control,"
preventing people from infecting others, said Dr.
Thomas Frieden, chief executive of Resolve to Save
Lives, an advocacy group, and former director of the
C.D.C., who wrote an editorial outlining weaknesses of
the research. "An N95 mask is better than a surgical
mask," Dr. Frieden said. "A surgical mask is better than
most cloth masks. A cloth mask is better than nothing".

The *NYT* also wrote

> The study's conclusion flies in the face of other research suggesting that masks do protect the wearer. In its recent bulletin, the C.D.C. cited a dozen studies finding that even cloth masks may help protect the wearer.

This was extraordinary, because, as even the *New York Times'* piece itself admits of these other papers,

> Most of them were laboratory examinations of the particles blocked by materials of various types.

They also quoted a scientist who should be ashamed of herself:

> Susan Ellenberg, a biostatistician at the University of Pennsylvania Perelman School of Medicine, noted that protection conferred by masks on the wearer trended "in the direction of benefit" in the trial, even if the results were not statistically significant. "Nothing in this study suggests to me that it is useless to wear a mask," she said.

Here's some very basic philosophy of science: if a paper finds that X doesn't work, you don't then say 'Nothing in this paper tells me that X is useless'.

The *Los Angeles Times* went even further, though, with its astonishingly misleading headline 'Face mask trial didn't stop coronavirus spread, but it shows why more mask-wearing is needed' (Kaplan, 20 Nov 2020). It quickly downplayed the negative results and claimed (ie. lied) that the study shows that *more* mask-wearing is needed, highlighting the apparently pro-mask comments of the study's authors that I mentioned above, as well making a big thing of the ridiculous comments by the trio of editors that I also mentioned above.

5.1.b. Other randomized controlled trials

In this section I look at the other published, peer-reviewed randomized controlled trials of face mask effectiveness in chronological order, apart from the only cloth mask RCT, which I look at in the next section, 5.1.c.

A 2005 randomized controlled trial entitled 'Effect of use of Face mask on Hajj-related Acute Respiratory Infection among Hajjis from Riyadh – A Health Promotion Intervention study' by Alabdeen et al, in the *Saudi Epidemiology Bulletin* (v.12, pp.27-8), concluded

> no association was observed between compliance with face mask wearing and developing ARI [acute respiratory illness].

What is remarkable here is not the study itself, which is of low quality, but that even as far back as 2005 the editors felt the need to add an afternote explaining that face masks are great, despite this study finding nothing to support their use:

> A simple prevention method against ARI that can break the cycle of disease transmission is using a simple face mask. Their regular use has been associated in previous studies with a substantial decrease in ARI incidence. The previous FETP [Field Epidemiology Training Program] study also reported that the use of face mask was associated with lower ARI attack rates, at least among males.

The conclusion the editors draw from the article they've just published is that it needs to be re-analysed, or another study needs to be done, until the right result is acquired:

> highlight[s] the need of in-depth analysis of the data or conducting another study with more objective measurement of ARI.

In the 2008 paper 'Preliminary Findings of a Randomized Trial of Non-Pharmaceutical Interventions to Prevent Influenza Transmission in Households' by Cowling et al, in *PLOS One* (v.3 (5), 7 May 2008), the authors studied whether an 'index case', ie. someone with influenza, infected others in the household. They concluded that

> The laboratory-based or clinical secondary attack ratios did not significantly differ across the intervention arms.

A 2009 randomized controlled trial funded by the CDC in *Annals of Internal Medicine* (Oct 6 2009) called 'Facemasks and Hand Hygiene to Prevent Influenza Transmission in Households: A Cluster Randomized Trial' by Cowling et al (a follow-up to their 2008 paper above), found that

> Hand hygiene with or without facemasks seemed to reduce influenza transmission, but the differences compared with the control group were not significant.

The study also claimed to show that

> Hand hygiene and facemasks seemed to prevent household transmission of influenza virus when implemented within 36 hours of index patient symptom onset

but the evidence that this was due to masks alone was underpowered (see Table 5 in the paper and the surrounding discussion).

In analysing this study in a meta-analysis titled 'Surgical Mask to Prevent Influenza Transmission in Households: A Cluster Randomized Trial' in *Plos One* (Nov 17 2010), Canini et al said in this study, no additional benefit was observed when facemask was added to hand hygiene by comparison with hand hygiene alone.

(Bear in mind that Cowling is a pro-masker – in interviews he has said that masks work and we should wear them.)

A 2009 randomized controlled trial called 'Face Mask Use and Control of Respiratory Virus Transmission in Households' by MacIntyre et al in *Emerging Infectious Diseases* (v.15 (2) Feb 2009, pp. 233–241) compared a P2 group (P2 is the Australian version of an N95), a surgical mask group, and a control group (called 'arms'). The main results 'showed no difference between arms'. The authors stated

Intent-to-treat analysis showed no significant difference in the relative risk of ILI in the mask use groups compared with the control group.

The authors tried to claim that the problem was that not enough people wore their masks, and that the masks were effective for those who wore them, but the evidence for this was tenuous, and the authors admitted that no causal link of this sort can be 'demonstrated because adherence was not randomized in the trial'.

A 2009 randomized controlled trial in the *American Journal of Infection Control* (37 (5), June 2009, pp.417-9) by Jacobs et al titled 'Use of surgical face masks to reduce the incidence of the common cold among health care workers in Japan: A randomized controlled trial' found

Face mask use in health care workers has not been demonstrated to provide benefit in terms of cold symptoms or getting colds.

A 2010 randomized controlled study in *Public Health Reports* (125 (2), Mar-Apr 2010, pp. 178-91) titled 'Impact of non-pharmaceutical interventions on URIs and influenza in crowded, urban households' by Larson et al said

> In this population, there was no detectable additional benefit of hand sanitizer or face masks over targeted education on overall rates of URIs [upper respiratory infections].

The study in fact found that those in the hand-hygiene group were significantly less likely to develop any symptoms of an upper respiratory infection (42 percent experienced symptoms) than those in the mask-plus-hand-hygiene group (61 percent), which suggests that wearing a mask actually undermines the benefits of hand hygiene, possibly due to touching the mask.

The study did also claim that 'mask wearing was associated with reduced secondary transmission'. *City Journal* says of this

> A multivariable analysis of this same study found a significant difference in secondary attack rates (the rate of transmission to others) between the mask-plus-hands group and the control group. On this basis, the authors maintain that mask-wearing "should be encouraged during outbreak situations." However, this multivariable analysis also found significantly lower rates in crowded homes—"i.e., more crowded households had less transmission"—which tested at a higher confidence level. Thus, to the extent that this multivariable analysis provided any support for masks, it provided at least as much support for crowding.

A 2010 randomized controlled trial in the *Journal of Infectious Diseases* (201 (4), Feb 15 2010, pp. 491-8) called 'Mask use, hand hygiene, and seasonal influenza-like illness among young adults: a randomized intervention trial' by Aiello et al looked at students in halls in 2006-07 who were assigned into three groups: face mask use, face masks with hand hygiene, or control, for six weeks. It said

> Face mask use alone showed a similar reduction in ILI compared with the control group, but adjusted estimates were not statistically significant.

There was no effect either for facemasks with hand hygiene:

> Neither face mask use and hand hygiene nor face mask use alone was associated with a significant reduction in the rate of ILI cumulatively.

A 2010 randomized controlled trial in PLOs One (17 Nov 2010) titled 'Surgical Mask to Prevent Influenza Transmission in Households: A Cluster Randomized Trial' by Canini et al said

> A cluster randomized intervention trial was conducted in France during the 2008–2009 influenza season... Households were randomized either to the mask or control group for 7 days... Influenza-like illness was reported in 24/148 (16.2%) of the contacts in the intervention arm and in 25/158 (15.8%) of the contacts in the control arm and the difference between arms was 0.40%. We observed a good adherence to the intervention. In various sensitivity analyses, we did not identify any trend in the results suggesting effectiveness of facemasks.

A 2011 randomized controlled study titled 'Findings from a household randomized controlled trial of hand washing and face masks to reduce influenza transmission in Bangkok, Thailand' by Simmerman et al, in *Influenza and Other Respiratory Viruses* (5 (4), July) concluded that

> Influenza transmission was not reduced by interventions to promote hand washing and face mask use.

In fact, masks and hand-washing made things worse, as the authors obliquely admit in the depths of the paper:

> Relative to the control group, the ORs [odds ratios] for ILI [influenza-like illnesses] among household members in the hand-washing arm and hand washing plus face mask arm were twofold in the opposite direction from the hypothesized protective effect.

A 2012 randomized controlled trial called 'Facemasks, Hand Hygiene, and Influenza among Young Adults: A Randomized Intervention Trial' by Aiello et al in *PLOS One* (v.7 (1), Jan 25 2012), was similar to their 2010 paper listed above, with similar numbers. It also looked at students in halls, in 2007-08 this time, who were assigned into three groups (face mask use, face masks with hand hygiene, or control) for six weeks. It said

> Both intervention groups compared to the control showed cumulative reductions in rates of influenza over the study period, although results did not reach statistical significance

and

> Masks alone did not provide a benefit.

A small 2012 randomized controlled trial called 'The role of facemasks and hand hygiene in the prevention of influenza transmission in households: results from a cluster randomised trial; Berlin, Germany, 2009-2011' by Suess et al in *BMC Infectious Diseases* (v.12, art. 26, Jan 26 2012). This is yet another survey where the authors play down the overall negative results and try to big up weakly-supported minor findings. Overall they found that

> In primary intention-to-treat analysis of all data, the interventions did not lead to statistically significant reductions of SAR in household contacts.

(SAR stands for 'secondary attack rates', ie. the percentage of people around the infected person who also got infected.)

They then say

> in a secondary analysis among households with full implementation of the intervention within 36 h [hours] after symptom onset, the combined participants from M and MH groups had a significantly lower chance of influenza infection compared to controls. With one exception (MH households in 2010/11), we observed a non-significant, but consistent and substantial reduction of the OR for influenza infection in both intervention groups (M, MH) and for both case definitions (laboratory confirmed and clinical).

Note that this applies to the mask and mask-and-hand-washing groups combined, so even if this result was valid we would not know how much of it was due to masks. Also, the authors admit the result is not statistically significant.

A 2014 randomized controlled trial titled 'Pilot Randomised Controlled Trial to Test Effectiveness of Facemasks in Preventing Influenza-like Illness Transmission among Australian Hajj Pilgrims in 2011' by Barasheed et al in *Infectious Disorders Drug Targets* (14 (2), pp. 110-6). This small study found that fewer people in the surgical mask group developed an influenza-like illness than in the control group, but this relied upon subjective self-reporting. Lab testing, on the other hand, revealed the opposite results, so we can conclude that this study did not provide any support for mask wearing.

In the 2016 paper 'Cluster randomised controlled trial to examine medical mask use as source control for people with respiratory illness' by MacIntyre et al in *BMJ Open* (v.6 (12), 30 Dec 2016), the authors found no statistically significant differences between the mask group and the control group.

The *BMJ* inserted a text box into the presentation with two possible excuses as to why no effect was found: firstly, the study was underpowered (which is true), and also the utterly ridiculous claim that

Removal of masks in the intervention arm during meal times may have reduced efficacy and biased the results towards the null.

In other words, maybe the masks didn't work because the mask-wearers took them off to eat. If only those silly mask-wearers had kept them on while eating they would have worked! Is this is the best pro-maskers can come up with? Do they really think we have to wear them even when eating, otherwise their magic is lost?

In a 2020 randomized controlled trial titled 'Facemask against viral respiratory infections among Hajj pilgrims: A challenging cluster-randomized trial' by Alfelali et al (a follow-up to the 2014 Barasheed paper mentioned above), in

PLoS One (v.15 (10), 13 Oct 2020), the authors concluded that

> This trial was unable to provide conclusive evidence on facemask efficacy against viral respiratory infections.

They claimed that this was most likely due to poor adherence to mask protocols, but the fact remains that this was yet another RCT that failed to show an effect.

Note that the authors initially expected facemasks to be worn for 24 hours a day. Yes, *24 hours a day*:

> Although facemasks were to be worn for 24 hours daily per protocol if possible, for the analysis, pilgrims who used at least one facemask each day during Hajj were considered to have used a facemask during that day, counter to the planned design.

So not only do some of these mask researchers expect people to wear their masks while eating, they expect people to wear them 24 hours a day, when eating, showing, sleeping, defecating, making love, walking in the countryside, etc. Mad.

5.1.c. The only cloth mask randomized-controlled trial

Finally we come to an important study, important because it remains the only ever randomized controlled trial of cloth masks that has been carried out and published in a peer-reviewed journal. Not a single such study has been performed and published on cloth masks since March 2020, an extraordinary and shocking situation seeing that so many health institutions having been pushing masks and so many countries have made it illegal not to wear one.

This study also had a reasonable number of participants.

This 2015 trial was called 'A cluster randomised trial of cloth masks compared with medical masks in healthcare workers' by MacIntyre et al, and appeared in *BMJ Open*. (v.5, 2015). As the title says, it compared the effectiveness of surgical masks and cloth masks in healthcare workers in hospitals.

So how did the cloth mask fare in this study? Terribly, it turns out. The cloth mask group was more than 13 times likely (see Table 2 in the study) to develop an influenza-like illness than those in the surgical-mask group. The authors said

Conclusions: This study is the first RCT of cloth masks, and the results caution against the use of cloth masks. This is an important finding to inform occupational health and safety. Moisture retention, reuse of cloth masks and poor filtration may result in increased risk of infection... as a precautionary measure, cloth masks should not be recommended for HCWs [healthcare workers], particularly in high-risk situations.

Note that this study did have a control group, but that group sometimes or often wore masks (mostly surgical but sometimes cloth as well) as this is standard practice in the hospitals in Vietnam where study took place. This led the authors to say

Owing to a very high level of mask use in the control arm, we were unable to determine whether the differences between the medical and cloth mask arms were due to a protective effect of medical masks or a detrimental effect of cloth masks.

We can reasonably suspect the latter, because there are so many studies on surgical masks that show that they have no effect (see section 5.7). As the authors themselves says,

The magnitude of difference between cloth masks and medical masks in the current study, if explained by efficacy of medical masks alone, translates to an efficacy of 92% against ILI, which is possible, but not consistent with the lack of efficacy in the two previous RCTs.

The authors also strongly imply that cloth masks made infection worse:

we found no significant difference in rates of virus isolation in medical mask users between the three trials, suggesting that the results of this study could be interpreted as partly being explained by a detrimental effect of cloth masks. This is further supported by the fact that the rate of virus isolation in the no-mask control group in the first Chinese RCT was 3.1%, which was not significantly different to the rates of virus isolation in the medical mask arms in any of the three trials including this one... The study suggests medical masks may be protective, but the magnitude of difference raises the possibility that cloth masks cause an increase in infection risk in HCWs. Further, the filtration of the medical mask used in this trial was poor, making extremely high efficacy of medical masks unlikely, particularly given the predominant pathogen was rhinovirus, which spreads by the airborne route.

The authors further caution about the risks of a cloth masks:

The physical properties of a cloth mask, reuse, the frequency and effectiveness of cleaning, and increased moisture retention, may potentially increase the infection risk for HCWs. The virus may survive on the surface of the face-masks, and modelling studies have quantified the contamination levels of masks. Self-contamination through repeated use and improper doffing is possible.

They also warned that double-masking is likely to make the problem worse:

> Observations during SARS suggested double-masking and other practices increased the risk of infection because of moisture, liquid diffusion and pathogen retention.

The authors also reported that cloth masks and surgical masks performed terribly with filtering tests, especially cloth masks which had virtually no filtering ability at all:

> Laboratory tests showed the penetration of particles through the cloth masks to be very high (97%) compared with medical masks (44%).

(No details are given on how they performed these tests.)

City Journal reports on an update on the situation with this paper (in 'Do Masks Work? A review of the evidence' by Jeffrey H. Anderson, 11 Aug 11, 2021):

> MacIntyre and several other authors of this study, perhaps under pressure from the CDC or other entities with similar agendas, released what the CDC calls a "follow up study," in September 2020. This follow-up isn't really a study at all, certainly not a new RCT, yet the CDC cites it favorably while disparaging the original study, which, the CDC asserts, "had a number of limitations." This 2020 follow-up pretty much amounts to publishing the finding that when hospitals washed the cloth masks, health-care workers were only about half as likely to get infected as when they washed the cloth masks themselves. Still, the 2020 publication says, "We do not recommend cloth masks for health workers," much as the 2015 one said.

5.1.d. An attempt at a new randomized controlled trial (the 'Bangladesh study')

A mask study funded by the US National Bureau of Economic Research called 'The Impact of Community Masking on COVID-19: A Cluster-Randomized Trial in Bangladesh' by Abaluck et al, and popularly known as the 'Bangladesh study' as it was set in Bangladesh, has been the subject of a lot of wild claims in media and social media and even government reports and science journals about how it supposedly provides enormously strong evidence for the effectiveness of masks. For example, NBC News said

> A study involving more than 340,000 people in Bangladesh offers some of the strongest real-world evidence yet that mask use can help communities slow the spread of Covid-19. The research, conducted across 600 villages in rural Bangladesh, is the largest randomized trial to demonstrate the effectiveness of surgical masks, in particular, to curb transmission of the coronavirus. Though previous, smaller studies in laboratories and hospitals have shown that masks can help prevent the spread of Covid, the new findings demonstrate that efficacy in the real world — and on an enormous scale.

Nature said

> Face masks protect against COVID-19. That's the conclusion of a gold-standard clinical trial in Bangladesh, which backs up the findings of hundreds of previous observational and laboratory studies.

It was used in the UK Health Security Agency report we looked at in part 4.4, which was itself a major source of evidence for the decision in early January 2022 to require face masks in classrooms in England again.

The Bangladesh study has not yet been published in a peer-reviewed journal. Various versions of it can be found on the internet (the authors' haphazard cataloguing of the study is perhaps indicative of the quality of their data-gathering.)

Even if we take the paper at face value, the results provide nothing at all for mask advocates to get excited about. The non-mask-wearing villages had 8.6% of people reporting Covid symptoms, compared to 7.6% in the mask villages, which meant that only 1% more people got Covid symptoms in the non-mask villages. If you put it in terms of what percentage the control group figure was reduced by, which those pushing this study like to do, that's an 11.6% reduction, which sounds bigger (although still not very big), but the fact remains that the absolute difference is slight. The difference between masks and non-masks was even less pronounced when it came to the numbers of people who gave blood which showed seroprevalence for SARS-CoV-2 IgG antibodies (about 40% from each group who had symptoms consented to testing): 0.76% versus 0.68%, which is less than 1%.

So even if these differences were real, they're too small to help pro-maskers anyway. As epidemiologist and biostatistician Martin Kulldorf said,

> As a vaccine advocate, I would be horrified if a vaccine trial showed 11% efficacy. Based on the 95% confidence intervals, we do not even know if surgical mask efficacy is more than 0%.

It also turns out that the differences, small as they were, were only seen with surgical masks, not cloth masks. With the seroprevalence results, the authors admit that they

> see no statistically significant effect for cloth masks.

So for cloth masks, which most Western countries are trying to force upon their citizens, the result was a big fat zero. And even for surgical masks, the differences were very small, and also possibly zero, given the confidence intervals.

What's more, these differences were only really seen in over-50's:

> We generally find that the impact of the intervention is concentrated among individuals over age 50.

This is very odd, and very suggestive of a sociological explanation like social desirability rather than anything to with Covid. (See below for more on the likely involvement of social desirability here.)

> So even taken at face value the study is hardly the resounding success story that the press headlines would have you believe, and hardly justifies the heavy-handed government action in mandating masks that we have seen all over the world.

But we should definitely not take the study at face value. The science blogger el gato malo (himself a very experienced and high-level working scientist) has savaged this study as complete junk:

> it violates pretty much every single tenet of setting up and running a randomized controlled experiment. Its output is not even sound enough to be wrong. It's complete gibberish... truly, a dismal day for the dismal science and those pushing it into public health.

There were multiple failures with the study's design. One of the biggest, el gato malo points out, was that

> to claim that masks caused any given variance in outcome, you need to isolate masks as a variable. They didn't. This was a whole panoply of interventions, signage, hectoring, nudges, payments, and psychological

games. It had hundreds of known effects and who knows how many unknown ones… We have zero idea what's being measured and even some of those variables that were measured showed high correlation and thus pose confounds. When you're upending village life, claiming one aspect made the difference becomes statistically impossible. The system becomes hopelessly multivariate and cross-confounded.

Another major fault was that the researchers' own observations on mask compliance in actuality showed that participant's reports on their own mask-wearing were wildly inaccurate, yet the study depended on self-reporting about symptoms:

> When we surveyed respondents at the end of April 2020, over 80% self-reported wearing a mask and 97% self-reported owning a mask… Anecdotally, mask-wearing was substantially lower than indicated by our self-reported surveys. To investigate, we conducted surveillance studies throughout public areas in Bangladesh in two waves. The first wave of surveillance took place between May 21 and May 25, 2020 in 1,441 places in 52 districts. About 51% out of more than 152,000 individuals we observed were wearing a mask. The second wave of surveillance was conducted between June 19 and June 22, 2020 in the same 1,441 locations, and we found that mask wearing dropped to 26%, with 20% wearing masks that covered their mouth and nose.

This by itself invalidates any assumptions about the accuracy of self-reporting in the study. (This also affects the testing results, because the only people who were tested were ones who had symptoms, so those who wore masks but declined to report symptoms didn't get tested, even though they might have tested positive.)

It gets worse. There was widespread government mask propaganda everywhere in Bangladesh. Also the researchers were strongly pushing masks. In fact, they were running a simultaneous study with the villages *to see how well they could increase compliance*. So the villagers knew full well what results the researchers wanted. This means there will have been a massive social desirability factor in operation, with mask wearers, especially amongst the older and more responsible ones, wanting to please the researchers. So there was motivation for mask wearers not to report symptoms, while there was the same motivation for non-mask wearers to report the very same symptoms. None of this is accounted for in the study, a shocking error. As El Gato says of this:

> This non-blinded issue combining with self reporting adds one tailed error bars so large to this system that they swamp any signal.

5.2. The effectiveness of face masks: other trials and studies

Part 5.2 contents

5.2.a. Other face mask trials and studies – Covid-era

5.2.b. Other face mask trials and studies – pre-Covid era

Many other studies, especially ones used by pro-maskers, are 'observational' studies. Here's what Carl Heneghan and Tom Jefferson, from Oxford's Centre for Evidence-Based Medicine, say about such studies in their *Spectator* article 'Landmark Danish study finds no significant effect for facemask wearers' (19 Nov 2020):

> The only studies which have shown masks to be effective at stopping airborne diseases have been 'observational' – which observe the people who ordinarily use masks, rather than attempting to create a randomised control group. These trials include six studies carried out in the Far East during the SARS CoV-1 outbreak of 2003, which showed that masks can work, especially when they are used by healthcare workers and patients alongside hand-washing.

> But observational studies are prone to recall bias: in the heat of a pandemic, not very many people will recall if and when they used masks and at what distance they kept from others. The lack of random allocation of masks can also 'confound' the results and might not account for seasonal effects. A recent observational study paper had to be withdrawn because the reported

fall in infection rates over the summer was reverted when the seasonal effect took hold and rates went back up. This is why large, randomised trials like this most recent Danish study are so important if we want to understand the impact of measures like face masks.

For this reason I have mostly avoided this sort of observational study here. Pro-maskers also like mannequin studies, and computer model studies. I don't regard these as adequate substitutes for real-life studies, and the computer model studies are particularly prone to bias, so I generally don't include them here unless they have been very influential and need commenting on (or unless they are used to show something they are more reliable on).

5.2.a. Other face mask trials and studies – Covid-era

In 2020 77 Marine recruits in a barracks tested positive despite extremely stringent restrictions, including constant mask-wearing with double layers. This was reported in 'SARS-CoV-2 Transmission among Marine Recruits during Quarantine' in the *New England Journal of Medicine* Dec 2020 (v.383, pp.2407-2416) by Letizia et al. They reported that

> All recruits wore double-layered cloth masks at all times indoors and outdoors.

In the CDC's *Morbidity and Mortality Weekly Report* (v.69 (36), Sep 11, 2020) there was a mask-wearing study titled 'Community and Close Contact Exposures Associated with COVID-19 Among Symptomatic Adults ≥18 Years in 11 Outpatient Health Care Facilities — United States, July 2020' by Fisher et al. It looked at mask-wearing before

Covid infection. It found that 85% of infected people they studied always or usually wore their masks. There was little difference in this respect with the control group of uninfected people.

A 2021 study in the *Southern Medical Journal* (114 (9), Sep, pp. 597-602) entitled 'Analysis of the Effects of COVID-19 Mask Mandates on Hospital Resource Consumption and Mortality at the County Level' by Schauer et al looked at a Texas hospital before after a mask mandate was introduced in mid-2020. It concluded that

> There was no reduction in per-population daily mortality, hospital bed, ICU bed, or ventilator occupancy of COVID-19-positive patients attributable to the implementation of a mask-wearing mandate.

In 2021's 'Mask mandate and use efficacy for COVID-19 containment in US States' by Guerra and Guerra in *International Research Journal of Public Health* (v.5 (55), 2021), the authors conclude that

> We did not observe association between mask mandates or use and reduced COVID-19 spread in US states... Our main finding is that mask mandates and use likely did not affect COVID-19 case growth. Mask mandates were associated with greater mask use but ultimately did not influence total normalized cases or post-mandate case growth... initial association between masks and lower COVID-19 growth rates that dissipated during the Fall-Winter 2020-21 wave is likely an artifact of fewer normalized cases begetting faster growth in states with coincidental low mask use.

In 'Transmission of COVID-19 in 282 clusters in Catalonia, Spain: a cohort study' by Marks et al in the *Lancet* (v.21 (5), 1 May 2021, pp. 629-636) the authors say

> We observed no association of risk of transmission with reported mask usage by contacts

and

> we did not find any evidence of decreased risk of transmission in individuals who reported mask use... we did not note any association between mask use and risk either in our unadjusted analysis (table 3) or in a multivariable model excluding type of exposure.

A team at the University of Waterloo tested the filtration ability of masks in 2021 and found that all types performed very badly. In 'Experimental investigation of indoor aerosol dispersion and accumulation in the context of COVID-19: Effects of masks and ventilation' by Shah et al, in *Physics of Fluids* (v.33, 17 May 2021), the authors report disastrous results for surgical and cloth masks:

> The results show that a standard surgical and three-ply cloth masks, which see current widespread use, filter at apparent efficiencies of only 12.4% and 9.8%, respectively.

Respirators fared better, but nowhere near as good as they were supposed to:

> Apparent efficiencies of 46.3% and 60.2% are found for KN95 and R95 masks, respectively, which are still notably lower than the verified 95% rated ideal efficiencies.

(An R95 is just like an N95 except that it is also resistant to oily particles; it is considered a better mask.)

The presence of a valve or a loose fit means you might as well not be wearing the mask at all:

> the efficiencies of a loose-fitting KN95 and a KN95 mask equipped with a one-way valve were evaluated, showing that a one-way valve reduces the mask's apparent efficiency by more than half (down to 20.3%), while a loose-fitting KN95 provides a negligible apparent filtration efficiency (3.4%).

Other mask tests come under fire for not considering fit:

> The present results provide an important practical contrast to many other previous experimental and numerical investigations, which do not consider the effect of mask fit when locally evaluating mask efficiency or incorporating mask usage in a numerical model.

Some researchers from the University of Wisconsin did a study called 'Reported COVID-19 Incidence in Wisconsin High School Athletes During Fall 2020' by Sasser et al in the *Journal of Athletic Training* (2021), which said

> There were no significant associations between COVID-19 incidence and face mask use during play for those sports with greater than 50 schools reporting on face mask use.

'Impact of non-pharmaceutical interventions against COVID-19 in Europe in 2020: a quasi-experimental non-equivalent group and time series design study' by Hunter, Brainard et al, in *Eurosurveillance* (v.26 (28), July 15, 2021) found little evidence for face masks, although they were at pains to avoid saying this, but the study should be regarded with scepticism anyway as it relied on a lot of computer modelling.

In 'Efficacy of face masks, neck gaiters and face shields for reducing the expulsion of simulated cough-generated aerosols' by Lindsley, in *Aerosol Science and Technology* (v.55 (4), pp.449-457), the authors claimed to find that masks were effective, and far more so than face shields, but this was another study that tested coughing:

> We used a cough aerosol simulator with a pliable skin headform to propel small aerosol particles (0 to 7 µm) into different face coverings. An N95 respirator blocked 99% (standard deviation (SD) 0.3%) of the cough aerosol, a medical grade procedure mask blocked 59% [etc.]… Our results suggest that face masks and neck gaiters are preferable to face shields as source control devices for cough aerosols.

In the influential paper 'Identifying airborne transmission as the dominant route for the spread of COVID-19' by Zhang in *Proceedings of the National Academy of Sciences* (v.117 (26), June 30, 2020 pp. 14857-14863), the authors say

> We conclude that wearing of face masks in public corresponds to the most effective means to prevent interhuman transmission.

Over forty academics and scientists – none of them 'anti-maskers' – sent a letter to the PNAS urging it to retract the paper because it was so bad. The letter said

> We are writing with deep concerns about a paper recently published in your journal, entitled 'Identifying airborne transmission as the dominant route for the

spread of COVID-19'. The paper made extraordinary claims about routes of transmission, the effectiveness of mask-wearing, and by implication, the ineffectiveness of other non-pharmaceutical interventions. While we agree that mask-wearing plays an important role in slowing the spread of COVID-19, the claims in this study were based on easily falsifiable claims and methodological design flaws. We present only a small selection of the most egregious errors here.

The Johns Hopkins Bloomberg School of Public Health also issued its own criticisms of the study:

this highly flawed paper provides no evidence on mask effectiveness at the population level... The claims made in this paper are not supported, and the journal editors should strongly consider retraction... This paper had two primary conclusions, neither of which were supported by the evidence presented... The authors made two false statements, which were key assumptions underpinning their primary conclusions.

The *New York Times* reported that the authors were allowed to choose their own reviewers.

The 2021 article 'Mask Use and Ventilation Improvements to Reduce COVID-19 Incidence in Elementary Schools — Georgia, November 16–December 11, 2020' by Gettings et al in the CDC's *Morbidity and Mortality Weekly Report* (v. 70 (21), 28 May 2021, pp.779–784), was touted by the CDC as good evidence for mask use, especially seeing it was involved 91,893 students in 169 schools in Georgia, and newspapers dutifully reported the CDC's summary, which said that

COVID-19 incidence was 37% lower in schools that required teachers and staff members to use masks' and said that 'Mask requirements for teachers and staff members and improved ventilation are important strategies in addition to vaccination of teachers and staff members that elementary schools could implement.

However, what was not mentioned was the finding that there was no statistically significant effect found with student masking:

The 21% lower incidence in schools that required mask use among students was not statistically significant compared with schools where mask use was optional.

A *New York Magazine* writer, David Zweig, who investigated this study in an article titled 'The Science of Masking Kids at School Remains Uncertain' (20 Aug 2021) wrote

Scientists I spoke with believe that the decision not to include the null effects of a student masking requirement (and distancing, hybrid models, etc.) in the summary amounted to "file drawering" these findings, a term researchers use for the practice of burying studies that don't produce statistically significant results. "That a masking requirement of students failed to show independent benefit is a finding of consequence and great interest," says Vinay Prasad, an associate professor in University of California, San Francisco's Department of Epidemiology and Biostatistics. "It should have been included in the summary." "The summary gives the impression that only masking of staff was studied," says Tracy Hoeg, an epidemiologist and the senior author of a separate CDC study on COVID-19 transmission in schools, "when in reality there was this additional important detection about a student-masking requirement not having a statistical impact."

'Community Use Of Face Masks And COVID-19: Evidence From A Natural Experiment Of State Mandates In The US', Lyu and Wehby, *Health Affairs* (v.39 (8), 16 June 2020).

City Journal says of this study:

> One widely cited study finds that states that enacted mask mandates in the spring saw lower growth rates in the following weeks—but those states were mostly early hotspots already closer to herd immunity, where one would naturally expect to see decelerating transmission.

('Do We Need Mask Mandates?' Harris, 22 March 2021.)

In 'Maximizing Fit for Cloth and Medical Procedure Masks to Improve Performance and Reduce SARS-CoV-2 Transmission and Exposure, 2021' by Brooks et al, published in the CDC's *Morbidity and Mortality Weekly Report* (v.70, Feb 19 2021, pp. 254–257), the authors boasted that they had experimented with ways to improve the fit of masks so that exposure to virus particles was reduced:

> During January 2021, CDC conducted experimental simulations using pliable elastomeric source and receiver headforms to assess the extent to which two modifications to medical procedure masks, 1) wearing a cloth mask over a medical procedure mask (double masking) and 2) knotting the ear loops of a medical procedure mask where they attach to the mask's edges and then tucking in and flattening the extra material close to the face (knotted and tucked masks), could improve the fit of these masks and reduce the receiver's exposure to an aerosol of simulated respiratory droplet particles of the size considered most important for transmitting SARS-CoV-2. The receiver's exposure was

maximally reduced (>95%) when the source and receiver were fitted with modified medical procedure masks.

But then, bizarrely, they ended up warning that

The findings of these simulations should neither be generalized to the effectiveness of all medical procedure masks or cloths masks nor interpreted as being representative of the effectiveness of these masks when worn in real-world settings... these findings might not be generalizable to children because of their smaller size or to men with beards and other facial hair, which interfere with fit. Finally, although use of double masking or knotting and tucking are two of many options that can optimize fit and enhance mask performance for source control and for wearer protection, double masking might impede breathing or obstruct peripheral vision for some wearers, and knotting and tucking can change the shape of the mask such that it no longer covers fully both the nose and the mouth of persons with larger faces.

These warnings are, in effect, saying 'These suggestions might be a load of rubbish in the real world, so take them with a grain of salt'.

In 'The airborne lifetime of small speech droplets and their potential importance in SARS-CoV-2 transmission' by Stadnytskyi in *Proceedings of the National Academy of Sciences* (v.117 (22), June 2020, pp.11875-7), a useful summary is given at the start of droplet fall science.

In 'Transmission of Severe Acute Respiratory Syndrome Coronavirus 2 via Close Contact and Respiratory Droplets Among Human Angiotensin-Converting Enzyme 2 Mice' by Bao et al, in the *Journal of Infectious Diseases* (v.222 (4), 2020, pp.551-5), the authors say

hACE2 mice cannot be experimentally infected via
aerosol inoculation until continued up to 25 minutes
[*sic.*] with high viral concentrations.

5.2.b. Other face mask trials and studies – pre-Covid era

A 2019 trial called 'N95 Respirators vs Medical Masks for
Preventing Influenza Among Health Care Personnel: A
Randomized Clinical Trial' by Radonovich et al in *Journal
of the American Medical Association* (v.322 (9), Sep 3,
pp.824-833) conducted across seven US medical centres said
this:

> Conclusions and relevance: Among outpatient health
> care personnel, N95 respirators vs medical masks as
> worn by participants in this trial resulted in no
> significant difference in the incidence of laboratory-
> confirmed influenza.

In 'Testing the Efficacy of Homemade Masks: Would
They Protect in an Influenza Pandemic?' by Davies et al in
Disaster Medicine and Public Health Preparedness (v.7 (4),
22 May 2013) say

> any mask, no matter how efficient at filtration or how
> good the seal, will have minimal effect if it is not used in
> conjunction with other preventative measures... An
> improvised face mask should be viewed as the last
> possible alternative if a supply of commercial face masks
> is not available... [but] these masks would provide the
> wearers little protection from microorganisms from
> others persons who are infected with respiratory
> diseases. As a result, we would not recommend the use

of homemade face masks as a method of reducing transmission of infection from aerosols.

A 2010 study called 'Simple Respiratory Protection— Evaluation of the Filtration Performance of Cloth Masks and Common Fabric Materials Against 20–1000 nm Size Particles' by Rengasamy, Eimer and Shaffer in *The Annals of Occupational Hygiene* (v.54 (7), Oct, pp.789–98) said

> Results obtained in the study show that common fabric materials may provide marginal protection against nanoparticles including those in the size ranges of virus-containing particles in exhaled breath.

A 2006 study 'Do N95 respirators provide 95% protection level against airborne viruses, and how adequate are surgical masks?' by Balazy et al, was published in the *American Journal of Infection Control* (v.34 (2), 1 March 2006, pp.51-57). I cannot access the full text, but the abstract reports that

> the tested surgical masks showed a much higher particle penetration because they are known to be less efficient than the N95 respirators. The 2 surgical masks, which originated from the same manufacturer, showed tremendously different penetration levels of the MS2 virions: 20.5% and 84.5%, respectively, at an inhalation flow rate of 85 L/min.

It also said that

> National Institute for Occupational Safety and Health (NIOSH)-certified N95 respirators can exceed an expected level of 5%.

This article has also been cited as suggesting that N95 performance decreases due to the electrostatic charge wearing out, and as evidence for masks not working when they are damp.

In 'Evaluating the efficacy of cloth facemasks in reducing particulate matter exposure' in the *Journal of Exposure Science and Environmental Epidemiology* (v.27 (3), May 2017, pp.352-357), Shakya et al found that cloth masks were of little use when compared to N95s as a baseline (surgical masks had more effectiveness):

> our results suggest that cloth masks are only marginally beneficial in protecting individuals from particles<2.5 μm. Compared with cloth masks, disposable surgical masks are more effective in reducing particulate exposure.

An interesting 2018 study in *Biocontrol Science* (v.23 (6), pp.61-9) titled 'Comparison of the Filter Efficiency of Medical Nonwoven Fabrics against Three Different Microbe Aerosols' by Shimasaki et al said that mask efficiency tests are normally conducted using a bacterium which is much larger than influenza-type virions (phi-X174 phage aerosols), so they conducted penetration tests of non-woven medical masks using inactivated influenza virions. Their conclusion was this.

> We compared the filter efficiency against each airborne microbe to analyze the dependency of filter efficiency on the microbial particle size. Our results showed that against the three types of spherical microbe particles, the filter efficiencies against influenza virus particles were the lowest and those against phi-X174 phages were the highest for both types of nonwoven fabrics... We conclude that the filter efficiency test using the phi-X174 phage aerosol may overestimate the protective

performance of nonwoven fabrics with filter structure
compared to that against real pathogens such as the
influenza virus.

In 'The bacterial and viral filtration performance of
breathing system filters' by Wilkes et al, in *Anaesthesia* (55
(5), May 2000, pp.458-65), the authors

> hypothesise that, since the droplet sizes are the same,
> both the bacterial and viral droplets impact on the filter
> media, but that the viruses, released from the droplet
> after contact with moisture accumulated on the filter, can
> be driven onwards by the flow of gas, whereas the
> bacteria remain attached to the filter media.

Although this is in an anaesthesia context, it does suggest
that when a mask is damp a virion can (whereas a bacteria
can't, or at least is far less likely to), be removed from the
mask by breath and carried off with the breath. It is not,
however, entirely clear what is being said here. But in the
Davies paper from part 4.1 it is said of this study that

> Although the droplet sizes for both virus and bacteria
> were the same and affected the filter media in a similar
> manner, it was suggested that the viruses, after contact
> with the moisture on the filter, were released from their
> droplet containment, and driven onward by the flow of
> gas.

In 'Respiratory Performance Offered by N95 Respirators
and Surgical Masks: Human Subject Evaluation with NaCl
Aerosol Representing Bacterial and Viral Particle Size
Range' by Lee et al, in *The Annals of Occupational Hygiene*
(v. 52 (3), Apr 2008, pp.177–185), the authors say

The study indicates that N95 filtering facepiece respirators may not achieve the expected protection level against bacteria and viruses.

In 'Evaluating the efficacy of cloth facemasks in reducing particulate matter exposure' by Shakya et al in *Journal of Exposure Science and Environmental Epidemiology* (v. 27, Aug 2017, pp.352–7), the authors say

our results suggest that cloth masks are only marginally beneficial in protecting individuals from particles<2.5 μm.

5.3. The effectiveness of face masks: reviews and meta-analyses

Part 5.3 contents

It is instructive to note that there have been far more meta-analyses and reviews of the literature than there have been randomized controlled trials, a sorry state of affairs. (Meta-analyses, although not easy to do, and certainly not easy to do well, are still easier and cheaper than a randomized controlled trial.

The Cato's Institute's comments about meta-analyses need to be borne in mind whenever anyone shows you a meta-analysis supporting mask-wearing:

> We identified 32 systematic reviews and meta-analyses evaluating the effects of community face masking against respiratory viral transmission. Of 16 quantitative meta-analyses (Table 2), 8 were critical or equivocal as to whether existing evidence was sufficient to support a

public recommendation of masks, and the remaining 8 supported a public mask intervention on the basis of existing evidence primarily due to the precautionary principle—i.e., based on the assumption that masks might help and are unlikely to harm—and on the basis of observational or other indirect evidence. Of the 15 solely qualitative reviews identified by the authors, seven concluded that evidence for the use of community masking was weak, seven cautiously concluded that mask benefits outweigh risks in various settings, often conceding that the evidence was only of low to moderate quality, and one unequivocally concluded that facemasks were beneficial. Despite their varying conclusions, these 15 qualitative reviews are largely redundant of one another and chiefly evaluate evidence already discussed above. The meta-analyses largely analyzed the same RCTs as one another but used different methodologies and sometimes included different non-RCT observational studies. None of these studies considered the SARS-CoV-2 virus specifically, and most looked at surgical—not cloth—face mask use in community settings.

5.3.a. The effectiveness of face masks: reviews and meta-analyses – post-Covid era

The Cato Institute's own meta-analysis from which the above quote is taken is itself a very comprehensive and in-depth review. It is titled 'Evidence for Community Cloth Face Masking to Limit the Spread of SARS-CoV-2: A Critical Review', by Liu, Prasad & Darrow and it came out in November 8th, 2021. It found that

evidence of facemask efficacy is based primarily on observational studies that are subject to confounding and on mechanistic studies that rely on surrogate endpoints (such as droplet dispersion) as proxies for disease transmission. The available clinical evidence of facemask efficacy is of low quality and the best available clinical evidence has mostly failed to show efficacy, with fourteen of sixteen identified randomized controlled trials comparing face masks to no mask controls failing to find statistically significant benefit in the intent-to-treat populations.

They also said

In non-healthcare settings, of the 14 RCTs identified by the authors that evaluated face mask efficacy compared to no-mask controls in protecting against respiratory infections other than COVID-19, 13 failed to find statically significant benefits from facemask use under intention-to-treat analyses. In communal living settings, four of five RCTs failed to show statistically significant benefits to masking, and the promising results of the fifth study were not confirmed when its authors sought to replicate the results in a much larger follow-up trial. Of eight RCTs that evaluated face mask efficacy against respiratory illness transmission in non-healthcare household settings, all eight failed to find a statistically significant benefit for the use of face masks alone compared to controls in their intention-to-treat analyses, and only three found statistically significant benefit in highly selective sub-group analyses.

A November 2020 review in the *Cochrane Database of Systematic Reviews* (v.11 (11), Nov 2020) titled 'Physical interventions to interrupt or reduce the spread of respiratory viruses' by Jefferson et al found that

There is low certainty evidence from nine trials (3507 participants) that wearing a mask may make little or no difference to the outcome of influenza-like illness (ILI) compared to not wearing a mask (risk ratio (RR) 0.99, 95% confidence interval (CI) 0.82 to 1.18. There is moderate certainty evidence that wearing a mask probably makes little or no difference to the outcome of laboratory-confirmed influenza compared to not wearing a mask.

They also said

The pooled results of randomised trials did not show a clear reduction in respiratory viral infection with the use of medical/surgical masks during seasonal influenza.

Note that Cochrane reviews are extremely rigorous and high-quality, and are generally superior to journal articles.

A meta-analysis titled 'Nonpharmaceutical Measures for Pandemic Influenza in Nonhealthcare Settings—Personal Protective and Environmental Measures' by Xiao, Cowling et al, published in the CDC's journal *Emerging Infectious Diseases* (v. 26 (5), May 2020), said

In our systematic review, we identified 10 RCTs that reported estimates of the effectiveness of face masks in reducing laboratory-confirmed influenza virus infections in the community from literature published during 1946–July 27, 2018. In pooled analysis, we found no significant reduction in influenza transmission with the use of face masks… We did not find evidence that surgical-type face masks are effective in reducing laboratory-confirmed influenza transmission.

(Note that Cowling is a pro-masker and still insists that masks work and we should wear them.)

Aggarwal et al in their 2020 meta-analysis 'Facemasks for prevention of viral respiratory infections in community settings: A systematic review and meta-analysis', in the *Indian Journal of Public Health* (64 (supp.), June 2020, pp.S192-S200), said

> There was no significant reduction in ILI either with facemask alone or facemask with handwash. Conclusion: Existing data pooled from randomized controlled trials do not reveal a reduction in occurrence of ILI with the use of facemask alone in community settings.

In 'Face masks effectively limit the probability of SARS-CoV-2 transmission' by Cheng et al in *Science* (v. 372 (6549), 25 June 2021, pp.1439-1443) the authors argue that masks are likely to be useless in virus-rich environments like hospitals:

> In indoor settings, it is impossible to avoid breathing in air that someone else has exhaled, and in hospital situations where the virus concentration is the highest, even the best-performing masks used without other protective gear such as hazmat suits will not provide adequate protection.

In 'Update Alert 3: Masks for Prevention of Respiratory Virus Infections, Including SARS-CoV-2, in Health Care and Community Settings' by Chou et al, in *Annals of Internal Medicine* (15 Dec 2020), the authors said that wearing a mask *all the time* may have some effect, but concluded

> Therefore, evidence for mask use versus nonuse and comparing mask types in health care settings remained

insufficient. There were no new studies on the effectiveness and safety of mask reuse or extended use.

Note that in the latest update in this series (Update 6, 31 July 2021), the authors say

> In community settings, the strength of evidence remains low for an association between any mask use versus no mask use or surgical mask use versus no mask use and decreased risk for SARS-CoV-1 infection.

'Do Masks Work? A Review of the Evidence' by Jeffrey H. Anderson in *City Journal* (Aug 11, 2021) contains very useful analyses of most of the randomized controlled trials, as well as many others studies, including those that purport to support mask use. For example:

> The CDC further recommends that all schoolchildren and teachers, even those who have had Covid-19 or have been vaccinated, should wear masks. The CDC asserts this even though its own statistics show that Covid-19 is not much of a threat to schoolchildren. Its numbers show that more people under the age of 18 died of influenza during the 2018–19 flu season—a season of "moderate severity" that lasted eight months—than have died of Covid-19 across more than 18 months. What's more, the CDC says that out of every 1,738 Covid-19-related deaths in the U.S. in 2020 and 2021, just one has involved someone under 18 years of age; and out of every 150 deaths of someone under 18 years of age, just one has been Covid-related. Yet the CDC declares that schoolchildren, who learn in part from communication conveyed through facial expressions, should nevertheless hide their faces—and so should their teachers.

In 'Do facemasks protect against COVID-19?' by Isaacs et al, in the *Journal of Paediatrics and Child Health* (v.56 (6), 16 June 2020, pp.976–7), the authors says

> There is no good evidence that facemasks protect the public against infection with respiratory viruses, including COVID-19.

They also say

> the questionable benefits arguably do not justify health-care staff wearing surgical masks when treating low-risk patients and may impede the normal caring relationship between patients, parents and staff. We counsel against such practice.

In 'Community use of face masks and similar barriers to prevent respiratory illness such as COVID-19: a rapid scoping review' by Brainard, Hunter et al, in *Eurosurveillance* (v.25 (49) 10 Dec 2020), the authors claim that the mask RCTs slightly underestimate the effectiveness of masks, although they claim so on very speculative grounds, and their estimate of effectiveness is still only 6-15%:

> Our best estimate is that the effect of wearing a face mask is between the effects seen in RCTs and the effects seen in cohort studies, or around 6 to 15% reduction in disease transmission.

Given the lack of precision involved in such issues, and given that this was a 'rapid review', this basically amounts to an expression of opinion along the lines of 'we didn't find an effect, but we still reckon there's got to be a small one there'. The authors also note that observational studies likely overestimate effects, as mask wearing might be associated with other risk-averse behaviours. GRADE was low or very low quality.

(Also bear in mind that this team has published on Covid-19 with Independent SAGE member and psy-op behavioural scientist Susan Michie.)

In 'Review of infective dose, routes of transmission and outcome of COVID-19 caused by the SARS-COV-2: comparison with other respiratory viruses' by Karimzadeh et al in *Epidemiology and Infection* (v.149, 14 April 2021), the authors made several interesting comments, particularly

the infective dose in humans for SARS-CoV-2 was estimated as 100 particles

which makes mask wearing pointless even if they work to some degree.

Also:

We estimate that the infective dose for SARS-CoV-2 is probably lower than for influenza virus (1000 TCID50) as it is more contagious with a slightly higher R_0. The only human study on a coronavirus we found was on HCoV-229E with the TCID50 comparison was 13…

the true measurement of infectious dose in animals and extrapolation to human is not possible. First, none of the animal studies reported the same clinical presentations and pathology after infection with SARS-CoV-2, and outcomes were highly variable as in humans. Second, different endpoints used for the measurement of infection, meanwhile susceptibility of animals can largely vary dependent on various species, ACE2 expression, age and comorbidities. Third, the route of inoculation can largely affect the response of animals to infection. All the animals infected by aerosol and other routes of exposure presented signs of infection whereas animals exposed by the intragastric route mostly remained asymptomatic (intranasal route being intermediate). In animals, the infective dose is generally lower with aerosol transmission than other routes. The infective dose in human could be lower than currently believed if transmission by aerosol is important. Moreover, aerosol transmission can allow the virus to penetrate into the lower respiratory tract of humans and cause severe symptoms...

Higher viral load is not necessarily correlated with more severe symptoms, with some studies finding higher viral load in mildly symptomatic or asymptomatic stages of disease...

COVID-19 shares important features with influenza in serial interval of disease, clinical presentation, transmission route, viral load, infective dose, viral shedding and correlation with outcome...

Exhaled breath of symptomatic patients with influenza can transmit an estimated 33 particles per minute in aerosol [89]. Twenty minutes of exposure would be required for the exposure to the median infective dose of H1N1 subtype. Similarly, almost 25 particles per minute (630 particles in 25 min) in aerosol were required to cause SARS-CoV-2 infection in hACE2 mice [21]. Exposure for a similar period to SARS-CoV-2 exhaled in normal breathing of infected patients could lead to the inhaling of our estimated hundreds of SARS-CoV-2 particles by aerosol, thus complementing infection by fomites and droplets. However, further studies are warranted to examine infective dose by the aerosol route and its correlation with COVID-19 severity and immune response both in animals through experiments and humans through observation.

In an influential WHO-commissioned review titled 'Physical distancing, face masks, and eye protection to prevent person-to-person transmission of SARS-CoV-2 and COVID-19: a systematic review and meta-analysis' by Chu et al in the *Lancet*, (v.395 (10242), 27 June–3 July 2020, pp. 1973-1987), the authors flip-flop around, claiming at various points that the data supported a large reduction from masks, but they also use the word 'suggest' a lot, and adding caveats like

> Nevertheless, in view of the limitations of these data, we did not rate the certainty of effect as high.

They also used Baysian and frequentist analyses to torture the data.

The American Institute for Economic Research pointed out (in 'Masking: A Careful Review of the Evidence', by Paul E. Alexander, 11 Feb 2021) that this study

> included 39 nonrandomized observational studies (weaker study designs) that were not always adjusted fully for confounders and reported that face masks could be effective. These studies had small sample sizes with small event numbers, and were plagued with potential selection bias and residual confounding bias. The body of evidence was judged to be of low quality and was also open to the risk of recall, and measurement bias. The studies focused principally on mask use in households or contacts of cases that arose from investigations of the SARS and MERS epidemics (but with limited date for Covid-19 too).

The AIER article goes on to say

Following publication in the Lancet of the WHO-sponsored review, researchers led by University of Toronto epidemiology professor Peter Jueni, have now come forward asking *Lancet* to retract the study, citing numerous serious methodological flaws such as (but not limited to):

i) 7 studies being unpublished and non-peer-reviewed observational studies

ii) failure to consider the randomized evidence

iii) 25 included studies are about the SARS-1 virus or the MERS coronavirus, both of which have very different transmission characteristics than SARS-CoV-2: they were transmitted almost exclusively by severely ill hospitalized patients and there was no assessment of community transmission; a serious concern in regard to the issues being discussed in this document

iv) of the 4 studies relating to the SARS-CoV-2, 2 were misinterpreted by the authors of the Lancet meta-study, 1 is inconclusive, and 1 focused on the impact of using N95 (FFP2) respirators which is irrelevant insofar as community transmission, especially in regard to asymptomatic people and also did not address the use of medical grade or cloth masks

v) this review is being used to guide global face mask policy for the general population whereby one included study was judged to be misclassified (relating to masks in a hospital environment), one showed no benefit of face masks, and one is a poorly designed retrospective study about SARS-1 in Beijing based on telephone interviews. None of the studies refer to SARS-CoV-2.

Jueni (aka Jüni), Professor of Medicine and Epidemiology at the University of Toronto, and scientific director of the Ontario COVID-19 Science Advisory Table, and a mask-wearer himself, described the study in an interview with a German newspaper as 'methodologically flawed' and 'essentially useless'.

'An evidence review of face masks against COVID-19' by Howard et al, *Proceedings of the National Academy of Sciences* (v. 118 (4), Jan 2021), was a very influential paper in 2020 when it first appeared as a preprint. It's a poor 'narrative review' of the evidence. It offers some lame excuses to disregard most of the mask RCTs (citing, amongst other papers, a Trish Greenhalgh opinion piece), and instead cherry-picks some weaker studies, particularly a raft of modelling studies, which even SAGE thought was a weak approach:

> Several modelling studies are reported within a recent systematic review (Howard et al, 2020) that also suggest substantial impacts on the value of R in a population, but are based on idealised assumptions around the efficacy and adherence to wearing face coverings.

(From the SAGE-EMG paper 'Application of physical distancing and fabric face coverings in mitigating the B117 variant SARS-CoV-2 virus in public, workplace and community'.)

The paper is also notable for the appearance of a couple of the pro-maskers' favourite failed arguments:

> The available evidence suggests that near-universal adoption of nonmedical masks when out in public, in combination with complementary public health measures, could successfully reduce R_e [the R_e is similar

to the R₀] to below 1, thereby reducing community spread if such measures are sustained.

And, in the abstract:

Public mask wearing is most effective at reducing spread of the virus when compliance is high.

It's only when we get deep into the paper that it's revealed that this dubious claim about compliance comes from the modelling studies:

Models suggest that public mask wearing is most effective at reducing spread of the virus when compliance is high.

And notice that the authors have turned a 'suggest' into something stronger here.

The most laughable element, though, is perhaps this:

Economic analysis suggests that mask wearing mandates could add 1 trillion dollars to the US GDP.

You've got to wonder whether any of these academics, in 2022, look back at their work, compare it to the masked US states which are still masked a year later with results no different to the unmasked states, and feel ashamed of how hopelessly wrong they got it, or are they still making excuses for why masks don't appear to have done anything? ('Compliance wasn't high enough, right?')

In 'Masks for prevention of viral respiratory infections among health care workers and the public: PEER umbrella systematic review' by Dugre et a, in *Canadian Family Physician* (v. 66 (7), 2020, pp.509-17) the authors say

Overall, the use of masks in the community did not reduce the risk of influenza, confirmed viral respiratory infection, influenzalike illness, or any clinical respiratory infection... The use of masks in households with a sick contact was not associated with a significant infection risk reduction in any analysis, no matter if masks were used by the sick individual, the healthy family members, or both.

'Trends in County-Level COVID-19 Incidence in Counties With and Without a Mask Mandate — Kansas, June 1–August 23, 2020', *Morbidity and Mortality Weekly Report* (v.69 (47), Nov 27, 2020, pp.1777-1781), by Van Dyke et al.

City Journal says of this (in the 11 Feb 2021 piece above):

The same problem affects an influential CDC study finding that, during the summer, Kansas counties with mask mandates had slower growth of Covid-19 cases than those without: mask-mandate counties had seen a large spike in cases just before the mandate went into effect and had consistently higher absolute infection rates.

Also, after more time went by, data came in that totally refuted this study. The second half of 2020 saw masked counties with the same figures as non-masked counties

5.3.b. The much-hyped '53% effectiveness' BMJ Talic meta-analysis

In November 2021 the media across the world made much fuss about a paper in the *British Medical Journal* that supposedly showed that masks were 53% effective in reducing Covid. The paper in question was a meta-analysis titled 'Effectiveness of public health measures in reducing the incidence of covid-19, SARS-CoV-2 transmission, and covid-19 mortality: systematic review and meta-analysis' by Talic et al, *BMJ* (v. 375, 17 Nov 2021).

The paper in fact spends very little time on analysing face masks (it looks at many different types of NPI). A mere one paragraph, as well as not-very-informative table, is devoted to its face mask meta-analysis:

Mask wearing and covid-19 incidence—Six studies with a total of 2627 people with covid-19 and 389 228 participants were included in the analysis examining the effect of mask wearing on incidence of covid-19. Overall pooled analysis showed a 53% reduction in covid-19 incidence (0.47, 0.29 to 0.75), although heterogeneity between studies was substantial (I2=84%). Risk of bias across the six studies ranged from moderate to serious or critical.

Six studies were included in the face mask section, including the Bundgaard DANMASK study. Here are their results. (W=weighting. RR=relative risk reduction – the lower the number the more effective the intervention. CI=confidence intervals.)

Bundgaard 2001:

W: 22.2%. RR: 0.82. (CI: 0.54 to 1.24.)

Doung-Ngern 2020:

W: 7.6%. RR: 0.23. (CI: 0.05 to 0.97.)

Krishnamachari 2021:

W: 26.6%. RR: 0.77. (CI: 0.71 to 0.84.)

Lio 2021:

W: 11.1%. RR: 0.30. (CI: 0.10 to 0.88.)

Xu 2020:

W: 23.6%. RR: 0.34. (CI: 0.24 to 0.48.)

Wang 2020:

W: 8.9%. RR: 0.21. (CI: 0.06 to 0.76.)

Notice the extremely wide confidence intervals in three of the studies that showed large effects. Doung-Ngern's CI is 0.05 to 0.97, Lio's is 0.10 to 0.88, Wang's is 0.06 to 0.76. A paper with such noisy data sources should never have been accepted for publication.

One of the studies that greatly affected the result was Xu 2020, which is 'Relationship Between COVID-19 Infection and Risk Perception, Knowledge, Attitude, and Four Nonpharmaceutical Interventions During the Late Period of the COVID-19 Epidemic in China: Online Cross-Sectional Survey of 8158 Adults' by Xu et al, *Journal of Medical Internet Research* (v. 22 (11), Nov 2020).

Yes, you read that right. The *Journal of Medical Internet Research*. It was a web survey. Yes, a web survey:

> An online survey of 8158 Chinese adults between
> February 22 and March 5, 2020, was conducted.

This study was given a weighting of 23.6% in the results, so it counted for almost one-quarter of the effect. It claimed to show a very large 66% reduction from mask wearing.

Bear in mind that only 57 out of the 8158 people – less than 1% – who filled in the survey had even gotten Covid.

> Of 8158 adults included, 57 (0.73%) were infected with
> COVID-19.

The words 'complete' and 'joke' may spring to mind.

Another paper included was 'Reduction of secondary transmission of SARS-CoV-2 in households by face mask use, disinfection and social distancing: a cohort study in Beijing, China', by Wang et al, *BMJ Global Health*. (v. 5 (5), May 2020). This claimed to show a massive 79% decrease in Covid transmission.

We mentioned the problem with this paper in part 4.2 (the DELVE report update also made use of it): it claimed that secondary transmission was reduced by mask-wearing, but the families that reported no secondary cases also engaged in far more other possible relevant behaviours than the families that did report secondary cases.

Pharmacy Professor David Seedhouse and several scientific and academic colleagues pointed out another serious issue with Wang's study – it

> investigated the effectiveness of mask-wearing in families in their homes of laboratory-confirmed Covid-19 cases in Beijing and concluded that face mask use was '79 per cent effective in reducing transmission'. Strangely, the paper contains a passage that seems to undermine the whole study: "As the compliance of UFMU (universal face mask use) would be poor in the home, there was difficulty and also no necessity for everyone to wear masks at home." This seems to imply that the use of face masks by family members in their households included in the study was sporadic and that therefore the study has no scientific merit.

Another paper that showed a massive effect (77%) was 'Case-Control Study of Use of Personal Protective Measures and Risk for SARS-CoV 2 Infection, Thailand' by Doung-Ngern, in *Emerging Infectious Diseases* (v. 26 (11), 2020, pp.2607-2616).

This was a non-randomized phone survey done with people located through the Thai contact tracing teams. This provides a high risk of bias. There is also other relevant behaviour which is difficult to separate out:

> contacts who always wore masks were more likely to practice social distancing.

The authors also give us a version of the old 'masks only work if you wear them all the time' line:

Wearing masks all the time during contact was independently associated with lower risk for SARS-CoV-2 infection compared with not wearing masks; wearing a mask sometimes during contact did not lower infection risk.

This is very peculiar. If masks are effective, then wearing them only sometimes should (in all likelihood) have some effect on transmission, not zero effect. A more likely explanation is that those extremely zealous individuals who wear them all the time are much more likely to stay well away from other people and practice every other measure they can think to avoid their exposure, in which case their mask-wearing may have nothing to do with the fact that fewer of them get Covid. (Plus, no doubt, the survey was producing rubbish.)

Another paper that also showed a very large effect (70%) was 'Effectiveness of personal protective health behaviour against COVID-19' by Lio et al, in *BMC Public Health*. (v. 21:827, 2021), another Chinese study. Like the others that showed a large effect, it was non-randomized, and also involved other potentially protective measures. It relied upon filling in a questionnaire. Over 60% of the planned control group refused to participate:

For the control group, 2981 travellers were initially included, 1813 of whom refused to participate.

This means that the risk of getting a biased sample is very high.

The authors admit that

in this study, the small sample size of patients with definite contact history limited the calculation of the actual effect size of these protective measures.

Overall we can conclude that the Talic meta-analysis pulls the same sort of trick as occurred in the Royal Society report (see part 4.3), where some dodgy Asian studies are thrown into the mix to produce the desired results.

We should also take note of the fact that only three out of the 35 studies that were included in the various meta-analyses in the Talic paper were rated as having a low risk of bias. For the six studies in the mask meta-analysis, not a single one was deemed to have a low risk of bias, while four were deemed to have a moderate risk of bias, and two (the Xu and Doung-Ngern studies) as having a high-to serious risk of bias. Why were such studies included when the authors admit this? This is ludicrous. And their assignment of 'moderate' ratings are laughable. The reasonably decent Bundgaard DANMASK RCT gets the same 'moderate' bias rating as the worthless Wang and Lio studies we looked at above.

One medical health Professor I spoke to said that he was angry that rubbish like this was being published. He said that normally, in his area, to get a meta-analysis published required a massive amount of work and extreme rigour, and it can take years before the evidence has built up enough to get that intervention introduced, whereas terrible mask studies that are not even at the level of an undergraduate project are being published at the drop of a hat, and masks are being pushed onto the public with no quality evidence behind them at all.

As well as the one measly paragraph on the meta-analysis, there were also two paragraphs which briefly mentioned five other weak, cherry-picked studies (which weren't in the meta-analysis). Included was Lyu and Wehby's 2020 *Health Affairs* paper, which we looked at in part 5.2.a – this was a paper that appeared very early on in the pandemic, and its results have long been superseded. Another paper, 'Mask-wearing and control of SARS-CoV-2 transmission in the USA: a cross-sectional study', by Rader et al in *Lancet Digital Health*. (v. 3 (3), March 2021), was based on web surveys.

Later on there is another paragraph containing a short and superficial comparison to other face mask reviews, in which it is admitted that

> transmission of SARS-CoV-2 largely arises in hospital settings in which full personal protective measures are in place, which suggests that when viral load is at its highest, even the best performing face masks might not provide adequate protection. Additionally, most studies that assessed mask wearing were prone to important confounding bias, which might have altered the conclusions drawn from this review (ie, effect estimates might have been underestimated or overestimated or can be related to other measures that were in place at the time the studies were conducted). Thus, the extent of such limitations on the conclusions drawn remain unknown.

This paper was practically begging to be rejected, but the *BMJ* accepted it regardless.

Those five paragraphs and a table are pretty much the extent of the discussion of face masks in this paper, a paper which received worldwide media attention for its mask results.

5.3.c. The effectiveness of face masks: reviews and meta-analyses – pre-Covid era

A 2017 meta-analysis titled 'Effectiveness of Masks and Respirators Against Respiratory Infections in Healthcare

Workers: A Systematic Review and Meta-Analysis' by Offeddu et al in *Clinical Infectious Diseases* (v.65 (11), 1 Dec 2017, pp.1934–42) found that

> evidence of a protective effect of masks or respirators against verified respiratory infection (VRI) was not statistically significant.

Inglesby et al say in their 2006 review 'Disease Mitigation Measures in the Control of Pandemic Influenza', in *Biosecurity and Bioterrorism: Biodefense Strategy, Practice, and Science* (v.4 (4), 2006, p. 372), that

> studies have shown that the ordinary surgical mask does little to prevent inhalation of small droplets bearing influenza virus. The pores in the mask become blocked by moisture from breathing, and the air stream simply diverts around the mask.

A 2010 meta-review in *Epidemiology & Infection* (v.138 (4), pp. 449-456) titled 'Face masks to prevent transmission of influenza virus: a systematic review', by Cowling, Zhou, Ip, Leung and Aiello, reviewed studies of the effectiveness of face masks on the spread of influenza and influenza-like illnesses in both healthcare and community settings. It concluded

> There is little evidence to support the effectiveness of face masks to reduce the risk of infection.

In regards to masks stopping an infected person spreading it, the review found some evidence to support this happening in 'controlled conditions', but said

> there is less evidence on whether this translates to effectiveness in natural settings.

It also noted that the evidence base is weak:

Current research has several limitations including underpowered samples, limited generalizability, narrow intervention targeting and inconsistent testing protocols, different laboratory methods, and case definitions.

A 1920 analysis of cloth mask use during the 1918 influenza pandemic, entitled 'An experimental study of the efficacy of gauze face masks', by Kellogg and MacMillan in the *American Journal of Public Health* (v.10 (1), Jan 1920, pp. 34-42), said

Studies made in the Department of Morbidity Statistics of the California State Board of Health did not show any influence of the mask on the spread of influenza in those cities where it was compulsorily applied... The masks, contrary to expectation, were worn cheerfully and universally, and also, contrary to expectation of what should follow under such circumstances, no effect on the epidemic curve was to be seen.

A 2012 systematic review titled 'The use of masks and respirators to prevent transmission of influenza: a systematic review of the scientific evidence' by bin-Reza et al in *Influenza and Other Respiratory Viruses* (v.6 (4), July 2012, pp.257–267) found that

none of the studies established a conclusive relationship between mask/respirator use and protection against influenza infection.

A 2017 Singaporean meta-analysis titled 'Effectiveness of Masks and Respirators Against Respiratory Infections in Healthcare Workers: A Systematic Review and Meta-Analysis' by Offedu in *Clinical Infectious Diseases* (v.65

(11), 1 Dec 2017) concluded that masks offered some protection, but also noted that

> the existing evidence is sparse and findings are inconsistent within and across studies.

A 2016 meta-analysis called 'Effectiveness of N95 respirators versus surgical masks in protecting health care workers from acute respiratory infection: a systematic review and meta-analysis' by Smith et al in the *Canadian Medical Association Journal* (v.188 (8), 17 May 2016) found that N95s were no better than surgical masks. And we know surgical masks themselves don't work. (Unfortunately the authors didn't include a no-mask control group.) They said

> In the meta-analysis of the clinical studies, we found no significant difference between N95 respirators and surgical masks in associated risk of (a) laboratory-confirmed respiratory infection... (b) influenza-like illness; or (c) reported workplace absenteeism.

A May 2020 meta-analysis titled 'Effectiveness of N95 respirators versus surgical masks against influenza: A systematic review and meta-analysis' by Long et al, in the *Journal of Evidence Based Medicine* (v.13 (2), May 2020, pp.93-101), found that N95s performed no better than surgical masks. They said

> There were no statistically significant differences in preventing laboratory-confirmed influenza, laboratory-confirmed respiratory viral infections, laboratory-confirmed respiratory infection, and influenza-like illness using N95 respirators and surgical masks.

They did find some protection against laboratory-confirmed bacterial colonization.

5.3.d. The effectiveness of face masks: reviews and meta-analyses – government and health institution reports

Note that none of these reports, as is usual with government or health institution reports, are peer-reviewed.

For the DELVE 2020 report, Royal Society 2020 report, and the UK government's January 2022 Evidence Summary for face masks, see part 4. For the June 2020 WHO report on masks see my discussion of it in part 1.

In 2019 WHO released a report called 'Non-pharmaceutical public health measures for mitigating the risk and impact of epidemic and pandemic influenza' (as part of their 'Global Influenza Programme'). Under the heading 'Overall Result of Evidence on Face Masks', the authors said

> Ten RCTs were included in the meta-analysis, and there was no evidence that face masks are effective in reducing transmission of laboratory-confirmed influenza.

Despite this the authors recommended surgical masks anyway:

> Face masks worn by asymptomatic people are conditionally recommended in severe epidemics or pandemics, to reduce transmission in the community. Disposable, surgical masks are recommended to be worn at all times by symptomatic individuals when in contact with other individuals. *Although there is no evidence that this is effective in reducing transmission,* [my

italics] there is mechanistic plausibility for the potential effectiveness of this measure.

In other words: 'All the studies show that they don't work in the real world, but we reckon that they should work, so wear them despite the evidence just because we say so'.

A Public Health England rapid review put out in June 2020 titled 'Face coverings in the community and COVID-19: a rapid review' found only weak or limited evidence for the effectiveness of masks:

> 28 studies were identified, but none of them provided high level evidence and 15 were non-peer-reviewed preprints (search up to 5 June 2020). The evidence was mainly theoretical (based on modelling or laboratory studies) and epidemiological (highly subject to confounders). There is weak evidence from epidemiological and modelling studies that mask wearing in the community may contribute to reducing the spread of COVID-19 and that early intervention may result in a lower peak infection rate.

In the 2020 UK government put out a report entitled 'Working safely during the COVID-19 in construction and other outdoor work: COVID-19 secure guidance for employers, employees and the self-employed'. In v. 2.0, updated on 14 June 2020, it says

> The evidence suggests that wearing a face covering does not protect you, but it may protect others if you are infected but have not developed symptoms… It is important to know that the evidence of the benefit of using a face covering to protect others is weak and the effect is likely to be small, therefore face coverings are not a replacement for the other ways of managing risk.

This guidance was later removed from updates to this report.

A 2014 British government review titled 'The Use of Facemasks and Respirators during an Influenza Pandemic: Scientific Evidence Base Review', by Dixon and Phin, commissioned by the Department of Health and produced by Public Health England, concluded that

Despite a further review of all the available evidence up to 30 November 2012 there is still limited evidence to suggest that use of face masks and/or respirators in health care setting can provide significant protection against infection with influenza when in close contact with infected patients… None of the studies in the review established a conclusive relationship between mask/respirator use (when used exclusively) and protection against influenza infection.

The Norwegian Institute of Public Health released a report into facemasks in June 2020, titled 'COVID-19-EPIDEMIC: Should individuals in the community without respiratory symptoms wear facemasks to reduce the spread of COVID-19? – a rapid review'. It said

Conclusion: In the current epidemiological situation in Norway, wearing facemasks to reduce the spread of COVID-19 is not recommended for individuals in the community without respiratory symptoms who are not in near contact with people who are known to be infected.

The Canadian government wrote in its pandemic preparedness review (titled 'Public health measures:

Canadian Pandemic Influenza Preparedness: Planning Guidance for the Health Sector') in 2018. It said

> Masks worn by ill individuals may protect uninfected individuals from virus transmission, but little evidence exists that mask use by well individuals avoids infection.

The European CDC published a review of evidence in Feb 2021, titled 'Using face masks in the community: first update: Effectiveness in reducing transmission of COVID-19'. It found very little evidence:

> there is only low to moderate certainty of evidence for a small to moderate effect of the use of medical face masks in the community for the prevention of COVID-19.

They went on to invoke the precautionary principle to justify recommending masks despite this.

On 8 April 2020 the US National Academies of Science, Engineering and Medicines put out a rapid review, authored by Besser and Fischhoff, called 'Rapid Expert Consultation on the Effectiveness of Fabric Masks for the COVID-19 Pandemic'. Their conclusion was that while

> evidence from these laboratory filtration studies suggests that such fabric masks may reduce the transmission of larger respiratory droplets,

in regards to aerosols

> There is little evidence regarding the transmission of small aerosolized particulates of the size potentially exhaled by asymptomatic or presymptomatic individuals with COVID-19.

In 'Wearing Masks in Public and COVID-19 – What We Know So Far', a review by Public Health Ontario (14 Sep 2020) said

> Masking to protect the wearer is unlikely to be effective in non-healthcare settings. Existing evidence demonstrates that wearing a mask within households after an illness begins is not effective at preventing secondary respiratory infections.

From 'COVID-19: Guidance for School Reopening' (29 July 2020), by the Hospital for Sick Children in Canada:

> The addition of NMMs [non-medical masks] may increase anxiety, interfere with the therapeutic learning environment, and increase inattention or distraction in children and youth, particularly for those who may already struggle with attention, such as those with attention deficit hyperactivity disorder (ADHD) or other developmental disorders.

In 2016 to 2018 there was a fight between the Ontario Hospital Association and the Ontario Nurses' Association over nurses being forced to get flu vaccines and wear masks. The arbitration decision was that:

> There is scant scientific evidence concerning asymptomatic transmission, and, also, scant scientific evidence of the use of masks in reducing the transmission of the virus to patients.

5.4. The effectiveness of face masks: preprints

I have mostly avoided referring to non-peer reviewed preprints in the body of this resource, but here are a few interesting ones.

In a preprint called 'COVID-19 Mitigation Practices and COVID-19 Rates in Schools: Report on Data from Florida, New York and Massachusetts' by Oster et al the authors conclude

> We do not find any correlations with mask mandates.

Researchers from Heidelberg Institute of Global Heath put up a preprint called 'COVID-19 transmission in educational institutions August to December 2020 in Germany: a study of index cases and close contact cohorts' by Schoeps et al.

Rational Ground said of this study

> During the study period, as infections increased, masking recommendations changed. On November 2, children over 10 were also recommended to wear masks in the classroom. It does not appear that this had any impact on case growth within the classroom—with November seeing the highest number of cases. Likely the curve simply reflects the seasonal arc of the disease.

Perski et al (including Independent SAGE member Susan Michie) published a preprint of their paper 'Face masks to prevent community transmission of viral respiratory infections: A rapid evidence review using Bayesian analysis' on the 'open peer review' site Qeios. Their Bayesian analysis showed

> a moderate likelihood of a small effect of wearing surgical face masks in community settings in reducing self-reported influenza-like illness... However, the risk of reporting bias was high and evidence of reduction of clinically- or laboratory-confirmed infection was equivocal... Observational studies yielded evidence of a negative association between face mask wearing and ILI but with high risk of confounding and reporting bias. Conclusions: Available evidence from RCTs is equivocal as to whether or not wearing face masks in community settings results in a reduction in clinically- or laboratory-confirmed viral respiratory infections.

5.5. The effectiveness of face masks: commentaries, editorials and academic letters

Two experts on respiratory protection from the University of Chicago, Prof Lisa M Brosseau and Dr Margaret Sietsema published a commentary on cloth masks at the University of Minnesota's Centre for Infectious Disease Research and Policy titled 'Masks-for-all for COVID-19 not based on sound data'. In it they said

> We do not recommend requiring the general public who do not have symptoms of COVID-19-like illness to routinely wear cloth or surgical masks because there is no scientific evidence they are effective in reducing the risk of SARS-CoV-2 transmission... Sweeping mask recommendations—as many have proposed—will not reduce SARS-CoV-2 transmission... Our review of relevant studies indicates that cloth masks will be ineffective at preventing SARS-CoV-2 transmission.

CIDRAP came under intense pressure from mask activists to remove this study. The authors added a note about some studies that had recently been referenced by the CDC in its guidelines, noting that they had reviewed these studies and

> found that many employ very crude, non-standardized methods'

They then reiterated that

> data from laboratory studies... indicate cloth masks or face coverings offer very low filter collection efficiency for the smaller inhalable particles we believe are largely responsible for transmission, particularly from pre- or asymptomatic individuals who are not coughing or

sneezing… The filter performance of a cloth material does not directly translate or represent its performance on an individual, because it neglects the understanding of fit.

In 'Open Schools, Covid-19, and Child and Teacher Morbidity in Sweden', in *New England Journal of Medicine* (v. 384, 18 Feb 2021, pp.669-71), the authors Ludvigsson et al say

The number of deaths from any cause among the 1,951,905 children in Sweden who were 1 to 16 years of age was 65 during the pre–Covid-19 period of November 2019 through February 2020, and 69 during 4 months of exposure to Covid-19 (March through June 2020).

How many children got Covid and had to go to ICU in this period?

From March through June 2020, a total of 15 children with Covid-19 (including those with MIS-C) were admitted to an ICU (0.77 per 100,000 children in this age group), 4 of whom were 1 to 6 years of age (0.54 per 100,000) and 11 of whom were 7 to 16 years of age (0.90 per 100,000). Four of the children had an underlying chronic coexisting condition (cancer in 2, chronic kidney disease in 1, and hematologic disease in 1).

How many of these children died?

No child with Covid-19 died.

But what about the teachers?

Data from the Public Health Agency of Sweden… showed that fewer than 10 preschool teachers and 20 schoolteachers in Sweden received intensive care for Covid-19 up until June 30, 2020 (20 per 103,596 schoolteachers, which is equal to 19 per 100,000). As compared with other occupations (excluding health care workers), this corresponded to sex- and age-adjusted relative risks of 1.10 (95% confidence interval [CI], 0.49 to 2.49) among preschool teachers and 0.43 (95% CI, 0.28 to 0.68) among schoolteachers.

So preschool teachers were possibly a teensy bit more at risk of going into ICU than other workers, whereas all the other teachers were far less at risk.

A guest editorial entitled 'Universal Masking in Hospitals in the Covid-19 Era' by Klompas et al in the *New England Journal of Medicine* (v.382, May 21, 2020) said

> We know that wearing a mask outside health care facilities offers little, if any, protection from infection.

The authors also admit that an important role of masks is as symbols to keep the Covid hysteria going, although of course they phrase it as decreasing fear and anxiety (which is obviously nonsense, as fear ramps up in the population when masks are mandated):

> It is also clear that masks serve symbolic roles. Masks are not only tools, they are also talismans that may help increase health care workers' perceived sense of safety, well-being, and trust in their hospitals. Although such reactions may not be strictly logical, we are all subject to fear and anxiety, especially during times of crisis. One might argue that fear and anxiety are better countered with data and education than with a marginally beneficial mask, particularly in light of the worldwide mask shortage, but it is difficult to get clinicians to hear this message in the heat of the current crisis. Expanded masking protocols' greatest contribution may be to reduce the transmission of anxiety, over and above

whatever role they may play in reducing transmission of Covid-19. The potential value of universal masking in giving health care workers the confidence to absorb and implement the more foundational infection-prevention practices described above may be its greatest contribution.

In 'Facial Masking for Covid-19' by Rasmussen in the *New England Journal of Medicine* (November 19, 2020; 383:2092-2094), the authors say

There is insufficient evidence to support the claim that masks reduce the infectious dose of SARS-CoV-2 and the severity of Covid-19, much less that their use can induce protective immunity… the infectious dose of SARS-CoV-2 is probably similar to that of SARS-CoV — approximately 300 virions… Normal talking can generate up to 3000 1-micron particles per minute in exhaled breath, and each particle could contain more than 250 virions, which means that a single minute of speaking potentially generates more than 750,000 virions. Cloth face coverings have highly variable efficacy depending on both filtering capacity and fit. Wearing a cloth face covering while being near an infected person for several minutes may not prevent the receipt of an infectious dose, which, as noted above, does not correlate with milder disease.

In 'Face masks in the general healthy population. Scientific and ethical issues' by Royo-Bordonada et al in *Gaceta Sanitaria* (v.35 (6), Nov-Dec 2021, pp.580–584) the authors say

At present, there is no evidence on the effectiveness of universal masking of healthy people in the community to prevent infection with respiratory viruses, including SARS-CoV-2.

A very cursory BMJ examination of mask evidence by Elisabeth Mahase, a *BMJ* editor, called 'Covid-19: What is the evidence for cloth masks?' *BMJ* (v.360, 7 April 2020), did contain this:

> Simon Clarke, associate professor in cellular microbiology at the University of Reading, said, "There is only very limited evidence of the benefits of wearing face masks by the general public, no evidence that wearing them in crowded places helps at all, and no evidence at all yet related to covid-19".

Cochrane collates medical evidence and is considered to have one of the highest standards of evidence in the world. It has a Covid-19 Resources page titled 'Do physical measures such as hand-washing or wearing masks stop or slow down the spread of respiratory viruses?'. On surgical masks it says

> Compared with wearing no mask, wearing a mask may make little to no difference in how many people caught a flu-like illness; and probably makes no difference in how many people have flu confirmed by a laboratory test.

On respirators it says

> wearing N95/P2 respirators probably makes little to no difference in how many people have confirmed flu; and may make little to no difference in how many people catch a flu-like illness or respiratory illness.

Trisha Greenhalgh wrote a response to her critics in a piece called 'Face coverings for the public: Laying straw men to rest' in *Evaluation in Clinical Practice* (v. 26 (4),

Aug 2020, pp.1070-7). It's the usual mix of weak evidence and evasiveness. RCTs are dismissed because she claims that she's only interested in source control, non-controlled anecdotal evidence is offered (such as the disease spreading at a choir practice where they didn't wear masks), the Czech Republic is said to prove masks work (as we saw, cases there skyrocketed soon after), modelling studies are praised (but there is zero discussion of them), and there's her usual invocation of the precautionary principle, which isn't discussed in any depth at all. In fact, the paper is so shallow that there's barely anything to analyse, but I did want to highlight this unbelievable gem:

> neither Martin et al nor the Jefferson systematic review which they cite offer any evidence whatsoever that the use of home-made face coverings by the lay public for source control has been shown to cause such harms. Indeed, there is no common sense reason why a covering made out of one's own old t-shirt would cause illness when the t-shirt itself was well-tolerated (and if it wasn't, why make a mask out of it?).

That's right: if you were able to wear a T-shirt as a T-shirt without any problems, then why would it cause harm when used in a completely different way? The fact that it is being used to *cover your airways* doesn't even come into it for Greenhalgh. Why, someone could use your old T-shirt to garrotte you, but it's just common sense to think that this can't cause you any harm, because that T-shirt was previously worn by you for years and was well-tolerated by your body then, so your body shouldn't have any problem with it now.

She also claims that

> if 60% of people wear a mask that is 60% effective, this
> is likely to be sufficient to substantially reduce the
> transmission of Sars-CoV-2.

Cloth masks don't, of course, reduce viral transmission by 60%, but you might still be interested to know what her basis for this claim is. It is, in fact, modelling studies. What's more, modelling studies that merely 'suggest' this, which Greenhalgh changes into a 'likely':

> Mathematical modelling suggests that a face covering
> that is 60% effective at blocking viral transmission and
> is worn by 60% of the population will reduce R0 to
> below 1.0.

In 'Face masks and COVID-19: don't let perfect be the enemy of good' in *Eurosurveillance* (v.25 (49), 10 Dec 2020) the authors Cowling and Leung say

> Nevertheless, there is compelling evidence that masks
> can contribute to the control of COVID-19

despite the fact that they had just admitted in various places in the paper that the evidence for them is poor. They claim that even if masks only have limited effectiveness their use would be justified because they are so cheap. The authors don't of course, provide any such justification, and of course they totally ignore the harms of masks.

The CDC, on its page about smoke inhalation, says

> Cloth masks that are used to slow the spread of COVID-
> 19 by blocking respiratory droplets offer little protection
> against wildfire smoke. They might not catch small,
> harmful particles in smoke that can harm your health.

(Smoke particles are about 25 times larger than SARS-CoV-2 virions.)

Before Covid, the California Department of Public Health said of respirators that

Children should not wear these masks – they do not fit properly and can impede breathing. If the air quality is poor enough that a child requires a mask, the child should remain indoors, in a safe place, and evacuation should be considered.

A group of Belgian doctors sent an Open Letter on 5 Sep 2020 to the Belgian authorities and media called 'Open letter from medical doctors and health professionals to all Belgian authorities and all Belgian media'. The letter says

The current crisis management has become totally disproportionate and causes more damage than it does any good. We call for an end to all measures and ask for an immediate restoration of our normal democratic governance and legal structures and of all our civil liberties... Oral masks belong in contexts where contacts with proven at-risk groups or people with upper respiratory complaints take place, and in a medical context/hospital-retirement home setting... Oral masks in healthy individuals are ineffective against the spread of viral infections.

The letter has currently been signed by 760 medical doctors, 2887 medically trained health professionals, and 22199 citizens,

5.6: The effectiveness of respirators in healthcare settings

Part 5.6 contents

5.6.a: Respirators in healthcare settings: reviews and meta-analyses

5.6.b: Respirators in healthcare settings: studies

5.6.a: Respirators in healthcare settings: reviews and meta-analyses

In 2020 The U.S. Department of Health and Human Services' (HHS) Agency for Healthcare Research and Quality funded a systemic review of all relevant randomized controlled trials on the effectiveness of mask-wearing in stopping respiratory infections. The resulting study was titled 'Masks for Prevention of Respiratory Virus Infections, Including SARS-CoV-2, in Health Care and Community Settings: A Living Rapid Review' by Chou et al, and was published in in *Annals of Internal Medicine* (6 Oct 2020). The authors said

> In health care settings, N95 and surgical masks were probably associated with similar risks for influenza-like illness and laboratory-confirmed viral infection... Review of RCTs indicates that N95 respirators and surgical masks are probably associated with similar risk for influenza-like illness and laboratory-confirmed viral infections in high- and low-risk settings... The only trial comparing N95 respirators versus surgical masks in a

low-risk (primary care) setting found no difference in risk for clinical respiratory illness.

They also found no difference in community settings:

Randomized trials in community settings found possibly no difference between N95 versus surgical masks and probably no difference between surgical versus no mask in risk for influenza or influenza-like illness.

A 2020 meta-analysis titled 'Effectiveness of N95 respirators versus surgical masks against influenza: A systematic review and meta-analysis' by Long et al in the *Journal of Evidence Based Medicine* (v.13, 2020, pp.93–101) said

There were no statistically significant differences in preventing laboratory-confirmed influenza, laboratory-confirmed respiratory viral infections, laboratory-confirmed respiratory infection, and influenza-like illness using N95 respirators and surgical masks... The use of N95 respirators compared with surgical masks is not associated with a lower risk of laboratory-confirmed influenza.

A 2016 meta-analysis titled 'Effectiveness of N95 respirators versus surgical masks in protecting health care workers from acute respiratory infection: a systematic review and meta-analysis' by Smith et al in the *Canadian Medical Association Journal* (v.188 (8), May 17, 2016 pp.567-574) said that N95s were no better than surgical masks:

we found no significant difference between N95 respirators and surgical masks in associated risk of (a) laboratory-confirmed respiratory infection, (b) influenza-like illness, or (c) reported work-place absenteeism.

5.6.b: Respirators in healthcare settings: studies

A 2019 randomized trial titled 'N95 Respirators vs Medical Masks for Preventing Influenza Among Health Care Personnel: A Randomized Clinical Trial' by Radonovich et al, in *Journal of the American Medical Association* (v.322 (9), 2019, pp.824-833), concluded that

> N95 respirators vs medical masks as worn by participants in this trial resulted in no significant difference in the incidence of laboratory-confirmed influenza.

A 2009 study titled 'Performance of an N95 Filtering Facepiece Particulate Respirator and a Surgical Mask During Human Breathing: Two Pathways for Particle Penetration' by Grinshpun et al in the *Journal of Occupational and Environmental Hygiene* (v.6 (10), 2009, pp.593-603) concluded that

> The number of particles penetrating through the faceseal leakage of the tested respirator/mask far exceeded the number of those penetrating through the filter medium. For the N95 respirator, the excess was (on average) by an order of magnitude and significantly increased with an increase in particle size... Facial/body movement had a pronounced effect on the relative contribution of the two penetration pathways... the priority in respirator/mask development should be shifted from improving the efficiency of the filter medium to establishing a better fit that would eliminate or minimize faceseal leakage.

In 'Surgical Mask vs N95 Respirator for Preventing Influenza Among Health Care Workers: A Randomized Trial' by Loeb et al in *Journal of the American Medical Association* (JAMA) (v.302 (17), 2009, pp.1865–1871), the authors found that

> Influenza infection occurred in 50 nurses (23.6%) in the surgical mask group and in 48 (22.9%) in the N95 respirator group.

So N95s were no better than surgical masks in this study.

'A Quantitative Assessment of the Efficacy of Surgical and N95 Masks to Filter Influenza Virus in Patients with Acute Influenza Infection' by Johnson et al in *Clinical Infectious Diseases* (v.49 (2), 15 July 2009, pp.275–7), was a small study that found that N95s performed no better than surgical masks in a healthcare setting:

> The findings also support the guidelines that N95 respirators (designed to prevent disease acquisition) may not be necessary, because they appear to offer no additional benefit over surgical masks.

5.7: The effectiveness of surgical face masks in surgical settings

Part 5.7 contents

5.7.a: Surgical face masks in surgical settings: reviews and meta-analyses

5.7.b: Surgical face masks in surgical settings: studies

5.7.a: Surgical face masks in surgical settings: reviews and meta-analyses

A Cochrane review (these are very high quality) in 2014 entitled 'Disposable surgical face masks for preventing surgical wound infection in clean surgery' by Vincent and Edwards (*Cochrane Database of Systematic Reviews* v.17 (2), Feb 2014) said

> Three trials were included, involving a total of 2113 participants. There was no statistically significant difference in infection rates between the masked and unmasked group in any of the trials.

(A later update reached the same conclusion.)

A 2015 Oxford meta-analysis called 'Unmasking the surgeons: the evidence base behind the use of facemasks in surgery' by Zhou et al and published in the *Journal of the Royal Society of Medicine* (v.108 (6), June 2015, pp.223–228) concluded that overall there is a lack of substantial evidence to support claims that facemasks protect either patient or surgeon from infectious contamination.

A 2015 review titled 'Facemasks for the prevention of infection in healthcare and community settings' by Macintyre and Chughtai in the *British Medical Journal* (v.350, 2015) which showed that surgical masks were no better than the no-mask control group when it came to preventing clinical respiratory illness or influenza-like illness.)

A 2003 review by Lipp in *Nursing Times* (v.99 (39), Sep 2003, p.2230) concluded that

The rationale for wearing surgical face masks has shifted from protection of the patient to protection of the health professional. Despite this there remains a need to base the decision to wear a mask on the best available evidence (Sackett et al, 1996). Unfortunately, there is a lack of robust evidence for protecting nurse and patient. Currently there is little evidence that wearing a surgical mask provides sufficient protection from all the hazards encountered in an acute health care setting.

In 'Do Anaesthetists Need to Wear Surgical Masks in the Operating Theatre? A Literature Review with Evidence-Based Recommendations' by Skinner et al in *Anaesthesia and Intensive Care* (v. 29 (4), 1 Aug 2001, pp.331-338), the authors say

The evidence for discontinuing the use of surgical face masks would appear to be stronger than the evidence available to support their continued use. In this climate of economic justification it would appear prudent to say

Hector Drummond

that the use of surgical face masks by non-scrub operating theatre staff cannot be scientifically justified.

It is essential that anaesthetists use appropriate standard precautions to reduce the potential for transmission of infectious agents to patients. Equally important is the protection of the anaesthetist in this environment.

There is little evidence to suggest that the wearing of surgical face masks by staff in the operating theatre decreases postoperative wound infections. Published evidence indicates that postoperative wound infection rates are not significantly different in unmasked versus masked theatre staff. However, there is evidence indicating a significant reduction in postoperative wound infection rates when theatre staff are unmasked. Currently there is no evidence that removing masks presents any additional hazard to the patient.

In 2013 the Canadian Agency for Drugs and Technologies in Health released a review of the use of surgical masks in the operating theatres, called 'Use of Surgical Masks in the Operating Room: A Review'. It said

Key Messages: No evidence was found to support the use of surgical face masks to reduce the frequency of surgical site infections. No evidence was found on the effectiveness of wearing surgical face masks to protect staff from infectious material in the operating room.

MedPageToday, in their own 2009 review of the evidence on surgical masks in operating theatres titled 'Unmasking the Surgical Mask: Does It Really Work?', (Oct 5), said this:

Lack of evidence has also plagued surgical masks in their traditional setting, and where their use is still nearly universal: the operating room. But not for lack of study. In fact, three large, randomized controlled trials were conducted in the 1980s to determine once and for all if surgical masks actually did prevent surgical wound infection. Here, where bacteria were the major concern in wound infection, the enemy targets were larger and might not require the fine filtration necessary to keep a respiratory virus away, researchers theorized. But the trials "showed absolutely no efficacy" for that original purpose, MacIntyre [a professor at the University of NSW who did a more recent study on surgical masks] noted. "Really, the surgeon might as well wear nothing on their face," she said.

A Danish review in 2014 titled 'Dubious effect of surgical masks during surgery' by Carøe in *Ugeskr Laeger* (v.176 (27), June 30 2014) said this:

A search performed in PubMed found four studies based on 6.006 patients. The studies described the use of surgical masks in surgery with post-operative infections as endpoint, and the studies had to include a control group. None of the four studies found a difference in the number of post-operative infections whether you used a surgical mask or not.

In 'Surgical mask filter and fit performance' by Oberg and Brosseau in the *American Journal of Infection Control* (v.36 (4), May 1 2008, pp.276-282) the authors aimed 'to evaluate the filter performance and facial fit of a sample of surgical masks'. They found that

All subjects failed the unassisted qualitative fit test on the first exercise (normal breathing). Eighteen subjects failed the assisted qualitative fit tests; 60% failed on the first exercise.

Their conclusion was that

None of these surgical masks exhibited adequate filter performance and facial fit characteristics to be considered respiratory protection devices.

In 'The evolution of the surgical mask: filtering efficiency versus effectiveness' by Belkin , in *Infection Control and Hospital Epidemiology* (v.18 (1), Jan 1997, pp.49-57), the author concludes that

both in-vitro and in-vivo studies indicate that a mask may not be universally necessary in today's surgical environment.

In 'Surgeon's garb and infection control: what's the evidence?' in *Journal of the American Academy of Dermatology* (v. 64 (5), May 2011), author Eisen writes

Conclusions: In 1959 Shooter et al wrote "Despite the experience of the last sixty years, there are still doubts as to the value of surgical masks in preventing infection." Little appears to have changed since then regarding masks or other forms of specialized garb.

Although much has been written on this topic, definitive evidence to support the use of most surgical garb appears to be lacking and its efficacy in the outpatient dermatology operatory, speculative.

5.7.b: Surgical face masks in surgical settings: studies

A 1975 article titled 'The operating room environment as affected by people and the surgical face mask' in *Clinical Orthopaedics and Related Research* by Ritter et al (v.111, Sep 1975, pp.147-50) concluded that

> The wearing of a surgical face mask had no effect upon the overall operating room environmental contamination and probably work only to redirect the projectile effect of talking and breathing. People are the major source of environmental contamination in the operating room.

A 1980 study titled 'The efficacy of standard surgical face masks: an investigation using "tracer particles"' in *Clinical Orthopaedics and Related Research* by Ha'eri and Wiley (v.148, May 1980, pp.160-2) said

> To examine the efficacy of currently used synthetic-fiber disposable face masks in protecting wounds from contamination, human albumin microspheres were employed as "tracer particles," and applied to the interior of the fact mask during 20 operations. At the termination of each operation, wound irrigates were examined under the microscope. Particle contamination of the wound was demonstrated in all experiments.

A 1981 study titled 'Is a mask necessary in the operating theatre?' by Neil Orr, published in the *Annals of the Royal College of Surgeons of England* (v.63), said

> No masks were worn in one operating theatre for 6 months. There was no increase in the incidence of wound infection... The conclusion is that the wearing of a mask has very little relevance to the wellbeing of

patients undergoing routine general surgery and it is a standard practice that could be abandoned.

The study also noted that

A review of the very considerable literature on prevention of infection in theatre shows a heavy bias in favour of history and hypothesis.

'Masks: a ward investigation and review of the literature' by Ransjö in the *Journal of Hospital Infection* (v.7 (3), May 1986, pp. 289-94), found that

The use of masks was related to the acquisition from patients of beta-haemolytic streptococci and Staphylococcus aureus in the nose/throat of staff in a burns unit. The study took place over 10 weeks; wearing multi-layer operating room masks for every visit to patient rooms had no effect on nose or throat carriage rates, although airborne dispersal from patients was high.

A 1989 study called 'Wearing of caps and masks not necessary during cardiac catheterization' in *Catheterization and Cardiovascular Diagnosis* by Laslett and Sabin (v.17 (3), July 1989) found no need for masks or caps.

Documentation of the value of caps and masks for this purpose is lacking. We, therefore, prospectively evaluated the experience of 504 patients undergoing percutaneous left heart catheterization, seeking evidence of a relationship between whether caps and/or masks were worn by the operators and the incidence of infection. No infections were found in any patient, regardless of whether a cap or mask was used. Thus, we found no evidence that caps or masks need to be worn during percutaneous cardiac catheterization.

A 1991 study called 'Surgical face masks in modern operating rooms—a costly and unnecessary ritual?' by Mitchell and Hunt in the *Journal of Hospital Infection* (v.18 (3), July 1, 1991) concluded that

> The wearing of face masks by non-scrubbed staff working in an operating room with forced ventilation seems to be unnecessary.

A 1991 study titled 'Postoperative wound infections and surgical face masks: A controlled study' in *World Journal of Surgery* by Tunevall (v.15, 1991, pp.383–387) noted that

> It has never been shown that wearing surgical face masks decreases postoperative wound infections. On the contrary, a 50% decrease has been reported after omitting face masks.

So the authors set out to test the effectiveness of surgical masks:

> During 115 weeks, a total of 3,088 patients were included in the study. Weeks were denoted as "masked" or "unmasked" according to a random list. After 1,537 operations performed with face masks, 73 (4.7%) wound infections were recorded and, after 1,551 operations performed without face masks, 55 (3.5%) infections occurred. This difference was not statistically significant (p> 0.05) and the bacterial species cultured from the wound infections did not differ in any way, which would have supported the fact that the numerical difference was a statistically "missed" difference.

> These results indicate that the use of face masks might be reconsidered. Masks may be used to protect the operating team from drops of infected blood and from

airborne infections, but have not been proven to protect
the patient operated by a healthy operating team.

In 'Aerosol penetration through surgical masks' in
American Journal of Infection Control (v.20 (4), Aug 1992,
pp.177-84), the authors Chen and Willeke say

Although surgical mask media may be adequate to
remove bacteria exhaled or expelled by health care
workers, they may not be sufficient to remove the
submicrometer-size aerosols containing pathogens to
which these health care workers are potentially exposed.

'Aerosol penetration and leakage characteristics of masks
used in the health care industry' by Weber et al in the
American Journal of Infection Control (v.21 (4), Aug 1993,
pp. 167-73), said

We conclude that the protection provided by surgical
masks may be insufficient in environments containing
potentially hazardous submicrometer-sized aerosols.

In 'Filtration Performance of FDA-Cleared Surgical
Masks' by Rengasamy et al in the *Journal of the
International Society for Respiratory Protection* (v.26 (3),
2009, pp.54-70), a study looking the filtration performance
of surgical masks, the authors (from the US National
Institute for Occupational Safety and Health, say

The wide variation in penetration levels for room air
particles, which included particles in the same size range
of viruses confirms that surgical masks should not be
used for respiratory protection.

A 2009 study entitled 'Use of surgical face masks to reduce the incidence of the common cold among health care workers in Japan: a randomized controlled trial' by Jacobs et al in the *American Journal of Infection Control* (v.37 (5), June 2009, pp.417-419) found that

> Face mask use in health care workers has not been demonstrated to provide benefit in terms of cold symptoms or getting colds.

'Use of face masks by non-scrubbed operating room staff: a randomized controlled trial' by Webster et al, in *ANZ Journal of Surgery* (v.80 (3), March 2010, pp.169-73), attempted to

> assess the impact on surgical site infections (SSIs) when non-scrubbed operating room staff did not wear surgical face masks.

Their conclusion was that

> Surgical site infection rates did not increase when non-scrubbed operating room personnel did not wear a face mask.

A 2011 study titled 'A cluster randomized clinical trial comparing fit-tested and non-fit-tested N95 respirators to medical masks to prevent respiratory virus infection in health careworkers', by MacIntyre et al in *Influenza and Other Respiratory Viruses* (v.5 (3), 2011, pp.170–9) found medical masks made no significant difference to rates of clinical respiratory illness, influenza-like illness, laboratory-confirmed respiratory virus infection, and influenza.

A 2014 study titled 'Comparison of Filtration Efficiency and Pressure Drop in Anti-Yellow Sand Masks, Quarantine

Masks, Medical Masks, General Masks, and Handkerchiefs'
by Jung et al in *Aerosol and Air Quality Research* (v. 14 (3),
April 2014) which tested 44 different mask brands,
concluded that

> Medical masks, general masks, and handkerchiefs
> were found to provide little protection against
> respiratory aerosols.

A 2014 study called 'Surgical attire and the operating
room: role in infection prevention' by Salassa in the *Journal
of Bone and Joint Surgery* (v.96 (17), Sep 3 2014, pp.1485-
92) concluded that

> Although there is some evidence that scrubs, masks, and
> head coverings reduce bacterial counts in the operating
> room, there is no evidence that these measures reduce
> the prevalence of surgical site infection.

(The authors also conclude that the use of gloves and
impervious surgical gowns does have some effect, but not
masks.)

5.8: Face mask harms

Part 5.8 contents

5.8.a: Face masks and oxygen depletion

5.8.a.i: Face masks and oxygen depletion: studies

5.8.a.ii: Face masks and oxygen depletion: other relevant
  literature

5.8.b: Studies and reviews on skin problems

5.8.c: Studies and reviews on other face masks harms

See also the sections 'Why the fuss about kids wearing
masks?, 'Is there any harder evidence of masks harming
children?' and 'Do masks harm the development of
children?' in part 1. For face masks and headaches, see the
section 'Is there an association between masks and
headaches?' in part 2.

5.8.a: Face masks and oxygen depletion

The first section of part 5.8 looks at trials and studies, the
second section looks at other relevant literature.

I should note that where the following research involves
respirators there is no guarantee that the respirators are worn
with a tight fit in the testing period, and most likely there
will not be a tight fit, especially when anything strenuous is
required. More dramatic results would probably be found if
respirators were tightly attached to the face so that air cannot
escape in and out the sides.

(Research on non-respirator masks is likely to find less effect as these have such wide side gaps.)

5.8.a.i: Face masks and oxygen depletion: studies

Researchers at the University Hospital of Leipzig tested the physical performance of healthy adults wearing FFP2/N95 masks and exercising and found the masks considerably reduce performance and resilience. 'Effects of surgical and FFP2/N95 face masks on cardiopulmonary exercise capacity' by Fikenzer et al in *Clinical Research in Cardiology* (v.109, 2020, pp. 1522–1530).

The authors say:

> Results: The pulmonary function parameters were significantly lower with mask... the ventilation was significantly reduced with both face masks. Peak blood lactate response was reduced with mask… Participants reported consistent and marked discomfort wearing the masks… Conclusion: Ventilation, cardiopulmonary exercise capacity and comfort are reduced by surgical masks and highly impaired by FFP2/N95 face masks in healthy individuals. These data are important for recommendations on wearing face masks at work or during physical exercise.

In a 2018 French study in *Revue des Maladies Respiratoires* (v.35 (3), March 2018, pp.264-268) called 'Effet du port d'un masque de soins lors d'un test de marche de six minutes chez des sujets sains' ('Effect of a surgical mask on six minute walking distance') by Person et al, 44 subjects were tested in a series of walking tests. The authors said

> Dyspnea [shortness of breath] variation was significantly higher with surgical mask and the difference was

clinically relevant…Conclusion: Wearing a surgical
mask modifies significantly and clinically dyspnea
without influencing walked distance.

A 2008 study entitled 'Preliminary report on surgical mask
induced deoxygenation during major surgery' by Beder et al
in (v.19 (2), April 2008, pp.121-6), studied surgeons who
wore masks during surgery. The authors said

Our study revealed a decrease in the oxygen saturation
of arterial pulsations (SpO_2) and a slight increase in
pulse rates compared to preoperative values in all
surgeon groups. The decrease was more prominent in the
surgeons aged over 35. Conclusions. Considering our
findings, pulse rates of the surgeon's increase and SpO_2
decrease after the first hour. This early change in SpO_2
may be either due to the facial mask or the operational
stress. Since a very small decrease in saturation at this
level, reflects a large decrease in PaO_2, our findings may
have a clinical value for the health workers and the
surgeons.

The authors, however, stress that this was a preliminary
study.

In a paper in *Medical Hypotheses* (v.144, Nov 2020)
'"Exercise with facemask; Are we handling a devil's
sword?" – A physiological hypothesis', the authors
Chandrasekaran and Fernandes outline scientific reasons to
suspect that

Exercising with facemasks may reduce available oxygen
and increase air trapping preventing substantial carbon
dioxide exchange. The hypercapnic hypoxia may
potentially increase acidic environment, cardiac
overload, anaerobic metabolism and renal overload,

which may substantially aggravate the underlying pathology of established chronic diseases.

In 'Respiratory consequences of N95-type Mask usage in pregnant healthcare workers-a controlled clinical study' by Tong et al in *Antimicrobial Resistance and Infection Control* (v.4 (48), Nov 16 2015), the authors studied the effects of pregnant nurses wearing N95 masks at work. They said

> Exercising at 3 MET while breathing through N95-mask materials reduced mean tidal volume (TV) by 23.0 %... and lowered minute ventilation (VE) by 25.8 %... Volumes of oxygen consumption (VO2) and carbon dioxide expired (VCO2) were also significantly reduced... Although no changes in the inspired oxygen and carbon dioxide concentrations were demonstrated, breathing through N95-mask materials during low intensity work (3 MET) reduced expired oxygen concentration by 3.2 %... and increased expired carbon dioxide by 8.9%... suggesting an increase in metabolism. Conclusions: Breathing through N95 mask materials have been shown to impede gaseous exchange and impose an additional workload on the metabolic system of pregnant healthcare workers, and this needs to be taken into consideration in guidelines for respirator use.

A 2004 article entitled 'The physiological impact of wearing an N95 mask during hemodialysis as a precaution against SARS in patients with end-stage renal disease' by Kao et al in the *Journal of the Formosan Medical Association* (v.103 (8), Aug 2004, 624-8) found that

> Seventy percent of the patients showed a reduction in partial pressure of oxygen (PaO2), and 19% developed various degrees of hypoxemia [an abnormally low level

of oxygen in the blood]. Wearing an N95 mask significantly reduced the PaO2 level... increased the respiratory rate... and increased the occurrence of chest discomfort... and respiratory distress... Conclusion: Wearing an N95 mask for 4 hours during HD [hemodialysis] significantly reduced PaO2 and increased respiratory adverse effects in ESRD [end-stage renal disease] patients.

In 'Carbon dioxide increases with face masks but remains below short-term NIOSH limits' by Rhee et al in *BMC Infectious Diseases* (v.21, 354, 2021), the authors say

Use of face masks (KN95 and valved-respirator) resulted in significant increases in CO2 concentrations, which exceeded the 8-h NIOSH exposure threshold limit value-weighted average

although the authors still recommended them as they were below the 15-minute limits set by National Institute for Occupational Safety and Health (NIOSH).

In 'Physiological impact of the N95 filtering facepiece respirator on healthcare workers' by Roberge in *Respiratory Care* (v.55 (5), May 2010 pp.569-77), reported that

the FFR dead-space carbon dioxide and oxygen levels were significantly above and below, respectively, the ambient workplace standards, and elevated P(CO2) is a possibility.

In 'Effects of wearing N95 and surgical facemasks on heart rate, thermal stress and subjective sensations' by Li, Tokura et al, *International Archives of Occupational and*

Environmental Health v. 78, pp. 501–509 (2005), the
authors said

> High breathing resistance made it difficult for the subject
> to breathe and take in sufficient oxygen. Shortage of
> oxygen stimulates the sympathetic nervous system and
> increases heart rate (Ganong 1997). It was probable that
> the subjects felt unfit, fatigued and overall discomfort
> due to this reason. White et al. (1991) found that the
> increases in heart rate, skin temperature and subjective
> ratings may pose substantial additional stress to the
> wearer and might reduce work tolerance. This could be
> the reason why Farquharson reported that working 12-h
> shifts while wearing an N95 mask had indeed been a
> challenge to their ED staff.

In 'Effects of long-duration wearing of N95 respirator and
surgical facemask: a pilot study' by Zhu et al, in the *Journal
of Lung, Pulmonary & Respiratory Research* (v.1 (4), 2014),
the authors said

> In conclusion, there is an increase of nasal resistance
> upon removal of N95 respirator and surgical facemask
> after 3 hours wearing which potentially due to nasal
> physiological changes, instead of the size of nasal
> airways. The nasal resistance was not recovered even
> after 1.5 hours removal of respirator/facemask. In
> addition, the N95 respirator caused higher post-wearing
> nasal resistance than surgical facemask with different
> recovery routines.

In 'Protective Face Masks: Effect on the Oxygenation and
Heart Rate Status of Oral Surgeons during Surgery' by
Scarano et al in *International Journal of Environmental*

Research and Public Health (v.28 (8), Feb 2021 2363), the authors say

> In conclusion, wearing an FFP2 covered by a surgical mask induces a reduction in circulating O2 concentrations without clinical relevance, while an increase of heart frequency and a sensation of shortness of breath, light-headedness/headaches were recorded.

5.8.a.ii: Face masks and oxygen depletion: other relevant literature

A team of Stanford engineers is so concerned about the fact that N95 masks make it difficult to breathe that they are trying to come up with a new type of mask:

> But in filtering those particles, the mask also makes it harder to breathe. N95 masks are estimated to reduce oxygen intake by anywhere from 5 to 20 percent. That's significant, even for a healthy person. It can cause dizziness and lightheadedness. If you wear a mask long enough, it can damage the lungs. For a patient in respiratory distress, it can even be life threatening.

In 'Masks, false safety and real dangers, part 3: Hypoxia, hypercapnia and physiological effects' by Borovoy et al, *Primary Doctor Medical Journal* (2 Nov 2020), the authors look at the sort of physiological changes that can occur with decreased oxygen.

Dr. Margarite Griesz-Brisson MD, PhD is a Consultant Neurologist and Neurophysiologist with a PhD in Pharmacology, with special interest in neurotoxicology, environmental medicine, neuroregeneration and neuroplasticity. She has gone on record saying

The rebreathing of our exhaled air will without a doubt create oxygen deficiency and a flooding of carbon dioxide. We know that the human brain is very sensitive to oxygen depravation. There are nerve cells for example in the hippocampus, that can't be longer than 3 minutes without oxygen – they cannot survive. The acute warning symptoms are headaches, drowsiness, dizziness, issues in concentration, slowing down of the reaction time – reactions of the cognitive system. However, when you have chronic oxygen depravation, all of those symptoms disappear, because you get used to it. But your efficiency will remain impaired and the undersupply of oxygen in your brain continues to progress.

5.8.b: Studies and reviews on skin problems

In 'Adverse skin reactions to personal protective equipment against severe acute respiratory syndrome--a descriptive study in Singapore' by Foo et al, in *Contact Dermatitis* (v.55 (5), Nov 2006, pp.291-4), the authors said

> Our aim was to study the prevalence of adverse skin reactions to PPE among healthcare workers in Singapore during the SARS outbreak... 109 (35.5%) of the 307 staff who used masks regularly reported acne (59.6%), facial itch (51.4%), and rash (35.8%) from N95 mask use... The use of PPE is associated with high rates of adverse skin reactions.

In 'Consensus of Chinese experts on protection of skin and mucous membrane barrier for health-care workers fighting against coronavirus disease 2019' by Yan et al, in *Dermatologic Therapy* (v.33 (4), July/Aug 2020), the authors say

To assess the potential skin damage, a recent cross-sectional study surveyed 330 HCWs working at fever clinics and inpatients ward of COVID-19 cases. The results showed that 71% of respondents reported self-perceived skin barrier damage. The main symptoms were burning, itch, and stinging. The most commonly reported types of eruptions were dryness or scales, papules or erythema, and maceration.

In the review paper 'Impact of personal protective equipment use on health care workers' physical health during the COVID-19 pandemic: A systematic review and meta-analysis', by Galanis et al, in the *American Journal of Infection Control* (v.49 (10), 1 Oct 20201, pp.1305-1315), the authors say

Our review included 14 studies with 11,746 HCWs. The estimated overall prevalence of adverse events among HCWs was 78% with a range from 42.8% to 95.1% among studies. Among others, the following factors were related to the risk of adverse events among HCWs due to PPE use: obesity, diabetes mellitus, smoking, pre-existing headache, longer duration of shifts wearing PPE, increased consecutive days with PPE, and increased exposure to confirmed or suspected COVID-19 patients. Conclusions: The frequency of adverse events among HCWs due to PPE use is very high.

In the review 'Occupational Dermatoses Related to Personal Protective Equipment Used During the COVID-19 Pandemic' by Abdali and Yu, in *Dermatologic Clinics* (v.39 (4), Oct 2021, pp. 555-68), the authors say

There has been a significant increase in prevalence of reported occupational dermatoses due to the enhanced infection prevention measures adopted by both health care workers and the general public in response to the COVID-19 pandemic... Prolonged wearing of PPE, frequent handwashing, and disinfecting of surfaces have resulted in an increased number of skin complaints in both HCWs and non-HCWs. One study surveyed 542 HCWs and 97% reported skin damage caused by enhanced infection-prevention during the COVID-19 outbreak.9 The associated dermatoses include allergic contact dermatitis (ACD), irritant contact dermatitis (ICD), seborrheic dermatitis (SD), acne, and rosacea.

In the study 'Evaluation of skin problems and dermatology life quality index in health care workers who use personal protection measures during COVID-19 pandemic' by Daye et al in *Dermatologic Therapy* (v.33 (6), Nov/Dec 2020), the authors said

Skin problems were found to be 90.2%, the most common were dryness, itching, cracking, burning, flaking, peeling and lichenification... Of all, 22.3% (n = 98) stated that the use of PPE increased the severity of their previously diagnosed skin diseases and allergies... Skin problems were higher in those using mask with metal nose bridge. As the mask using period prolonged, acne was more common.

In 'Skin reactions of N95 masks and medial masks among health-care personnel: A self-report questionnaire survey in China' by Zuo in *Contact Dermatitis* (v.83 (2), April 2020, pp.145-147), the authors report that

49.0% reported mask-related skin reactions, of which 41.8% had facial skin problems. 17.1% reported respiratory tract problems, 6.2% had eye symptoms.

8.9% removed their masks because they could not tolerate it... N95 masks were associated with more reactions than medical masks.

5.8.c: Studies and reviews on other face masks harms

In 'Impacts of face coverings on communication: an indirect impact of COVID-19' by Saunders et al in the *International Journal of Audiology* (v.60 (7), 2021), the authors concluded that

> face coverings impacted the content of communication, feelings of interpersonal connection and willingness to engage in conversation, and that they had strong negative impacts on anxiety levels, stress, and self-confidence. They also reported that face coverings make communication fatiguing, frustrating, and embarrassing.

In 'Face Mask-Associated Ocular Irritation and Dryness' by Moshirfar in *Ophthalmology and Therapy* (v.9 (3), Sep 2020, pp.397–400), the authors say

> we have become aware of potential effects on the eye specifically. In our community and patient population, we have seen a marked increase in dry eye symptoms among regular mask users at multiple local clinics. This group includes individuals who have never previously suffered from dry eyes. Individuals using masks regularly for an extended duration appear more likely to show symptoms...

> We saw numerous individuals at our practice who were regular mask wearers, including both patients and staff. These individuals described a subjective worsening in symptoms assessed in the Ocular Surface Disease Index.

Patients showed a deterioration in corneal staining, as well as a distinct increase in dryness reported by cataract patients on postoperative day 1. The majority of individuals described an awareness of air blowing upward from the mask into their eyes. This increased airflow likely accelerates the evaporation of the tear film which, when continuous for hours or days, may result in ocular surface irritation or inflammation. In addition to air convection, other factors are also likely at play.

If you think you can tape your mask to your upper cheeks to prevent what is being called 'mask eye', think again:

Staff members using taped masks to prevent air convection toward the eyes also complained of corneal irritation. In these cases, we postulate that the tape adhering to the skin of the upper cheek may interfere with the normal excursion of the lower eyelid, possibly inducing mechanical ectropion with secondary lagophthalmos.

In 'Wearing Face Masks Strongly Confuses Counterparts in Reading Emotions' by Carbon in *Frontiers of Psychology* (v.25, Sep 2020), the author says

Lower accuracy and lower confidence in one's own assessment of the displayed emotions indicate that emotional reading was strongly irritated by the presence of a mask. We further detected specific confusion patterns, mostly pronounced in the case of misinterpreting disgusted faces as being angry plus assessing many other emotions (e.g., happy, sad, and angry) as neutral.

In 'Surgical face masks impair human face matching performance for familiar and unfamiliar faces' by Carragher and Hancock, in *Cognitive Research: Principles and Implications* (v. 5, art. no. 59, 2020), the authors say

> We found that surgical face masks have a large detrimental effect on human face matching performance, and that the degree of impairment is the same regardless of whether one or both faces in each pair are masked/... Our findings demonstrate that surgical face masks impair the ability of humans... to perform perceptual face matching tasks.

In 'Inconveniences due to the use of face masks during the COVID-19 pandemic: A survey study of 876 young people' by Matusiak et al in *Dermatologic Therapy* (v.33 (4), July/Aug 2020), the authors say

> Out of 876 participants, only 27 people (3.1%) did not complain of any problems related to face mask wearing. Out of all reported inconveniences, difficulty in breathing appeared to the most common one (35.9%), followed by warming/sweating (21.3%), misting up of the glasses (21.3%), and slurred speech (12.3%).

Even allowing that these sorts of surveys usually get a biased sample, this still shows some of the downsides of mask-wearing.

In 'Downsides of face masks and possible mitigation strategies: a systematic review and meta-analysis', by Bakhit et al in *BMJ Open* (v.11 (2), Feb 22, 2021), the authors reported that science is failing in not investigating the downsides of masks:

> Conclusions: There are insufficient data to quantify all of the adverse effects that might reduce the acceptability, adherence and effectiveness of face masks. New research

on face masks should assess and report the harms and downsides. Urgent research is also needed on methods and designs to mitigate the downsides of face mask wearing, particularly the assessment of possible alternatives.

In 'The implications of face masks for babies and families during the COVID-19 pandemic: A discussion paper' by Green et al in the *Journal of Neonatal Nursing* (v.27 (1), Feb 2021, pp.21–25), the authors say

For an infant, this has the potential for long reaching effects in the early stages of neurobehavioral development. A mask covering the face may affect the infant's ability to develop facial processing and orientating to or focusing on another person's face. To re-iterate, newborns prefer looking at faces and clearly have an innate ability to recognise what a face is (Otsuka, 2014). Furthermore, newborns can recognise familiar faces, especially ones where a close connection exists (Pascalis et al., 2011), important because newborns are dependent entirely on their parents for survival and need to recognise them (Simion and Giorgio 2015). Crucial for this process, is the newborn's ability to visualise facial expressions. For infants and children to feel safe, there is a heavy dependence on facial expressions as they rely on their parents' emotional cues via facial expression to regulate their responses towards them or to potentially threatening situations.

In 'Effect of facemasks on empathy and relational continuity: a randomised controlled trial in primary care' by Wong et al in *BMC Family Practice* (v.14, Dec 2013), the authors say a negative impact on the patient's perceived empathy and relational continuity can reduce potential therapeutic effects such as decreased depression, improved immune response, improved quality of life and improved health outcomes.

In 'Investigation of adverse reactions in healthcare personnel working in Level 3 barrier protection PPE to treat COVID-19', by Yuan et al, in BMJ's *Postgrad Medical Journal* (v.97 (1148), 2020, pp.351-4), the authors say

A total of 122 (94.57%) healthcare professionals experienced discomfort while wearing L3PPE to treat patients with COVID-19. The main reasons for adverse reactions and discomfort include varying degrees of adverse skin reactions, respiratory difficulties, heat stress, dizziness and nausea... Our study discovered that the high rates of adverse reactions experienced by healthcare personnel due to the usage of L3PPE in treatment of COVID-19 not only include previously reported skin mucosa discomfort reactions but include multiple adverse reactions linked to the respiratory, nervous and digestive systems.

In 'Effects of Prolonged Use of Facemask on Healthcare Workers in Tertiary Care Hospital During COVID-19 Pandemic' by Purushothaman et al in the *Indian Journal of Otolaryngology and Head & Neck Surgery* (v.73, 20201, pp.59–65) the authors say

This study suggests that prolonged use of facemasks induces difficulty in breathing on exertion and excessive sweating around the mouth to the healthcare workers which results in poorer adherence and increased risk of susceptibility to infection.

In 'We need better evidence on non-drug interventions for covid-19' (28 Aug 2020), in an opinion piece for the *British Medical Journal*, the author Dr Margaret McCartney said that

> Nor have we considered enough about the broader societal impact. People with histories of trauma, or who have hearing difficulties, are placed at disadvantage. Yet those who do not wear face coverings are categorised, by proponents of face coverings, as "deviants from the new norm." Societal cohesion is risked by dividing, rather than understanding behaviour. These are all harms. Nor do we have a clear "end" strategy.

In 'Science, society, and policy in the face of uncertainty: reflections on the debate around face coverings for the public during COVID-19' by Martin, Dingwall et al, in *Critical Public Health* (v.30 (5), 2020), the authors say

> some scientists have argued for policies to encourage or compel the use of face coverings in community (non-clinical) settings, despite acknowledged gaps in the evidence base for the effectiveness of such a measure. This commentary has two objectives. First, in the face of strong arguments that face coverings are a commonsense intervention, with negligible downsides, that can only do good, we make the case for caution in changing policy. Many seemingly benign public health interventions have the potential to cause harm, and that harm is often socially differentiated. We present five arguments for caution in policy change. Second, we reflect on the wider implications of the increasingly overt approaches to policy advocacy taken by some scientists. Drawing from the theory of post-normal science, we argue that the

science–policy interface in the case of face coverings has taken a surprisingly traditional form, falling short of interdisciplinary integration and failing to incorporate insights of the full range of relevant experts and affected stakeholders. We sketch a vision for an alternative, more mature, relationship between science and society that accepts uncertainty, embraces deliberation, and rises to the challenge of developing knowledge to improve public health.

Masks promote mouth-breathing, and mouth-breathing can have disastrous effects, as outlined in 'Mouth breathing: adverse effects on facial growth, health, academics, and behavior' by Jefferson in *General Dentistry* (v.58 (1), Feb 2010, pp.18-25):

The vast majority of health care professionals are unaware of the negative impact of upper airway obstruction (mouth breathing) on normal facial growth and physiologic health. Children whose mouth breathing is untreated may develop long, narrow faces, narrow mouths, high palatal vaults, dental malocclusion, gummy smiles, and many other unattractive facial features, such as skeletal Class II or Class III facial profiles. These children do not sleep well at night due to obstructed airways; this lack of sleep can adversely affect their growth and academic performance. Many of these children are misdiagnosed with attention deficit disorder (ADD) and hyperactivity.

In 'The Damage of Masking Children Could be Irreparable' (Brownstone Institute, 3 Nov 2021), author Eric Hussey says

Face-identification ability is specific. Humans have a specific face identification area of the brain, known in research as the FFA: the Fusiform Face Area. The FFA is in the right hemisphere of the brain... If the input from the left eye very early in development is impaired, as in congenital cataract, development of the FFA can be impaired... The vision science analogizes how we detect faces by describing the human face as a horizontal bar code. So, just for the moment, imagine checking out at the grocery store with half of each bar code covered... Blocking input to the FFA with a congenital cataract up to 2 to 6 months of age range interferes with recognizing changes in spacing of facial features... Delaying visual input by as little as 2 months results in permanent deficits... 9 more years of development after cataract surgery doesn't fix it.

5.9. Relevant media reports (a small selection)

A researcher at Duke University attacks a Duke University report about measures taken against Covid in schools, including masks, in a *Wall St Journal* story entitled 'Sophistry at Duke in Defense of Masks: A baseless conclusion about Covid in schools flows from an elementary error of logic' (July 8, 2021):

> On June 30 the collaborative shared findings in a report and news conference touting the effectiveness of masks. The impression was that the data from schools led them to this conclusion, though the way North Carolina chose to reopen did not allow for a control group. The report nonetheless declared wearing masks 'an effective strategy to prevent in-school COVID-19 transmission.

In 'Do face masks work? A note on the evidence' in the *Spectator* (19 April 2020), Dr John Lee wrote

> A laboratory study by the Health and Safety Executive looking at influenza virus, which is a similar size to coronavirus, found live virus in the air behind all surgical masks tested. They tested masks on a human volunteer using an 'inert aerosol challenge' (a simulated sneeze), and on a breathing dummy head using a live virus aerosol challenge. The numbers of particles were reduced by a factor of two for the human volunteer, and six for the dummy head; probably not very effective in reducing infection when infective aerosols – the droplets emitted from someone's cough or sneeze, or even during talking – may contain hundreds of thousands, or millions, of tiny particles.

But the thing to understand about this science is that those breathing-in factors represent the very best that could possibly be achieved. The masks were adjusted 'in order to obtain the best fit possible' and 'the test subject was asked to remain still during the test'. Obviously, the dummy head was completely still – in real life this just doesn't apply. Masks don't fit snugly, people move all the time, the mask material gets damp and air gets around the side.

Quebec's public health director Horacio Arruda attacked masks, telling the Montreal Gazette that masks are a bad idea. For one thing,

> masks get saturated with moisture from the mouth and nose after about 20 minutes. Once they're wet, they no longer form a barrier against viruses trying to come through or exit'. In addition to this, 'If a person's hand has come in contact with the virus, and they touch their mask to adjust it in the vicinity of their eyes, nose and mouth, it can transmit the disease.

Seventy doctors in Belgium wrote to the Flemish Minister of Education asking for masks to be abolished in schools due to the harms it causes:

> In an open letter to the Flemish Minister of Education Ben Weyts (N-VA), 70 doctors ask to abolish the mandatory mouth mask at school, both for the teachers and for the students. Weyts does not intend to change course. The doctors ask that Minister Ben Weyts immediately reverses his working method: no mouth mask obligation at school, only protect the risk group and only the advice that people with a possible risk profile should consult their doctor.

The decision to introduce a mandatory mouth mask at school for pupils from the age of 12 is of great concern to the signatories, mainly GPs. 'In recent months, the general well-being of children and young people has come under severe pressure. We see in our practices an increasing number of children and young people with complaints due to the rules of conduct that have been imposed on them. We diagnose anxiety and sleep problems, behavioral disorders and fear of contamination. We are seeing an increase in domestic violence, isolation and deprivation. Many lack physical and emotional contact; attachment problems and addiction are obvious.

The mandatory mouth mask in schools is a major threat to their development. It ignores the essential needs of the growing child. The well-being of children and young people is highly dependent on the emotional connection with others. (…) The aim of education is to create an optimal context so that a maximum development of young people is possible. The school environment must be a safe practice field. The mouth mask obligation, on the other hand, makes the school a threatening and unsafe environment, where emotional connection becomes difficult.

In the *Wall St Journal* article 'Kansas Democrats' Covid Chart Masks the Truth' (Aug 26 2020), author Allysia Finley accused Kansas Democrats of data-tampering:

Democrats and their public health experts often manipulate data, and their dishonesty is more insidious because it gets a pass in the press. A case in point is a chart created by Kansas Democratic Gov. Laura Kelly's Department of Health and Environment that purported to show her July 3 face-mask mandate has been a viral success.

In a *MedPage Today* article titled 'Climbing the Pandemic Failures Chart: Research on Masking Kids' (7 July 2021'), Prof Vinay Prasad says

Major scientific bodies, funding agencies, public health authorities, and researchers have abdicated the hard work of running trials to reduce uncertainty and hopefully answer the question. Instead, we performed retrospective, confounded, selectively reported studies on a politically divided population with preconceived notations that will forever reach opposing conclusions.

The Epoch Times reports on a study by Rationalground which examined a 229-day period in the US and compared the days in which state governments had imposed mask mandates and the days when they hadn't, and found that there were far less cases when there weren't mask mandates.

In states with a mandate in effect, there were 9,605,256 confirmed COVID-19 cases, which works out to an average of 27 cases per 100,000 people per day. When states didn't have a statewide order—including states that never had mandates, coupled with the period of time masking states didn't have the mandate in place—there were 5,781,716 cases, averaging 17 cases per 100,000 people per day.

This was only published as Twitter thread, unfortunately, and it could be complained that it lacks scientific rigour, and many excuses could be made (and have been) for why the numbers turn out the opposite way they should, but it is remarkable how a supposedly successful mask strategy just never seems to have any figures to back it up, despite the enormous amount of masking that has been done, and the enormous amount of mask data that is available.

The *New York Post* reported in 'Wearing a used mask could be worse than no mask amid COVID-19: study' (Dec 16 2020) that

> Wearing a used mask could be more dangerous than not wearing one at all when it comes to warding off COVID-19, a new study has found. A new three-layer surgical mask is 65 percent efficient in filtering particles in the air — but when used, that number drops to 25 percent, according to the study published Tuesday in the *Physics of Fluids*. Researchers from the University of Massachusetts Lowell and California Baptist University say that masks slow down airflow, making people more susceptible to breathing in particles — and a dirty face mask can't effectively filter out the tiniest of droplets. "It is natural to think that wearing a mask, no matter new or old, should always be better than nothing," said author Jinxiang Xi. "Our results show that this belief is only true for particles larger than 5 micrometers, but not for fine particles smaller than 2.5 micrometers".

Note though, that this study was just a computer modelling study, so take this with a grain of salt.

In 'Not wearing masks to protect against coronavirus is a 'big mistake,' top Chinese scientist says' (27 March 2020) *Science* interviewed (by text, phone calls and e-mail) George Gao, head of the Chinese Center for Disease Control and Prevention. Gao easily fobbed them off.

> The big mistake in the U.S. and Europe, in my opinion, is that people aren't wearing masks. This virus is

transmitted by droplets and close contact. Droplets play a very important role—you've got to wear a mask, because when you speak, there are always droplets coming out of your mouth. Many people have asymptomatic or presymptomatic infections. If they are wearing face masks, it can prevent droplets that carry the virus from escaping and infecting others.

Q: What about other control measures? China has made aggressive use of thermometers at the entrances to stores, buildings, and public transportation stations, for instance.

A: Yes. Anywhere you go inside in China, there are thermometers. You have to try to take people's temperatures as often as you can to make sure that whoever has a high fever stays out.

The next day *Science* published a mask-pushing article called 'Would everyone wearing face masks help us slow the pandemic?', partly based on what Gao said, as well as other mask-pushing scientists like Benjamin Cowling.

Also of interest here is that there is a note on this article saying 'Science's COVID-19 reporting is supported by the Pulitzer Center.' The Pulitzer Center presents itself as a philanthropic non-profit organisation that pays for journalism that commercial organisations are unwilling to do because of its costs. In reality the Center is yet another billionaire-funded leftist-globalist political project, funded by the likes of Bill Gates, the Rockefeller Foundation, the UN, the Carnegie Corporation, and many other usual suspects. For an example of what the Center does, you can note that it is funding the push to take the misleading and propagandist 1619 Project into the classroom.

In 'The Case Against Masks for Children' in the *Wall Street Journal* on 8 Aug 2021, Makary and Meissner say

> Do masks reduce Covid transmission in children? Believe it or not, we could find only a single retrospective study on the question, and its results were inconclusive... Some children compensate for such difficulties by breathing through their mouths. Chronic and prolonged mouth breathing can alter facial development. It is well-documented that children who mouth-breathe because adenoids block their nasal airways can develop a mouth deformity and elongated face.

> The possible psychological harm of widespread masking is an even greater worry. Facial expressions are integral to human connection, particularly for young children, who are only learning how to signal fear, confusion and happiness. Covering a child's face mutes these nonverbal forms of communication and can result in robotic and emotionless interactions, anxiety and depression. Seeing people speak is a building block of phonetic development. It is especially important for children with disabilities such as hearing impairment.

> The adverse developmental effects of requiring masks for a few weeks are probably minor. We can't say that with any confidence when the practice stretches on for months or years.

In 'The Cult of Masked Schoolchildren' in the *Tablet* on 20 Jan 2022, author Prof Vinay Prasad says there has been an

> increased pressure on kids to wear masks in school. Some private schools have gone beyond cloth-masking and mandated N95 (or equivalent) masks for children as

young as 4. The Berkeley Unified School District in California recently began transitioning students to N95-level masking. This isn't a matter of protecting children, their teachers, or their grandparents; it's delusional and dangerous cultlike behavior…

Data from Spain on masking kids is sobering. The figure below shows the R value—a measure of how fast the virus spreads—by age. Spain mandated masks at a specific age cutoff. If masks have a visible effect, we should see a step down in the graph at the age kids start to wear them (i.e., the spread should drop at the age masking begins). But as you can see, there is only a slow, deliberate, upward trend with no steps down. Based on the evidence only, it would be impossible to guess which age groups are wearing masks and which are not.

In 'Have San Francisco policies done more harm to children than COVID?' in *SFGate* on 20 Jan 2022, Laura Fagan says

As a parent, I have become increasingly concerned by the lack of cost-benefit analysis and rigor over which policies are the most effective or even necessary, and which policies may be causing long-term damage… Masks have been required for children ages 2 and up in all public settings, even when the mask mandate was briefly lifted for vaccinated adults in summer 2021… the impact of these rules are not benign. Real and lasting harms to development, learning and physical and mental health from these childhood interruptions continue to surface…

Students must qualify for Fedorko's special education services through a number of tests, none of which teachers were allowed to administer virtually. Closed schools meant the kids that needed this service had it delayed for a year.

"We committed educational malpractice,'" said Fedorko. Now back in the classroom, every student is struggling with pronunciation or recognizing letter sounds. "I am often the only adult they interact with that can articulate the sounds, but they can't see my mouth." Fedorko adds that it is especially hard on autistic students who already have trouble reading faces and emotions.

Fedorko has also witnessed an ELL student with such severe eczema that mask wearing has caused open cuts behind her ears. And yet the mask wasn't immediately removed because the child didn't have an exemption. "She's 5 years old. Just take it off. It's like all humanity is lost." Fedorko used to live in South Korea and has many expat friends living abroad. "Why are we one of the few places in the world that puts a mask on a kid with autism, eczema or speech issues? We claim to follow 'the science' here. What about the science of education?" said Fedorko.

'The Case Against Masks at School' by Smelkinson, Bienen, and Noble, in the *Atlantic*, 26 Jan 2022, says

We reviewed a variety of studies—some conducted by the CDC itself, some cited by the CDC as evidence of masking effectiveness in a school setting, and others touted by media to the same end—to try to find evidence that would justify the CDC's no-end-in-sight mask guidance for the very-low-risk pediatric population, particularly post-vaccination. We came up empty-handed.

Appendix A:
A short guide to
the units of measurement

Micron, aka micrometre, often written as μm = one thousandth of a millimetre, or 0.001 millimetres. In metres it is one millionth of a metre.

Nanometre = one thousandth of a micron, or one millionth of a millimetre (one billionth of a metre).

So, for example, 0.3 microns = 300 nanometres.

A Covid particle is around 60-140 nanometres, or 0.06-0.14 microns (μm).

The unaided human eye can generally see (in optimum viewing conditions, up close) particles larger than 40 microns, or 40,000 nanometres. This is 0.04 millimetres, or one-twenty-fifth of a millimetre.

For the latest updates on the author, visit:

www.hectordrummond.com